BRITISH GEOLOGICAL SURVEY
RESEARCH REPORT RR/01/06

Geology of the Isle of Man and its offshore area

R A Chadwick, D I Jackson, R P Barnes, G S Kimbell, H Johnson, R C Chiverrell,
G S P Thomas, N S Jones, N J Riley, E A Pickett, B Young, D W Holliday,
D F Ball, S G Molyneux, D Long, G M Power, and D H Roberts

Keyworth, Nottingham: British Geological Survey 2001

First published 2001

ISBN 0 85272 395 4

Bibliographic reference

Chadwick, R A, Jackson, D I, Barnes, Kimbell, G S, Johnson, H, Chiverrell, R C, Thomas, G S P, Jones, N S, Riley N J, Pickett, E A, Young, B, Holliday, D W, Ball, D F, Molyneux, S, Long, D, Power, G M, and Roberts, D. 2001. Geology of the Isle of Man and its offshore area. *British Geological Survey Research Report,* RR/01/06.

The printing of this report was funded by the Department of Trade and Industry

Topography and the grid, where used on the figures, is taken from Ordnance Survey map number 95, and the Isle of Man Government topographic base map.

Authors

R A Chadwick, MA, PhD, CGeol
N S Jones, BSc, PhD
G S Kimbell, BSc
S G Molyneux, BSc, PhD
N J Riley BSc, PhD, CGeol
British Geological Survey
Keyworth

D F Ball, BSc
R P Barnes, BSc, PhD
H Johnson, BSc, CGeol
D Long, BSc, CGeol
E A Pickett, BA, PhD
B Young, BSc, PhD, CGeol
British Geological Survey
Edinburgh

D W Holliday, MA, PhD, CGeol
Honorary Research Associate
British Geological Survey
Keyworth

G M Power, BSc, PhD
University of Portsmouth

D I Jackson, MA, CGeol
19 Swanston Crescent
Edinburgh

R C Chiverrell, BSc, MSc, PhD
G S P Thomas, BSc, PhD
University of Liverpool

D H Roberts, BSc, PhD
Environmental Research Centre
Department of Geography
University of Durham

Printed in the UK for the British Geological Survey
by Halstan & Co. Ltd, Amersham.
C10 10/01

Contents

Figures

Plates

Tables

ACKNOWLEDGEMENTS

The preparation of this report was generously sponsored by TotalFinaElf Exploration UK PLC and their partners Enterprise Oil plc and Amerada Hess Limited. Particular thanks are extended to P J Newman of TotalFinaElf Exploration UK PLC and other TotalFinaElf Exploration UK PLC staff in Aberdeen for their help and advice. K B Bawden, the Chief Executive of the Isle of Man's Department of Trade and Industry, is also especially thanked for his guidance during the work programme. The DTI generously sponsored the printing of this report.

The following organisations and individuals are warmly thanked for contributing data to the report: Amerada Hess Limited; BG International; Enterprise Oil plc; ExxonMobil International Limited; Fugro Airborne Surveys (formerly World Geoscience: UK Ltd); Isle of Man Department of Trade and Industry; Department of Local Government and the Environment; Jebco Seismic (UK) Limited (Old Westminster House, 38 Upper Mulgrave Road, Cheam, Surrey SH2 7AZ); Manx National Heritage; Marathon Oil (UK) Limited; TotalFinaElf Exploration UK PLC; Wardell Armstrong; WesternGeco Ltd; D J Burnett and D G Quirk, Oxford Brookes University; R C Chiverrell and G S P Thomas, University of Liverpool; J H Morris, Geological Survey of Ireland; G M Power, University of Portsmouth; D H Roberts, Environmental Research Centre, Department of Geography, Durham.

The following authors have produced the chapters in this report:

1	Introduction	H Johnson
2	Crustal structure	R A Chadwick and G S Kimbell
3	Lower Palaeozoic	R P Barnes, S G Molyneux and G M Power
4	Post-Caledonian structure	R A Chadwick
5	Devonian and Carboniferous	N S Jones and N J Riley
6	Permian	D I Jackson
7	Triassic and Jurassic	D I Jackson
8	Post-Jurassic–Palaeogene igneous rocks	R A Chadwick and G S Kimbell
9	Quaternary	R C Chiverrell, G S P Thomas, D Long and D H Roberts
10	Economic geology	B Young, D W Holliday and D F Ball

In addition to the work of the authors, the report has drawn extensively upon the knowledge and expertise of colleagues from academia, industry and BGS. In particular, the authors and editors are grateful to the following for constructive comment: D J Burnett, J R Davies, A A McMillan, P J Newman, D G Quirk, J D Ritchie, G Warrington and N H Woodcock.

The production of this report was co-ordinated by H Johnson, R P Barnes and A A McMillan. The report was compiled by E A Pickett; editing was by E A Pickett and A A Jackson. The figures were draughted by J Barclay, C E Carson and A M Stewart, BGS Cartography, Edinburgh.

NOTES

BGS offshore boreholes are registered in chronological order and prefixed with the year of drilling; they are cited in the text as, for example, Borehole 87/9. Commercial holes are referred to as Well and given the appropriate drilling number.

Numbers preceded by the letters P and GS quoted in the plate captions refer to the BGS photograph collections, held at Murchison House, Edinburgh and Keyworth, Nottingham.

Palynology samples collected from the Manx Group were registered in the MPA Series of the British Geological Survey, and bear the numbers MPA 49357-MPA 49452 and MPA 49465-MPA 49499. Slides, residues and remaining rock are stored at BGS Keyworth.

Numbers in the text that are preceded by the letter L refer to the Lamplugh collection. Thin sections are held at BGS Keyworth; they are indexed in an electronic database, BRITROCKS, which is the BGS corporate petrographic collection

Foreword

The Isle of Man is a self-governing dependency of the British Crown that is not part of the United Kingdom. The Island forms an upstanding part of a horst block within the Irish Sea, and is largely composed of deformed Lower Palaeozoic metasedimentary rocks and associated granitic intrusions. Relatively undeformed Upper Palaeozoic to Mesozoic sedimentary successions encroach onto the fringes of the Island, and are widespread and thickly developed in the surrounding offshore Peel, Solway and East Irish Sea basins. Geological processes have shaped the Manx landscape and also given rise to significant mineral resources. For example, lead, zinc and copper ores hosted within the Lower Palaeozoic succession and granitic intrusions were the basis of an important mining industry on the Island during the late 19th and early 20th centuries. More recently, the offshore sedimentary basins surrounding the Isle of Man have been the focus of hydrocarbon exploration, following commercial successes in the central and southern East Irish Sea Basin to the south.

This regional report integrates the results of targeted geological mapping on the Isle of Man, with an assessment of recently released hydrocarbon exploration data from the offshore basins, and with recent published and unpublished research. The report complements a new British Geological Survey (BGS) 1:50 000 Series geological map sheet covering the Isle of Man, which provides a revision of the meticulous, but outdated, mapping carried out between 1892 and 1897 by G W Lamplugh. Sponsorship of this report, together with the accompanying new geological map and an associated popular publication, was generously provided by TotalFinaElf Exploration UK PLC and their partners Enterprise Oil plc and Amerada Hess Limited. This oil industry group actively explored around the Island between 1994 and 1997 and generated important new geological and environmental data. The potential value of these new data was recognised by the Isle of Man Government and the group, and a programme of geological and environment work was planned in collaboration with the Island's Department of Trade and Industry. The geological work was led by the BGS, while Port Erin Marine Laboratory (part of the Centre for Marine and Coastal Studies of the University of Liverpool) conducted the environmental work. Copyright for the geological products, including this new report, the popular publication, the geological map, and associated Geographic Information System (GIS) digital databases, is jointly vested with the BGS (part of the Natural Environment Research Council) and the Isle of Man Government.

The geological work programme has benefited greatly from extensive collaboration with many organisations and individuals, including members of a multidisciplinary, academic research team that was mainly active during the period 1995 to 1998, and which was funded by the Natural Environment Research Council (NERC). The research team's data were integrated with detailed information from Lamplugh's field slips, published information and a wide range of data contributed by many organisations, including the Isle of Man Government, Fugro Airborne Surveys (formerly World Geoscience: UK Ltd), Jebco Seismic (UK) Limited, Schlumberger Geco-Prakla, WesternGeco Ltd and Wardell Armstrong. To facilitate efficient reinterpretation of the large and diverse data sets, they were captured and manipulated as themes within a specially customised GIS.

Many practical benefits are anticipated to follow from this programme. This report, the new map and the associated GIS will provide much previously unavailable detailed information. This information will assist the addressing of issues such as planning of major development projects, management of contaminated land and optimal exploitation of mineral resources.

D A Falvey PhD
Director
British Geological Survey
Kingsley Dunham Centre
Keyworth
Nottingham
NG12 5GG

Frontispiece The Neolithic chambered cairn at Cashtal yn Ard [SC 463 892]. Behind the cairn lie the hills of the Manx Uplands, composed of Manx Group (P 018717).

1 Introduction

The Isle of Man is about 45 km long and up to 16 km wide, and forms an upstanding part of a horst block within the Irish Sea (Figure 1). Two upland massifs dominate the Manx landscape and are separated by the central valley, which runs from Douglas to Peel. Deformed Lower Palaeozoic metasedimentary rocks and associated granitic intrusions underlie the areas of high ground (Figure 2), the highest point of which is Snaefell at 621 m. Upper Palaeozoic and Mesozoic sedimentary successions encroach onto the fringes of the Island, and are widespread and thickly developed in the surrounding offshore Peel, Solway† and East Irish Sea basins (Figure 3). The Manx Designated Area extends to 12 nautical miles offshore and is characterised bathymetrically by platforms with water depths generally less than 40 m. The relatively deep-water North Channel lies mainly outside the designated area to the west and north-west. With the exception of a veneer of Quaternary and Recent sediments, mid-Jurassic and younger sedimentary rocks are absent from the Island and the offshore designated area. This is principally a result of two phases of uplift and erosion during Cainozoic times. Thick Quaternary and Recent sediments blanket the northern plain and much of the plain of Malew in the south of the Island (Figure 29). Offshore, these deposits range in thickness from zero close inshore around the south of the Island to about 150 m off the Point of Ayre.

The account presented in this report summarises the geology of the Isle of Man and its offshore-designated area (Figure 1). It represents a tangible result from a collaborative research programme of closely related projects, which has also led to the publication of a new 1:50 000 scale Solid and Drift geological map of the Isle of Man (BGS, 2001) and a popular publication to explain the geology and landscape of the Isle of Man (Pickett, 2001). This report integrates and builds on recent scientific advances by Woodcock et al. (1999a), Quirk (1999), Meadows et al. (1997) and Jackson et al. (1997), and also draws upon new information resulting from the recent resurvey of the Island and a substantial amount of recently acquired offshore hydrocarbon exploration data.

HISTORY OF RESEARCH

There is a long history of investigation regarding the geology of the Isle of Man (e.g. Ford et al., 1999; Wilson, 1999), though the detailed work of Lamplugh (1903) forms the basis for much of our present view of the geology. A synthesis of the Lower Palaeozoic stratigraphy, structure, metamorphism and intrusions was provided by Simpson (1963a, b, 1964a, b, 1965, 1968) although subsequent biostratigraphical work by Molyneux (1979) indicated that Simpson's stratigraphy was significantly flawed. The geology of the Island was summarised by Dackombe and McCarroll (1990), and the publication of a field guidebook by Ford (1993) stimulated much field-based research that focused on the Lower Palaeozoic rocks. This research was co-ordinated through a multidisciplinary project, the results of which were summarised by Woodcock et al. (1999a). The guidebook by Ford (1993) has recently been updated in the light of the new research (Ford et al., 2001).

The preparation of the new geological map of the Isle of Man involved a phase of collaborative research that was led by the British Geological Survey (BGS) during 2000. Before the new field investigations began, pre-existing field data were made available to BGS by the research team who had contributed to the Lower Palaeozoic synthesis of Woodcock et al. (1999a). These data, together with many other data types contributed by the oil industry and government, were integrated within a customised Geographic Information System (GIS) which allowed efficient redisplay and interpretation of the information. Researchers from Oxford Brookes University assisted the BGS with construction of this GIS, and also with the following field survey (Burnett et al., 2001). Much of the fieldwork was focused on defining the location and nature of the boundaries between Lower Palaeozoic lithostratigraphical units recognised by Woodcock et al. (1999a), and investigating whether additional formations were present. An important component of the field investigations was sampling for new biostratigraphical analysis (Molyneux, 2001). Although much of the field survey was targeted at the Lower Palaeozoic rocks, the Devonian and Carboniferous successions were also re-examined, including all the available Carboniferous type localities and key reference sections of Dickson et al. (1987). Similarly, a re-evaluation of the Quaternary geology in the field, largely by academic co-workers, builds on recent research (e.g. Dackcombe and Thomas, 1989; Chiverrell et al., 2001).

In the offshore area surrounding the Island, geological information has come from two main sources:

i Exploration for hydrocarbons has generated hundreds of line-kilometres of seismic reflection profiles, together with information from deep wells. Such exploration activities and datasets have stimulated much research regarding the hydrocarbon-rich East Irish Sea Basin (e.g. Parker, 1993; Jackson and Johnson, 1996; Meadows et al., 1997; Quirk, 1999). Recent exploration campaigns by TotalFinaElf Exploration UK PLC and their partners in the Peel and Solway basins have also provided significant new information on the geology and hydrocarbon potential of these previously little-

† In this report, the term Solway Basin is used to describe the Carboniferous Basin in the Solway Firth, whereas the term Solway Firth Basin is used for the Permo–Triassic and younger basin in this area.

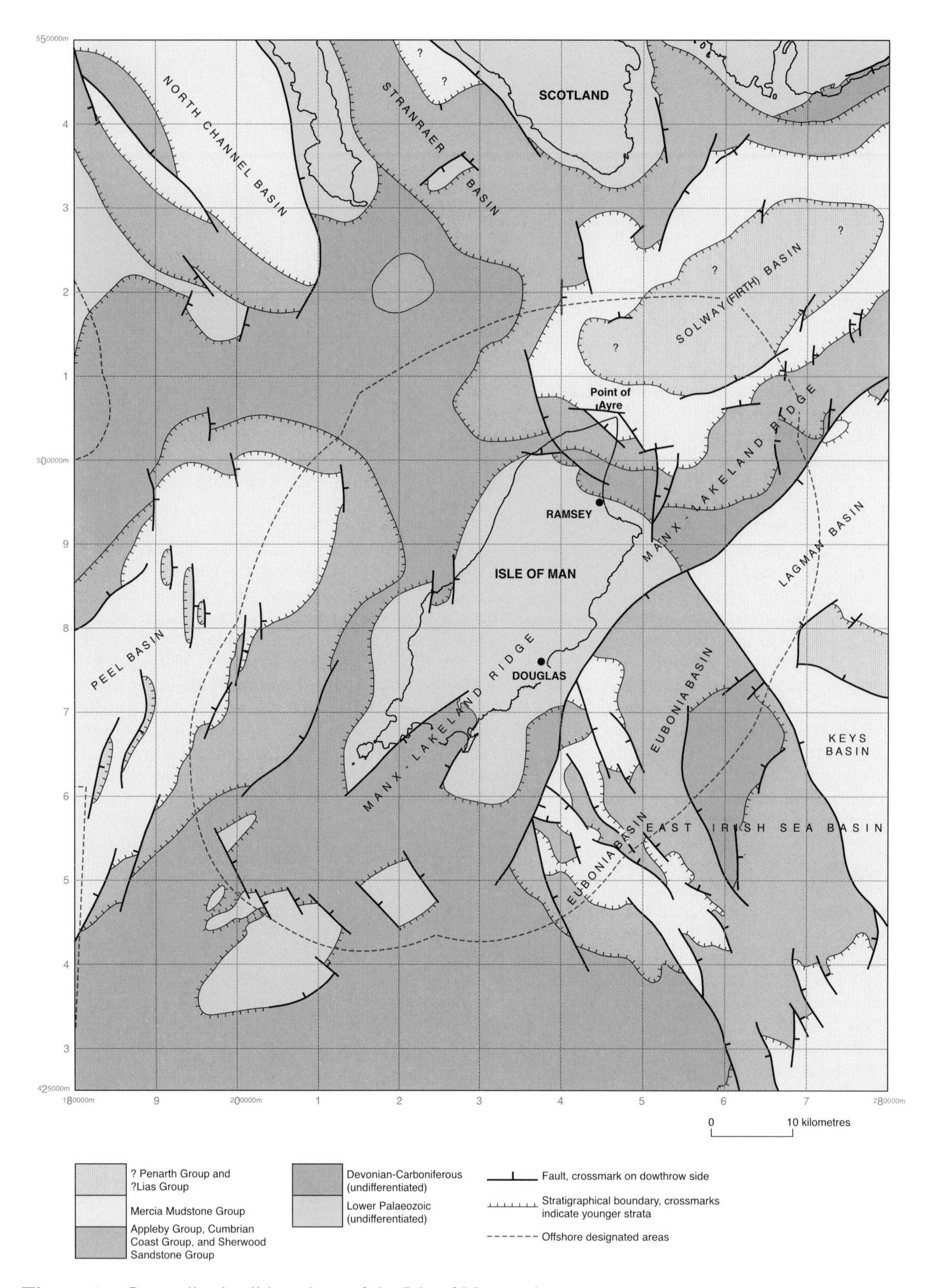

Figure 1 Generalised solid geology of the Isle of Man region.

explored areas (Newman, 1999) and this report draws freely on data and borehole reports generously loaned by the company.

ii BGS has undertaken a systematic offshore regional mapping programme of the UK continental shelf, including the Isle of Man offshore designated area. These surveys were funded largely by the Department of Energy (now the Department of Trade and Industry), and the results are incorporated into the BGS 1:250 000 map series. This map series is complemented by the BGS UK Offshore Report Series (e.g. Jackson et al., 1995), which integrates the results of surveys of BGS and commercial organisations with other published data, including important deep-seismic reflection surveys (e.g. Beamish and Smythe, 1986; Todd et al., 1991).

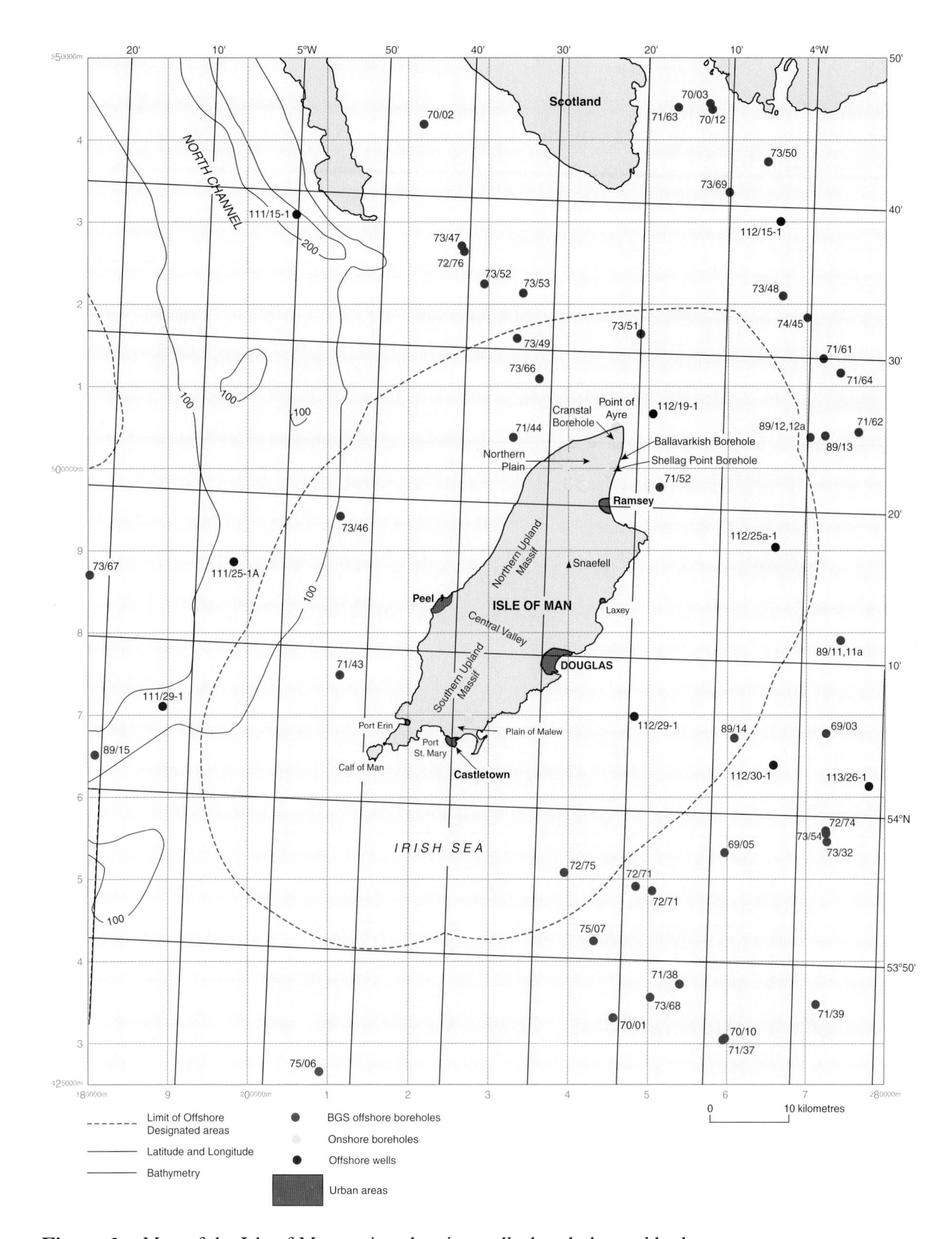

Figure 2 Map of the Isle of Man region showing wells, boreholes and bathymetry.

GEOLOGICAL SUMMARY

In earliest Ordovician times the continental crust that now underlies the Isle of Man lay within the southern hemisphere and formed part of Eastern Avalonia, a microcontinent on the northern margin of the Gondwana supercontinent (Cocks and Fortey, 1982, 1990). At this time, the wide Iapetus Ocean separated Eastern Avalonia from the Laurentian continent. During the early Ordovician, Eastern Avalonia drifted northwards and eventually collided, in Silurian times, with Laurentia during the Caledonian Orogeny. As a result of this collision, three distinct zones can be recognised within the crustal structure of the Isle of Man region. These are termed, from north to south, Laurentian crust, the Iapetus Convergence Zone, and Avalonian crust (see Figures 4 and 5). The Iapetus Convergence Zone includes the 'Iapetus Suture' and

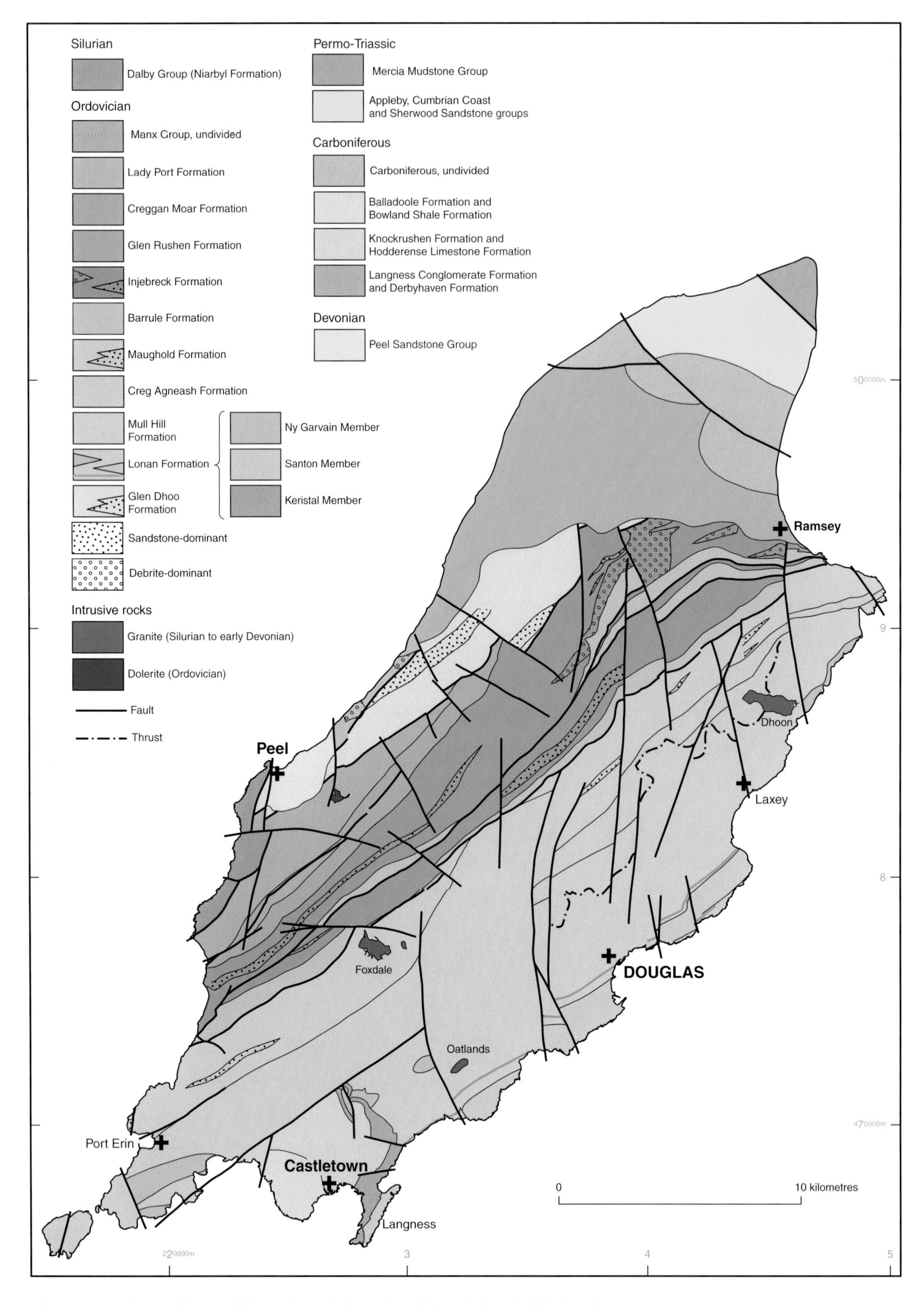

Figure 3 Generalised solid geology of the Isle of Man (after BGS, 2001).

is associated with a north-east-trending, low aeromagnetic anomaly of long wavelength. This may indicate the presence of metasedimentary rocks, originally deposited at the northern margin of Eastern Avalonia, which were subsequently partially subducted during final closure of the Iapetus Ocean (Kimbell and Stone, 1995). Notably, recently released commercial seismic data to the south-west of the Isle of Man indicate additional north-west-dipping basement reflectors (see Figure 8) that are interpreted as a Caledonian imbricate thrust stack (Barrule Thrust Zone) that may link with the lower crustal interface interpreted as the Iapetus Suture (Brewer et al., 1983).

The oldest rocks at outcrop on the Isle of Man are termed the Manx Group. These rocks were deposited during the Ordovician on the continental margin of Avalonia, at the southern margin of the Iapetus Ocean. They dominantly comprise turbiditic strata of laminated mudstone and siltstone, but also include units of typically fine-grained sandstone. Locally, volcanic rocks form a minor component of the succession. Generally, the Manx Group forms a steeply dipping and north-west-younging succession, although it is disrupted by a number of strike-parallel faults (Figure 3). Previous structural models that invoked a large-scale synclinorium through the Isle of Man (e.g. Lamplugh, 1903; Simpson, 1963a) are undermined by biostratigraphical data (Molyneux, 1979, 2001). Biostratigraphical evidence has also been crucial in demonstrating that Silurian strata crop out to the south of Peel (Howe, 1999). These rocks, which were formerly included in the Manx Group, are now separated as the Dalby Group (Morris et al., 1999). They consist predominantly of turbiditic rocks and represent a fragment of a succession that accumulated across both the Avalonian and Laurentian margins during the final closure of the Iapetus Ocean. The Dalby Group consists predominantly of fine- to medium-grained sandstone and silty mudstone, but includes very thinly laminated hemipelagite and rare bentonite beds. Within the Lower Palaeozoic succession, evidence of three phases of ductile deformation is preserved in folds and cleavages (S_1–S_3), and a variety of faults indicate brittle deformation. Subduction of the Iapetus Ocean beneath Laurentia during Ordovician and Silurian times resulted in progressive deformation of deposits on the Laurentian margin (e.g. Barnes et al., 1989; Barnes and Stone, 1999). Deposits on the Avalonian margin were subjected to periodic upheaval, but ductile deformation of the succession did not occur until the early Devonian, when the Avalonian margin was thrust beneath the leading edge of Laurentia. The first two phases of deformation, which affect both the Ordovician Manx Group and the Silurian Dalby Group, are considered to be equivalent to the 'Acadian' deformation of north-west England (Soper et al., 1987). The third tectonic phase is evident only locally and comparable with structures in the Carboniferous rocks, and therefore may be Variscan in age (Fitches et al., 1999).

A range of Palaeozoic intrusive rocks occurs at outcrop on the Isle of Man. Although granitic rocks may underlie much of the Island at depth (Cornwell, 1972), they crop out as three small bodies: the Dhoon granodiorite in the north-east, the Foxdale granite in the central part of the Island, and the Oatlands Complex in the south-east (Figure 3). The Dhoon granodiorite has a minimum age of syn-S_1 while the Foxdale granite, with an isotopic age of around 400 Ma (personal communication, S F Crowley and P S Kennan) postdates the formation of S_2. A suite of acid sheets crops out along the central spine of the Island, and other minor intrusions with a range of compositions are abundant in the Manx Group. The basic intrusive complex at Poortown comprises dykes and sills of dolerite and andesite and may have been emplaced during widespread volcanic activity associated with subduction of the Iapetus Ocean during the late Ordovician (Piper et al., 1999).

Red beds of interpreted Devonian age crop out around Peel, and are termed the Peel Sandstone Group. The group consists of up to about 2000 m of interbedded red sandstone and conglomerate, with minor siltstone, claystone and calcrete palaeosol horizons. These were deposited in dominantly continental braided river and distal alluvial fan environments, though some aeolian sandstone is also present. A semi-arid climate is suggested by the presence of calcrete-bearing soil horizons within the succession. Plate reconstructions suggest that the Peel Sandstone Group accumulated when the Isle of Man region lay at a palaeolatitude of 15° to 20° south of the equator (Allen and Crowley, 1993). The age of the Peel Sandstone Group is contentious owing to a lack of indigenous fossils, but Piper and Crowley (1999) assigned an early Devonian age on the basis of palaeomagnetic evidence. It remains uncertain whether the continental Peel Sandstone Group was deposited in conformity with the underlying marine Silurian rocks, including the Dalby Group, or in a separate unconformable basin (Woodcock et al., 1999b). Presumed exhumation and erosion of the Iapetus collision zone occurred during an early Devonian peak of orogenic activity. The Peel Sandstone Group does not contain a definite Caledonian cleavage, and must have been deposited late in the deformation history (Woodcock et al., 1999b).

Following the Caledonian Orogeny, regional uplift led to near peneplanation of the basement surface before the resumption of deposition in early Carboniferous times (Woodcock et al., 1999). Generally, the relatively weakly deformed sedimentary cover rocks rest with strong unconformity on the Caledonian basement. The cover rocks are locally over 9000 m thick and are cut by predominantly normal faults, with only localised reverse faulting and folding; the Permian to Jurassic succession is also affected by salt-related structures.

During Carboniferous times, the Isle of Man region is thought to have lain a few degrees to the south of the equator and was gradually drifting northwards (Scotese et al., 1979). Carboniferous rocks onshore are restricted to the northern and southern parts of the Island, though only the southern area crops out at the surface (Figure 3). In the north, Carboniferous rocks are concealed by Permo–Triassic strata and Quaternary deposits. Carboniferous sedimentary rocks form an important and extensive part of the offshore succession around the Isle of Man (Jackson et al., 1995; Jackson and Johnson, 1996), though uplift and erosion associated with Variscan inversion have commonly restricted the coal-bearing and red-bed Silesian successions to the centres of major basins or zones adjacent to major faults (Newman, 1999).

The broad tectonosedimentary setting for Carboniferous times is interpreted to be similar to that seen in Ireland and the UK, with rifting during Dinantian times and postextensional 'sag' subsidence during the Silesian. Rift trends were strongly influenced by the grain of the Caledonian basement. In the south of the Island, the Langness Conglomerate Formation lies at the base of the Carboniferous succession and essentially comprises a red-bed sequence. In mid-Dinantian times, a marine transgression introduced a predominantly carbonate succession in this area, initially deposited in a ramp setting, but evolving into a platform environment (Plate 1). In the late Dinantian, this was replaced by more basinal conditions, though 'Yoredale type' successions are more commonly developed beneath the north of the Island. Parts of the Carboniferous succession on the Island can be lithologically and biostratigraphically compared with the succession in northern England, and a revised lithostratigraphical nomenclature that recognises this is used in this report.

Seismic data suggest that about 2500 to 3000 m of Carboniferous sedimentary rocks may be preserved within the Solway Basin (Newman, 1999). The absence of a possible base-Carboniferous reflector in the Peel Basin means that the thickness of the Carboniferous succession is less well constrained in that area. In basinal areas east of the Solway Basin, Dinatian strata are estimated to be over 4000 m thick, and are thought to consist of mainly shallow-water to deltaic deposits (Newman, 1999). In contrast, over platform areas such as the Manx–Lakeland Ridge, the Dinantian is represented by a thin succession of shallow-water carbonates. Within the Eubonia and Keys sub-basins of the East Irish Sea Basin, up to 4000 or 5000 m of Carboniferous sedimentary rocks may be preserved (Jackson et al., 1995). The shallow-water Dinantian facies inferred for the Peel, Solway, Lagman and Keys basins and onshore Cumbria contrast significantly with the deep-water hemipelagic facies described from the southern tip of the Isle of Man and the Craven Basin and Garstang areas.

The Namurian marked a change from the deposition of carbonate-dominated successions to siliciclastic-dominated sedimentation. The Isle of Man, the Solway Basin and the Lake District are characterised by cyclic shallow-water deltaic successions during the Namurian, with the Isle of Man and the Lake District forming highs where sedimentation was intermittent. To the south, basinal conditions appear to have persisted throughout most of the Namurian and led to the accumulation of thick packages of mudstone, which include good petroleum source rocks. By the start of Westphalian times, a flat, low-lying fluviodeltaic environment was widely developed. Only erosional remnants of the once more extensive Westphalian succession are preserved owing to Variscan uplift and erosion. Westphalian rocks are recorded in boreholes from the northern part of the Isle of Man, in the centre of the Solway Basin, on the Ogham Platform, in the Eubonia Basin and onshore in the Canonbie area of west Cumbria.

Variscan deformation, in latest Carboniferous times, is recorded in the Isle of Man region by reversal on pre-existing normal faults and associated basin inversion (see Figure 15). The basin inversion appears to have been most pronounced over, and to the north of, the Manx–Lakeland Ridge, where Dinantian strata commonly subcrop the Permo–Triassic cover. In an alternative model for end-Carboniferous uplift, Corcoran and Clayton (1999) and Quirk et al. (1999a) postulated a process of thermal doming.

Plate 1 Monoclinal fold in bedded limestone of the Scarlett Point Member (Bowland Shale Formation). Scarlett Point (P 018733).

Following Variscan inversion and regional uplift and erosion, the resumption of deposition occurred during the Late Permian. Throughout much of Permo–Triassic times, the Isle of Man region formed part of a rift system that extended from the English Channel Basin to the western Scottish offshore basins. As in early Carboniferous times, rift trends were strongly influenced by basement structure and some aspects of basin configuration were similar to those of the Carboniferous rift system, though new major, basin-margin, normal faults with north-north-west or north-west trends were developed. In early Triassic times, rifting intensified during deposition of the Sherwood Sandstone Group and continued during deposition of the Mercia Mudstone Group, though with an increasing component of thermal subsidence. The deposition of salt, both in the Permian Cumbrian Coast Group and the Triassic Mercia Mudstone Group, led to the local development of salt-related folds, detachment faults and major collapse graben (see Figure 18).

At the base of the Permian succession of the Isle of Man region, the Appleby Group comprises scattered accumulations of largely aeolian sandstone that pass laterally into the locally developed alluvial fan breccia of the Appleby and Enler groups. These strata are overlapped by the widespread evaporitic and marginal marine (locally aeolian) deposits of the Cumbrian Coast and Belfast groups (see Figure 21). The Appleby Group is characterised by abrupt changes in thickness, but over most of the Isle of Man region it is probably less than 10 m thick. In basinal areas of low relief, the widespread absence of the Appleby Group and equivalents may be partly related to low surface run off in an arid climate, and the development of karstic topography with underground drainage systems beneath the penecontemporaneous Dinantian limestone surface outcrop. The Enler Group is recognised within the North Channel Basin where it comprises a breccia formation overlain by a sandstone formation. Within the Isle of Man region, the Cumbrian Coast Group reaches up to about 200 m in thickness and comprises two broad facies belts. In the basinal areas, which were characterised by more rapid subsidence, evaporites formed during successive transgressions of the Bakevellia Sea, and are overlain by mudstone. Towards the more slowly subsiding basin margins, this facies belt passes into marginal marine, estuarine and fluvial/lacustrine mudstone, which is commonly overlain by aeolian sandstone. The Belfast Group, in the North Channel Basin, is laterally equivalent to the Cumbrian Coast Group, and consists dominantly of arenaceous strata.

Triassic rocks within the Isle of Man region comprise the arenaceous Sherwood Sandstone Group overlain by the argillaceous and evaporitic Mercia Mudstone Group, which is itself overlain by the relatively thin Penarth Group (see Figures 23 and 24). The Sherwood Sandstone Group reaches up to about 1400 m in thickness, and consists of predominantly fluvial and aeolian sandstone. Initially, a large braided river on a northerly directed palaeoslope laid down fluvial deposits (Rottington Sandstone Member). Subsequently, aeolian and sabkha depositional environments became widespread with periodically dominant fluvial conditions (Calder Sandstone Member and Ormskirk Sandstone Formation). The Mercia Mudstone Group reaches about 2000 m in thickness within the Solway Firth Basin, but over 3000 m in the East Irish Sea Basin; it comprises alternating units of mudstone and halite (Jackson et al., 1995). Depositional environments alternated between episodes of halite precipitation from brine pans and phases dominated by the accumulation of lacustrine laminate and aeolian dust (Jackson and Johnson, 1996). The succession is extensively deformed by halokinetic structures, such as salt pillows, diapirs and shallowly dipping *décollements*. The Mercia Mudstone Group was probably deposited across virtually the entire Isle of Man region, but post-Early Jurassic erosion has left only large erosional remnants, which are probably coincident with areas of greatest Late Triassic subsidence. The overlying Penarth Group comprises dark grey pyritous marine mudstone overlain by grey-green mudstone and limestone. The pyritous mudstone was formed during a marine transgression that encroached from the south as a precursor to a major early Jurassic transgression.

The dominantly marine mudstone and bituminous limestone of the Lias Group were deposited over practically the entire Isle of Man region, though subsequent erosion has reduced their present-day distribution to scattered remnant outliers (Figure 1). Indeed, the post-Early Jurassic tectonostratigraphical history of the Isle of Man region is difficult to reconstruct, because with the exception of a veneer of Quaternary and Recent sediments, mid-Jurassic and younger sedimentary deposits are absent from the Island and the adjacent offshore area. This is principally the result of two phases of uplift and erosion in Cainozoic times. Uplift and erosion during the Palaeogene were associated with the development of the Iceland Plume (e.g. White and Lovell, 1997), whereas Miocene uplift and erosion were probably related to Alpine movements (Newman, 1999). During the Palaeogene, the north-west British Isles and the Atlantic Margin formed part of the North Atlantic Igneous Province, which was characterised by the development of extensive lava flows, sill complexes, dyke swarms and central igneous complexes. In the offshore Isle of Man region, Palaeogene igneous rocks comprise a suite of mafic minor intrusions that are most evident from their strong magnetic signature within the less magnetic Permo–Triassic sedimentary cover (see Figures 23 and 24). Onshore, east-south-east-trending olivine dolerite dykes are best exposed on the coasts of the Isle of Man. One of the most prominent Palaeogene dykes in the Isle of Man region, known as the Fleetwood Dyke, forms a large and complex intrusion comprising a number of separate dykes and sheets arranged *en échelon*.

The glacial succession exposed on the Isle of Man largely formed during the last or Late Devensian cold stage (oxygen isotope stage 2) and comparatively little is known about the deposits of earlier glacial and interglacial stages that locally occur at depth. The succession can be divided into high-level and low-level suites (see Figure 29). The high-level suite occupies upland areas underlain by the Manx Group and comprises relatively thin and locally derived glacial diamicts reworked by periglacial processes. The low-level suite, occupying the whole of the northern plain, parts of the plain of Malew and the Peel embayment, is dominantly composed of material foreign to the Island. These deposits comprise a wide variety of glacigenic sediments, including diamict, sand and gravel and massive and laminated clay; they are associated with a prominent glacial morphology. The Quaternary deposits on the northern plain reach up to about 250 m in thickness, and include the Bride Moraine, which forms one of the largest and most complex moraine structures in the British Isles. The offshore Quaternary deposits around the Isle of Man are a complex succession of glacial diamict, outwash, glaciomarine and marine sediments that range in age to oxygen isotope stage 6 or earlier. These deposits are recognised on seismic profiles both by their unconformable relationship with pre-Quaternary strata and their commonly subhorizontal layering. They range in thickness from zero close inshore around the south of the Island to about 150 m off the Point of Ayre, though 30 to 40 km offshore the Quaternary deposits consistently exceed 50 m in thickness. The Quaternary deposits are being actively reworked in the modern environment. Gravel-rich sea-bed sediments predominate within 10 to 20 km of the coast, passing into sand-dominated sediments and finally mud to the east and west of the Island (Jackson et al., 1995).

2 Crustal structure

In earliest Ordovician times the crust which now underlies the Isle of Man lay at high southerly latitudes close to the northern margin of the Gondwanan supercontinent, and was separated from the equatorial Scottish (Laurentian) terranes by the wide Iapetus Ocean (Cocks and Fortey, 1982, 1990). The Isle of Man, together with the southern parts of Britain and Ireland, lay on a microcontinental component of Gondwana which has been termed 'Eastern Avalonia' because of similarities to the Avalon terrane of eastern Newfoundland and parts of maritime Canada (Soper, 1986). Eastern Avalonia rifted from Gondwana in the early Ordovician, drifted northwards and converged with Laurentia during Silurian times. The collisional boundary between terranes originating from the Laurentian and Avalonian sides of the ocean is known as the 'Iapetus Suture', and now lies in the vicinity of the Isle of Man.

Caledonian basement outcrops within the Manx region (Figure 3) are limited to the Isle of Man (see Chapter 3) and the Southern Uplands, and the main evidence for regional crustal structure comes from geophysics. Seismic reflection and potential field (gravity and magnetic) data provide information on both lower and upper crustal structure and allow the identification of three distinct crustal structural zones. These are termed, from north to south, Laurentian crust, the Iapetus Convergence Zone and Avalonian crust (Figure 4).

Three main basement structural trends are evident, although over substantial parts of the region these can only be inferred from trends in the sedimentary cover. The important north-east–south-west 'Caledonian' basement trend is widespread, but most clearly defined over the Iapetus Convergence Zone. A north-west–south-east cross-trend is prominent in both Laurentian and Avalonian crustal zones and is interpreted as reflecting a greater heterogeneity of basement trends. Structures with the north-west–south-east structure may have formed in Caledonian times (Kelling and Walsh, 1970) as 'transfer' faults, compartmentalising the Caledonian thrust stacks, or may be much younger, Variscan, features (England and Soper, 1997). A third trend, north-north-east–south-south-west, is restricted to the Iapetus Convergence Zone west of the Isle of Man.

LAURENTIAN CRUST

Laurentian crust lies beneath the northernmost part of the Manx region (Figure 4). At surface, its southern margin is made up of a succession of fragmentary volcanic arcs and backarc basins accreted during the Early Palaeozoic, culminating in the accretionary thrust stack of the Southern Uplands terrane (Barnes et al., 1987; Stone, 1995; Barnes and Stone, 1999). The latter comprises north-east-trending, near vertical, fault-bounded slices within each of which a thin sequence of oceanic mudrock passes up northwards into a thick turbidite sandstone sequence. The sandstone in each slice represents a restricted stratigraphical interval which, with the age of the transition from the mudrock, becomes progressively younger in successive slices southwards. It is supposed that similar structures extend south-west beneath the northern part of the Manx region, where the regional structural grain follows the north-east-south-west Caledonian trend. The prominent north-west–south-east 'transfer' trend is well developed locally, in particular as structures in the Upper Palaeozoic sedimentary cover, owing to reactivation of some of these faults as basin-bounding structures (e.g. to the North Channel and Stranraer basins) (see Chapter 4).

The Laurentian crust in the Manx region has geophysical characteristics which distinguish it from the area to the south. Seismic reflection data from the WINCH 2 profile indicate that the Laurentian middle crust is poorly reflective (Figure 5; Brewer et al., 1983; Hall et al., 1984). Aeromagnetic anomalies over south-west Scotland and central Ireland (Figure 6a) indicate that it contains blocks of magnetic mid-crustal material (Kimbell and Stone, 1995; Morris and Max, 1995). These may be composed of Precambrian crystalline basement and/or magnetic igneous rocks generated by arc magmatism associated with the closure of the Iapetus Ocean (Kimbell and Stone, 1995). The Laurentian lower crust in the Manx region appears mostly unreflective on the WINCH 2 profile, with a poorly imaged Moho (Figure 5), although this may be due to problems with seismic data quality in the North Channel.

IAPETUS CONVERGENCE ZONE

A broad zone, here termed the Iapetus Convergence Zone, trends north-east-south-west through the middle of the Manx region (Figure 4). Rocks within the Iapetus Convergence Zone are likely to be of predominantly Avalonian affinity, with structures lying parallel or near parallel to the Iapetus Suture. This is seen in the strong north-east–south-west trends in the overlying cover rocks (Chapter 4). The Iapetus Convergence Zone is geophysically quite distinct from the Laurentian and Avalonian crust to the north and south.

Long wavelength aeromagnetic anomalies are aligned broadly north-east–south-west, with a magnetic low corresponding to the Iapetus Convergence Zone (Figure 6). This may be caused, in part, by a depression in the underlying magnetic basement rocks beneath the Solway Firth and Peel basins (there is a correlation between the lowest magnetic values and the depocentres of these basins). However, the continuity of the magnetic low over central and southern Ireland (Figure 6a) indicates a significant contribution from rocks of anomalously low magnetisation in the underlying, pre-Carboniferous basement (Figure 5). It may be that these are

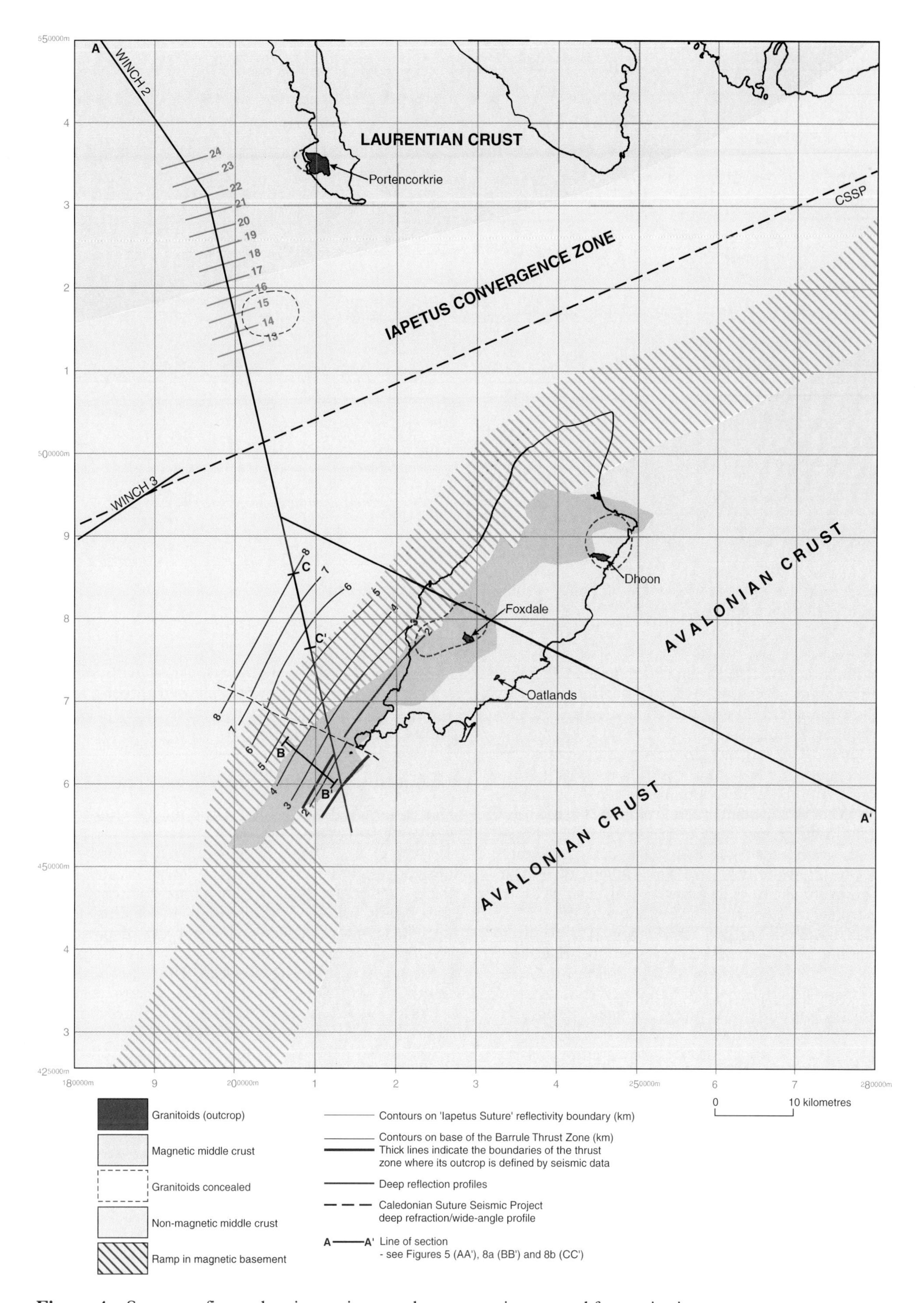

Figure 4 Summary figure showing main crustal structures interpreted from seismic and magnetic data.

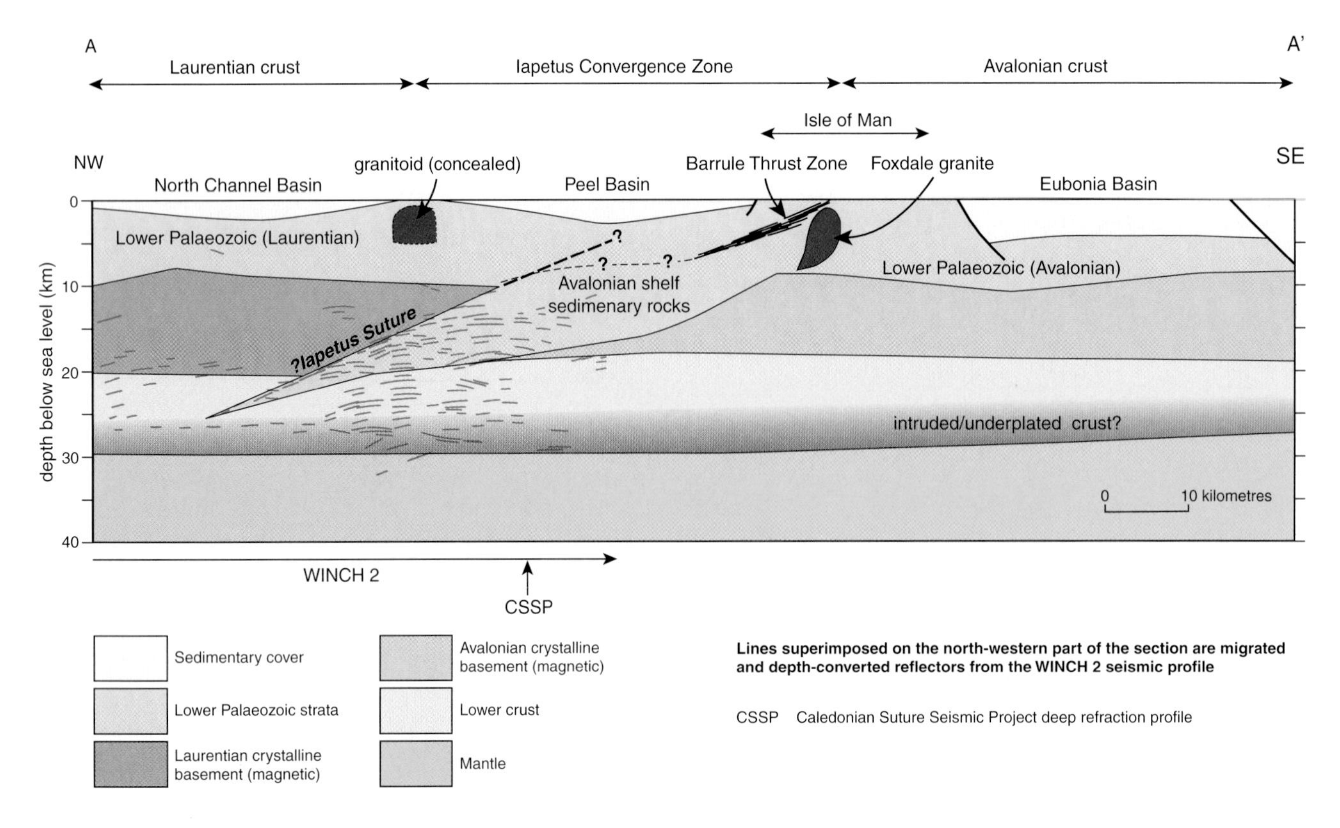

Figure 5 Crustal cross-section including part of the WINCH 2 seismic profile (see Figure 4 for location).

metasedimentary rocks, originally deposited at the northern margin of Eastern Avalonia and subsequently partially subducted during the final closure of the Iapetus Ocean (Kimbell and Stone, 1995).

The Iapetus Convergence Zone is the only area in the Manx region where the north-east–south-west Caledonian trend was the dominant structural control on subsequent sedimentary basin evolution (Chapter 4). Variations in the gravity field are mainly caused by structures in the sedimentary cover, so gravity images (Figure 7) help to illustrate this structural inheritance. The north-westward extent of the Iapetus Convergence Zone is somewhat indeterminate. At shallow depths it is expressed by the southward termination of the north-west-trending Permo–Triassic basins of the Southern Uplands. Locally, gravity data clearly indicate that the North Channel and Luce Bay basins are truncated to the south by a north-east-trending lineament (Figure 7; Stone, 1995). East of this the boundary of the Iapetus Convergence Zone appears to be offset southwards, as indicated by the north-west-trending Dumfries Basin which extends farther south (Akhurst et al., in press).

The south-east margin of the Iapetus Convergence Zone corresponds to the north-west margin of the magnetic Avalonian middle crust. The ramp-like geometry of this boundary was modelled by Kimbell and Quirk (1999) who estimated that it lies at depths of 8 to 10 km beneath the south-eastern part of the Isle of Man but dips north-west to much greater depth (Figures 4, 5). When projected upwards, the ramp aligns roughly with a prominent zone of anomalous magnetisation at shallow levels, corresponding to a belt of short wavelength magnetic disturbances extending north-east–south-west along the axis of the Isle of Man (Figures 4, 6b; Kimbell and Quirk, 1999). The ramp is also spatially associated with dipping seismic reflectors in Lower Palaeozoic rocks to the south-west of the Isle of Man, here termed the Barrule Thrust Zone (see below).

Iapetus Suture and Barrule Thrust Zone

The earliest seismic evidence for the Iapetus Suture was provided by the WINCH 2 deep seismic profile (Brewer et al., 1983), which imaged a north-west-dipping reflectivity boundary at lower crustal levels north-west of the Isle of Man. This boundary separates poorly reflective 'Laurentian' lower crust to the north from more reflective lower crust of presumed 'Avalonian' affinity, to the south, and was interpreted as the Iapetus Suture (Hall et al., 1984; Beamish and Smythe, 1986; Soper et al., 1992). Depth contours on this lower crustal interface are illustrated on Figure 4.

Additional north-west-dipping basement reflections are imaged updip of the lower crustal feature, at much shallower depths, both on a grid of seismic lines south-west of the Isle of Man (Figure 8a) and also on WINCH 2 (Figure 8b; Hall et al., 1984). These shallow reflections can be mapped over an area of some 300 km^2, depth contours on the basal event being illustrated on Figure 4. The basal reflector dips roughly west-north-west at 22°, from close to the sea bed to depths of about 8 km. The reflections are interpreted as a Caledonian imbricate thrust stack (Quirk et al., 1999b), here termed the Barrule Thrust Zone. The thrust stack has a maximum perpendicular thickness of at least 1300 m; the higher thrusts are steeper than the basal thrust, locally dipping at more than 30°. Structure contours on the basal thrust trend

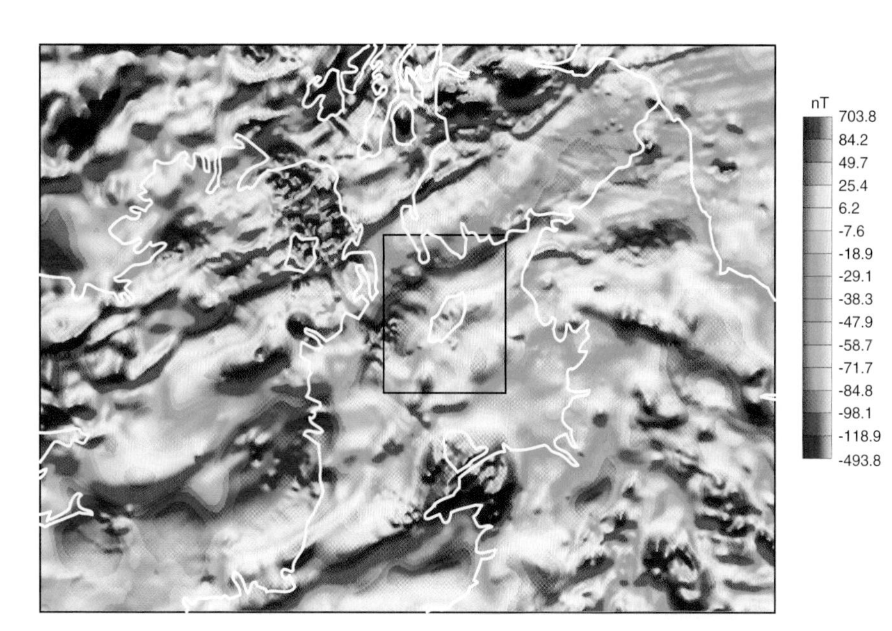

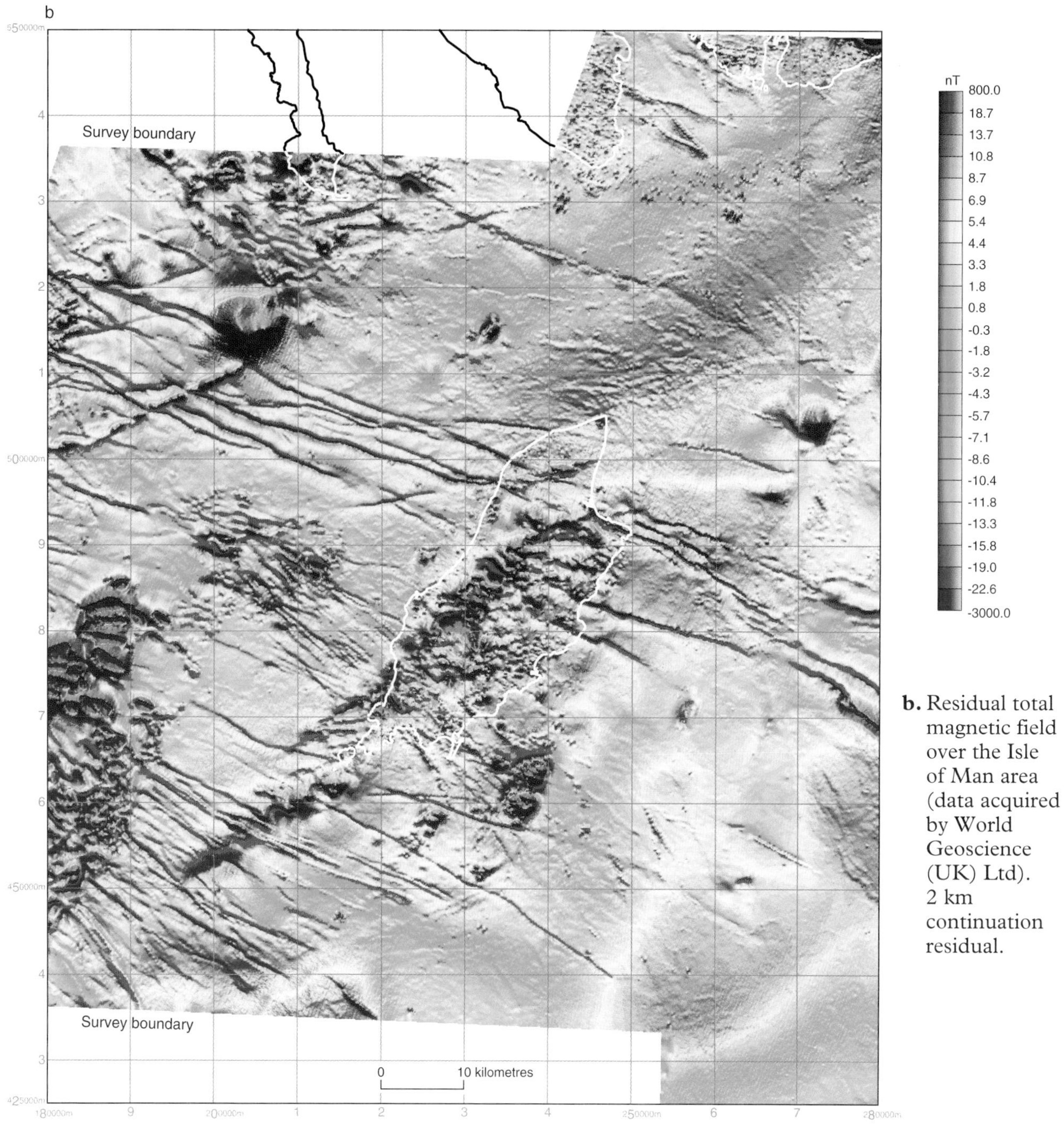

Figure 6 Aeromagnetic images (colour shaded-relief, illuminated from the north).

a. Regional reduced-to-pole magnetic field (BGS data). 2 km upward continued.

b. Residual total magnetic field over the Isle of Man area (data acquired by World Geoscience (UK) Ltd). 2 km continuation residual.

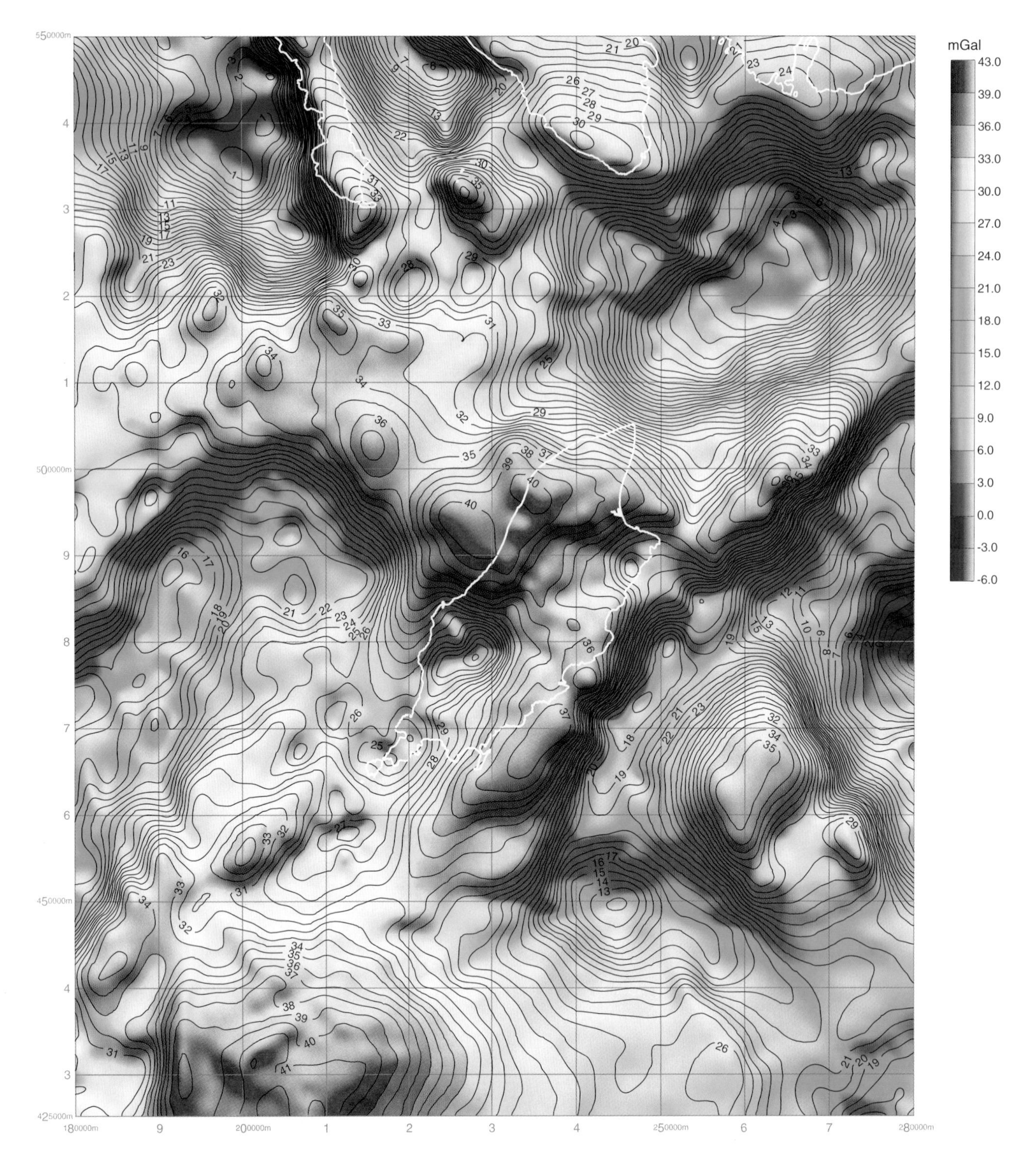

Figure 7 Colour shaded-relief image of gravity data from the Isle of Man area. Illumination is from the north. Superimposed contours are at 1 mGal intervals. Based on surveys by Cornwell (1972), BGS and Western Geophysical. Bouguer reduction density = 2.7 Mgm^{-3} (onshore) and 2.2 Mgm^{-3} (offshore).

north-north-east, with a possible small sinistral 'transfer' offset south-west of the Calf of Man (Figure 4). Projecting the seismically imaged reflections updip (south-eastwards) towards the surface suggests that the basal thrust would crop out on the Isle of Man, along a trend closely corresponding to the north–east-trending belt of magnetic anomalies that lies along the axis of the Island (Figure 6). Although no specific thrust structure can be identified onshore, Quirk et al. (1999b) have suggested that the offshore Barrule Thrust Zone correlates with a belt of imbricate structures in the Lower Palaeozoic rocks of the Isle of Man, traversing the Island from south-west to north-east. Zones of high strain in the uppermost part of the thrust stack, or in its hanging wall block, may explain features such as the Niarbyl Shear Zone (Chapter 3), which crops out on the west coast of the Island. The Barrule Thrust Zone is markedly reflective. This may be caused by a thick development of altered or mineralised fault rocks, but is also consistent with the presence of igneous material intruded into the fault zone (see Chapter 8).

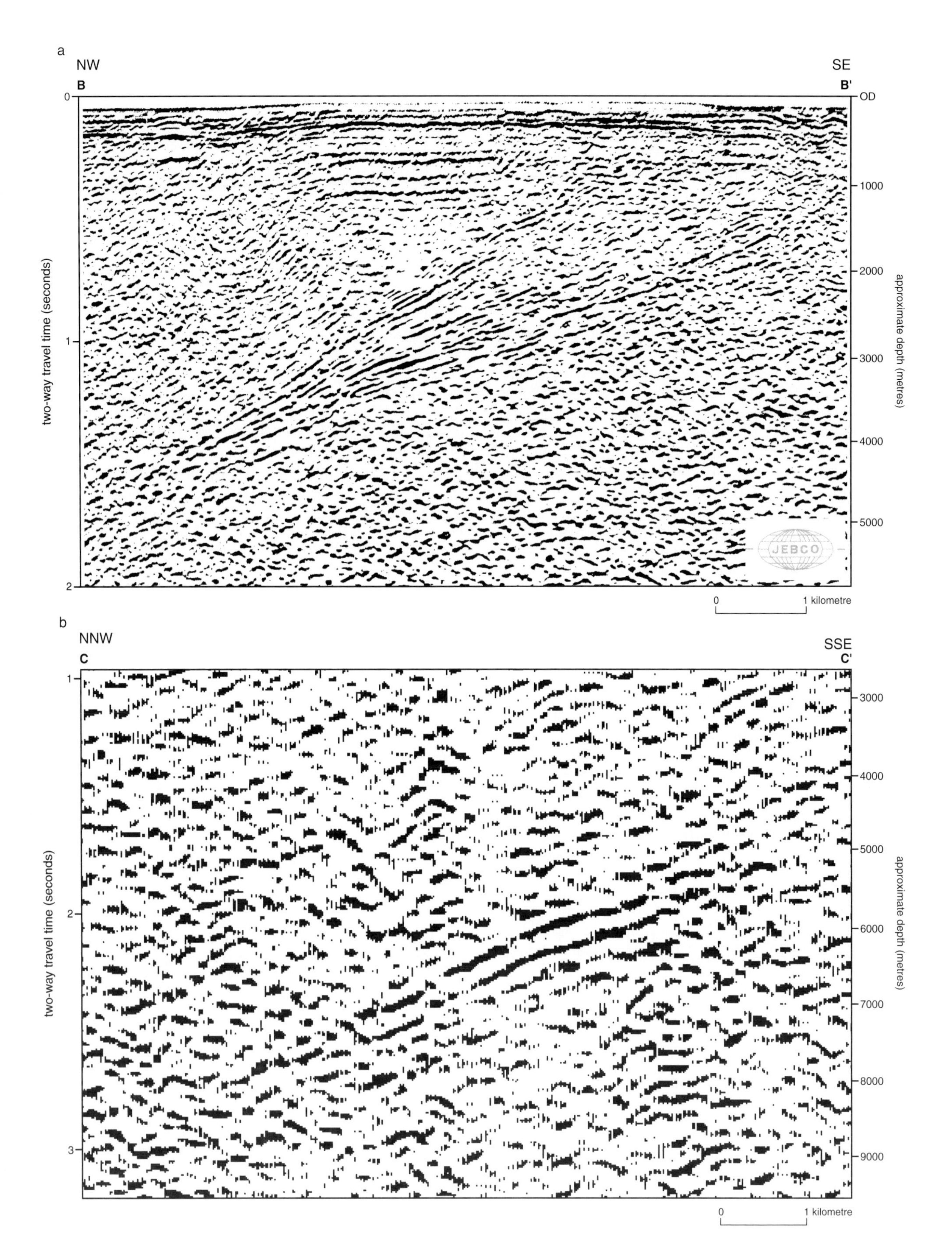

Figure 8 Seismic profiles south-west of the Isle of Man, Barrule Thrust Zone.

a. Imbricate thrusts penetrating close to the sea bed. Data supplied courtesy of JEBCO Seismic (UK) Ltd.

b. Basal thrust at greater depth on WINCH 2. (See Figure 4 for location.)

The reason for the anomalous shallow magnetisation associated with this zone is not known but it may be speculated that it arose as a result of secondary processes perhaps also associated with the observed higher metamorphic grade along this axis. For example, ilmenite is abundant as a metamorphic mineral phase formed during the early phases of deformation in the pelitic rocks within this zone (e.g. Power and Barnes, 1999). In addition, as discussed above, the effects of igneous material intruded into the fault zone cannot be ruled out.

The structure of the Barrule Thrust Zone at depth is uncertain. It lies above the north-west-dipping ramp at the edge of magnetic Avalonian middle crust (Figure 4). Kimbell and Quirk (1999) suggested a linkage between the basement ramp and overlying thrust zone, but this requires a steeper dip for the latter than is indicated by the seismic evidence (Figure 5). An alternative suggestion is that the Barrule Thrust Zone passes downward at a somewhat lower angle to link with the lower crustal interface interpreted as the Iapetus Suture. The resultant ramp-flat-ramp geometry (Figure 5) is very similar to that proposed by Chadwick and Holliday (1991) for Acadian thrusting within the Iapetus Convergence Zone beneath northern England. In the model of Chadwick and Holliday (1991) thrusts observed near the surface are situated entirely within Avalonian crust, well to the south of the (faunally defined) Iapetus Suture at shallow depths. This is consistent with the presence of rocks of Avalonian affinity on both sides of the Barrule Thrust Zone on the Isle of Man. A possible objection to linking the lower and upper crustal structures in this way lies in their apparently differing strikes. The Barrule Thrust Zone trends north-north-east, whereas the (admittedly poorly constrained) strike of the Iapetus Suture appears to be more east-north-east or north-east (Figure 4; Soper et al., 1992). Support for this change in direction also comes from the regional aeromagnetic data (Figure 6; Kimbell and Quirk, 1999).

Kimbell and Quirk (1999) suggested that a structural precursor to the Barrule Thrust Zone was initiated in Avalonian basement before the closure of the Iapetus Ocean. It may have originated when the basement was assembled in late Precambrian to early Cambrian times and was then reactivated during early Palaeozoic extension and subsequent continental collision. A possible analogue is provided by the Causey Pike Fault in the Lake District, which lies in a similar position with respect to the regional magnetic anomaly pattern. The Causey Pike Fault is an Acadian compressional structure which appears to have been formed by reactivation of a major, early Ordovician normal fault close to the margin of Eastern Avalonia (Webb and Cooper, 1988; Cooper et al., in press).

Chadwick and Holliday (1991) proposed that the Acadian basement thrusts of northern England suffered extensional reactivation in early Carboniferous times, thereby controlling development of the Northumberland–Solway Basin. It may be that the Barrule Thrust Zone behaved in a similar manner. Although the south-east margin of the Carboniferous Peel Basin is not clearly imaged on the seismic data, the apparent presence of north-west-dipping normal faults and tilt blocks in the hanging wall block of the thrust zone, suggest that its extensional reactivation played a part in controlling the Dinantian development of the basin.

AVALONIAN CRUST

Avalonian crust lies beneath the south-eastern part of the Manx region (Figure 4), demarcated to the north-west by the magnetic basement ramp in the middle crust. The Foxdale and Dhoon granites were intruded into the north-west flank of the Avalonian crustal block and appear to have contributed to the development of a rigid basement 'buttress' at depth beneath the Isle of Man. This structure maintained its integrity throughout the subsequent evolution of the region, forming the elevated Manx–Lakeland Ridge (Chapter 4). The basement buttress is of regional extent, passing eastwards into the Lake District and Alston blocks of northern England, themselves elevated blocks underpinned by granitic intrusions.

Seismically the Avalonian lower crust is quite reflective, with a well-defined seismic reflection Moho (Figure 5; Hall et al., 1984). The magnetic middle crust is interpreted to be the north-western part of a broad area of crystalline Avalonian basement that extends beneath southern Britain and the south-eastern part of Ireland (Figure 6a), where such basement crops out in the Rosslare Terrane (Kimbell and Quirk, 1999). As with the Laurentian crust, a north-west–south-east basement trend is important within the sedimentary cover, for example controlling the development of the very large Keys Fault (Chapter 4) in the East Irish Sea Basin. There are numerous faults with a similar trend on the Isle of Man (e.g. Quirk et al., 1999b), though only a few of these show large displacements.

CALEDONIAN INTRUSIONS

Large numbers of minor intrusions of a wide range of compositions occur within the Palaeozoic rocks of the Isle of Man, many of which were deformed by the Caledonian (early Devonian) orogenic events. Larger intrusions at outcrop are restricted to three relatively small granitic plutons and a basic intrusive complex, all hosted within the Ordovician metasedimentary rocks of the Manx Group. The Dhoon granodiorite body in the north-east of the Island [SC 46 87], was emplaced before, or during the formation of S_1 cleavage (Power and Barnes, 1999). To the south-west, the Foxdale granite [SC 29 77] was emplaced somewhat later, postdating the S_2 cleavage; combined whole-rock and muscovite Rb–Sr data indicate an age of about 400 Ma, although with a high degree of uncertainty (personal communication, S F Crowley and P S Kennan). A series of acid sheets crop out along the central spine of the Island (Lamplugh, 1903; Simpson, 1964) and may be related to the granitic bodies described above, or to underlying granites. A third granitic body is present at Oatlands in the south-east of the Island [SC 323 725]. Now poorly exposed, it was described by Lamplugh (1903) as ranging in composition from diorite to granite. The basic intrusive complex which crops out at Poortown [SC 269 832] comprises dykes and sills of pyroxene-rich and plagioclase-rich dolerite and plagioclase-phyric andesite. It is attributed to the widespread volcanic activity associated with subduction of the Iapetus Ocean during the late Ordovician (Piper et al., 1999; Power and Crowley, 1999).

Gravity data (Figure 7) indicate that substantial, low density plutons underlie the granite outcrops at Foxdale and Dhoon (Figure 4; Cornwell, 1972). Cornwell's (1972) model for the Foxdale pluton extended to a depth of about 10 km, and had a relatively shallow roof region underlying an area about 10 km long (in a north-east–south-west direction) by 4 to 5 km wide. Samples from the Dhoon granite have an average density of 2.71 Mgm^{-3}, which is similar to that of the surrounding Manx Group (2.73 Mgm^{-3}). The density contrast is insufficient to explain the observed anomaly, so it is necessary to postulate that the exposed granite is underlain by a lower density component (Cornwell, 1972). Although there is some evidence of a relative gravity low along the axis of the Island between the two plutons, the sharp gradient on its north-west side indicates that it is likely to be the result of density contrasts within the exposed Lower Palaeozoic rocks or shallow underlying basement rather than related to deep-seated granite components (Cornwell, 1972). This feature may therefore be a further shallow expression of the Barrule Thrust Zone (Kimbell and Quirk, 1999). Furthermore, the gravity data (Figure 7) suggest that emplacement of the Foxdale and Dhoon bodies was perhaps controlled by the intersection of the Barrule Thrust Zone and north-west-trending basement 'transfer' structures.

Although the Foxdale and Dhoon bodies lie within the north-east-trending belt of magnetic disturbance along the axis of the Island (Figure 6), magnetic field variations over the shallow parts of the plutons are small compared with other parts of the disturbance, so it is unlikely that the granitic rocks are the source of the anomalies. Magnetic basic intrusive rocks of probable Ordovician age occur at Poortown [SC 269 832], but airborne (Figure 6) and ground magnetic surveys (Piper et al., 1999) indicate that this is a small, isolated occurrence which does not lie within the main anomaly belt.

Further magnetic Caledonian intrusions occur in the Manx region to the north of the Iapetus Suture; the Portencorkrie diorite–granodiorite complex is exposed on the Rhins of Galloway [NX 090 350] and a similar, but concealed, body may be the source of a circular magnetic anomaly about 20 km to the south-south-west, just south of the North Channel Basin (Stone, 1995).

MOHO

The seismic reflection Moho beneath Laurentian crust is not clearly imaged on the deep seismic data (WINCH 2), but to the south it becomes clearer. Beneath the wedge of Avalonian crust that lies under the Iapetus Convergence Zone (Figure 5), the Moho lies at about 9 seconds of two way travel time (approximately 28 km depth), deepening gradually southwards to about 10 seconds of two way travel time (about 31 km depth), south of the Isle of Man. The seismic reflection evidence is somewhat at variance with data from the CSSP deep refraction profile (Figure 4), which indicate a rapid increase in seismic velocity from 6.8 kms^{-1} at 24 km to 7.8 kms^{-1} at 26 km depth. The refraction velocity field was interpreted as a shallow Moho by Jacob et al. (1985), but Lewis (1986) interpreted the data as signifying a high velocity lower crust. The latter could be caused by either pervasive intrusion or underplating of the lower crust with mafic material. Both are consistent with the Palaeogene igneous episode (Chapter 8) and the latter is consistent with the proposed Paleocene epeirogenic uplift which affected the region (Chapter 4). The gravity evidence supports the presence of an area of crust characterised by either a relatively shallow Moho or dense lower crust, centred about 80 km south-east of the Isle of Man (compare with Cope, 1994).

3 Lower Palaeozoic

The Caledonian basement rocks cropping out over much of the Isle of Man and its nearshore area comprise a thick pile of Lower Palaeozoic metasedimentary strata. They are mainly turbiditic rocks dominated by laminated mudstone and siltstone but varying from mudstone to units composed largely of thin- to medium-bedded, typically fine-grained sandstone. Debrite (pebbly mudstone) composed of intrabasinal material also occurs in parts of the succession. Volcanic rocks form a minor component of the succession locally. The succession is essentially steeply dipping to vertical and north-north-east- to east-north-east-striking such that outcrops of the different formations lie parallel to the axis of the Island (Figure 3). In detail, however, the dip varies widely due to folding.

The history of geological research on the Lower Palaeozoic rocks of the Isle of Man was reviewed by Ford et al. (1999). Until recently these rocks were thought to be entirely of Ordovician (Arenig) age and broadly equivalent to the Skiddaw Group of north-west England (e.g. Harkness and Nicholson, 1866; Cooper et al., 1995), although the 'Manx Slate Series' was separately designated by Lamplugh (Geological Survey, 1898; Lamplugh, 1903). In line with modern nomenclature, the term 'Manx Group' was introduced by Simpson (1968). However, Howe (1999) showed that part of the succession is Silurian (probably Wenlock) in age and hence it has since been separated as the 'Dalby Group' (Morris et al., 1999). Minor intrusions are abundant, many predating or contemporaneous with late Silurian or early Devonian deformation of the succession. Three large granitic intrusions range from syn-tectonic to post-tectonic and may represent a much larger granitic body at depth (see Chapter 2).

The primary geological survey of the Isle of Man was carried out in the 1890s by G W Lamplugh, and a map at the scale of one inch to one mile was published (Geological Survey, 1898) (Figure 9) as well as a substantial memoir (Lamplugh, 1903). Together with his field maps and interpreted clean copies this still provides the most comprehensive and detailed set of observations available on the geology of the Island and all subsequent work has drawn heavily on this information. Within his 'Manx Slate Series', Lamplugh distinguished four mappable lithostratigraphical units (Figure 9), intercalated with an otherwise undivided succession of variably laminated mudrocks. Two units, part of the 'Lonan Flags' on the south-east of the Island and the 'Niarbyl Flags' on the north-west coast, comprise interbedded sandstone and mudstone and were tentatively correlated as the lowest exposed part of the succession. Much of the succession considered to overlie the flags was undivided but three facies were distinguished. Sporadic outcrops dominated by quartz arenite were mapped as the 'Agneash and other Grits' and outcrops of black mudstone were mapped as the 'Barrule Slates'. A facies now recognised as pebbly mudstone was regarded by Lamplugh (1903, pp.55–71; Lamplugh and Watts, 1895) as being of tectonic origin and mapped as 'crush-conglomerate' without primary stratigraphical significance. Lamplugh considered the large-scale structure of the Island to be a 'synclinorium' with a north-east-trending hinge along the centre of the Island to explain the repetition of the outcrop of Barrule Slates and correlation of the Lonan and Niarbyl flags. In detail, the outcrop pattern was considered to be controlled by intense upright folding, locally causing near horizontal sheet dip.

Blake (1905) proposed that the 'crush-conglomerates' of Lamplugh (1903) were primary fragmental deposits, based on their association with a host sedimentary rock of dark mudstone and their limited stratigraphical range. He considered that the succession from the Agneash Grit upwards was repeated by large reverse faults rather than by folding, although he suggested that the flags formed an unconformable cover to this assemblage.

There was a hiatus in study of the Manx Group until the 1950s. Way-up evidence was used for the first time by Gillott (1956) to confirm Lamplugh's view that the Lonan Flags passed stratigraphically up into the Agneash Grits. He substantiated Blake's views on the origin of the breccia units and their stratigraphical position above the Barrule Slates, and defined two higher units, the Sulby Flags and the Cronk Sumark Slates, in the north of the Island. Detailed consideration of the structure was undertaken by Simpson (1963), broadly following Lamplugh's ideas but invoking a large, relatively simple syncline refolded by later structures. Simpson also added to the stratigraphical subdivision (Figure 10).

Fossils had thus far played little part in consideration of the Manx Group, being mostly either of dubious organic origin or trace fossils of little value for dating (Lamplugh, 1903, pp.89–95). A single early Ordovician graptolite specimen from Cronk Sumark (Bolton, 1899; Rushton, 1993) proved the age of the succession and the general correlation with the Skiddaw Group. Studies of microfossil assemblages (Downie and Ford, 1966; Molyneux, 1979) eventually provided a major advance. Diagnostic microfloras from a few localities (Molyneux, 1979, 1999) demonstrated that earlier structural models of the Manx Group were untenable but the new data were insufficient to establish an alternative model. Speculation on the structure and stratigraphy therefore continued (e.g. Roberts et al., 1990; Cooper et al., 1995), although a new graptolite locality in the Lonan Flags (Rushton, 1993) supported the early Arenig age assigned to that unit.

A further attempt in the mid-1990s to resolve the stratigraphy and structure of the Manx Group (Woodcock et al., 1999a) was based primarily on studies of the coastal sections but also extended into some inland areas. A parallel PhD thesis study by Burnett (1999) covered more of the inland outcrop. Lithostratigraphical subdivision of the Ordovician rocks was formalised by Woodcock et al. (1999c),

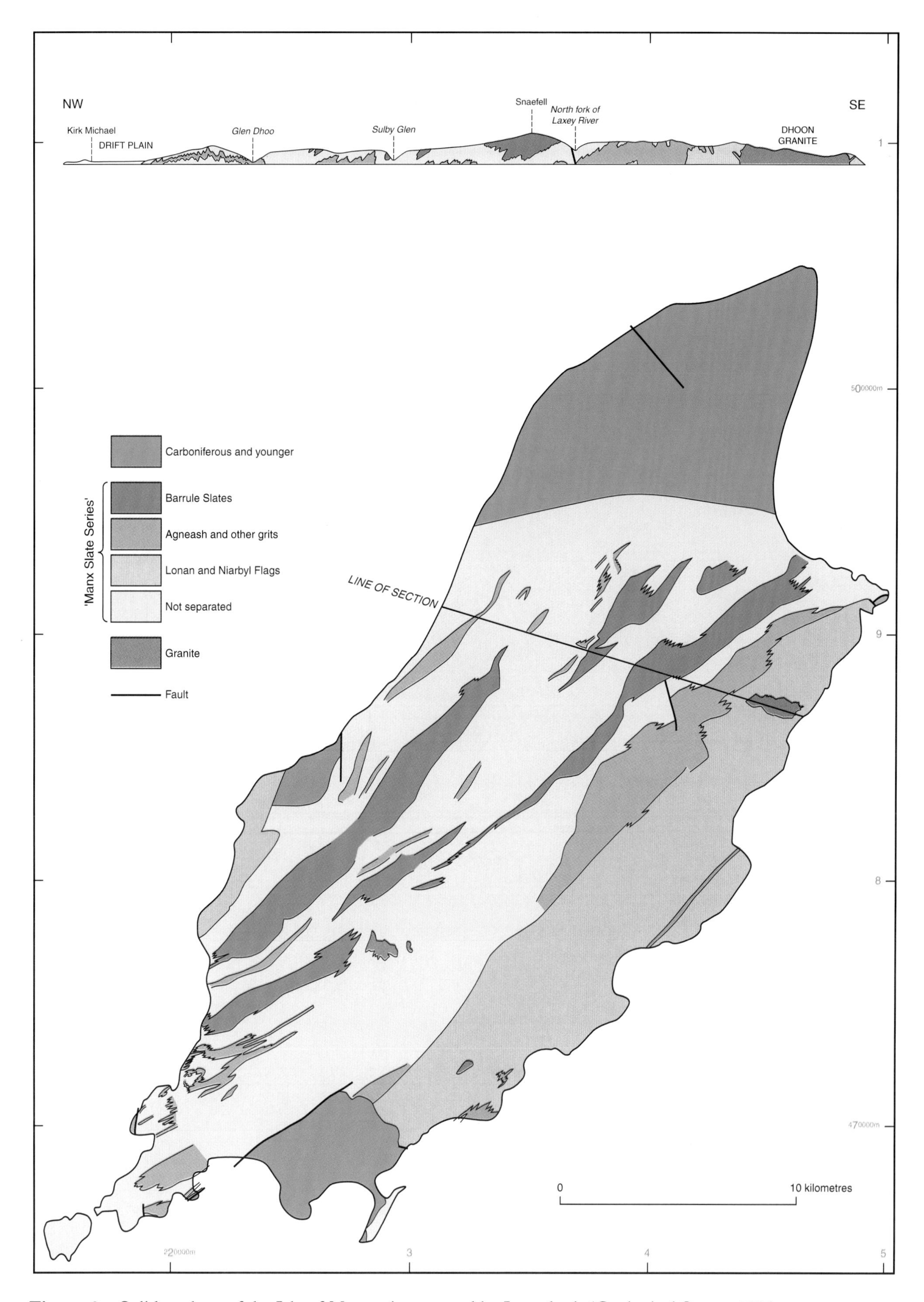

Figure 9 Solid geology of the Isle of Man as interpreted by Lamplugh (Geological Survey 1898; Lamplugh, 1903).

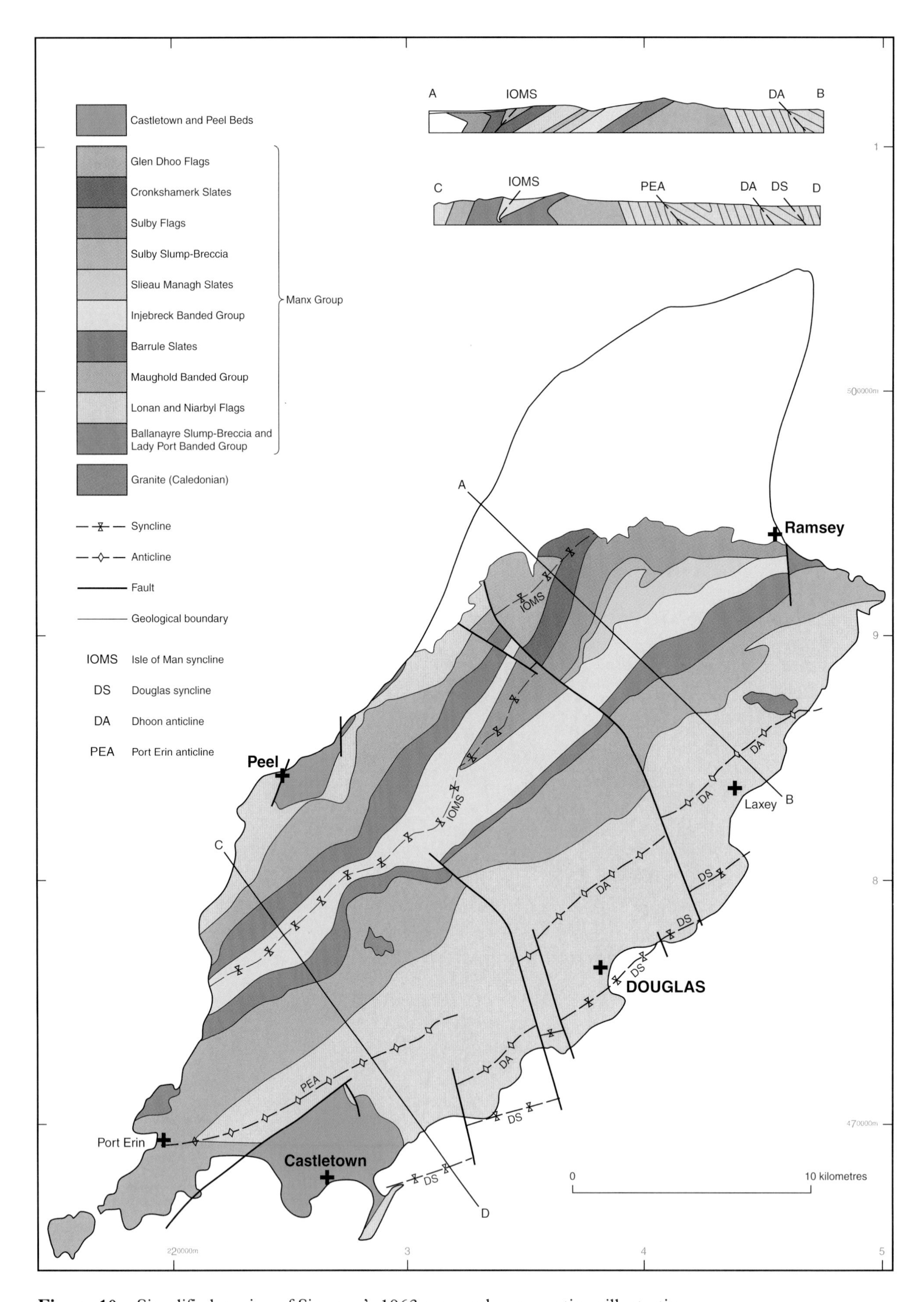

Figure 10 Simplified version of Simpson's 1963 map and cross-sections illustrating the Manx Slate Series and structural interpretations.

based where possible on the previous nomenclature of Lamplugh (1903) and Simpson (1963). Previously, the same lithostratigraphical terms had been applied to similar rock types in separate outcrops, suggesting repetition by faulting or folding and precluding the possibility of facies repetition at different levels in the succession. Consequently, Woodcock et al. (1999c) introduced new lithostratigraphical names where correlation between outcrops could not be demonstrated. Particular attention was paid to identifying stratigraphical contacts and the order of succession, but the work met with limited success owing to poor way-up control in some formations and faulting in coastal exposures. Because of the limited biostratigraphical control and the possibility that major strike-parallel faults separate the lithostratigraphical units it was important to allow for some degree of uncertainty in the stratigraphical classification. This was achieved through the characterisation of the successions in a series of north-east-trending tracts (Figure 11) within which there was reasonable certainty of stratigraphical continuity but between which no continuity could be demonstrated and faulted boundaries were demonstrable or possible (Fitches et al., 1999; Woodcock et al., 1999c). A few tracts contain evidence of an Arenig age whereas others remain undated. However, the westernmost tract, comprising the Niarbyl Formation (formerly the Niarbyl Flags), was shown from sedimentological and biostratigraphical evidence (Morris et al., 1999) to be Wenlock in age and was separated from the Manx Group into a newly defined 'Dalby Group'. This had major implications for the large-scale structure as it removed any possibility of correlation with the Lonan Formation. Rocks in the northern part of the Manx Group outcrop, only exposed inland between Kirk Michael and Ramsey, were not incorporated into the new lithostratigraphical scheme proposed by Woodcock et al. (1999c), although an interpretation of this area was proposed by Quirk and Burnett (1999).

The development of the new 1:50 000 Series geological map of the Isle of Man (BGS, 2001) focused on the principal uncertainties of the Woodcock et al. (1999c) model. Fieldwork was supported by palynological analysis of 130 rock samples representing most of the main Ordovician units (Molyneux, 2001). The lithostratigraphical units defined by Woodcock et al. (1999c) in the coastal sections have been traced inland and the nomenclature rationalised where appropriate (Figure 3). The significance of the interpreted tract boundaries was investigated through further examination of relationships in the field, and by inference from the additional biostratigraphical control. Observations made by Lamplugh (recorded on his field maps, at six inches to one mile, and clean copies) were used where no modern information was available, and the location of most of the dykes, mineral veins and mine entries are based on his maps. Where possible, dyke rock nomenclature has been revised, based on a re-examination of Lamplugh's original thin sections by G M Power.

This account of the Ordovician rocks (Manx Group) of the Isle of Man is based partly on new work and otherwise draws on Woodcock et al. (1999c). The description of the Silurian rocks (Dalby Group) is summarised from Morris et al. (1999).

Regionally, the Manx Group is equivalent to the Skiddaw Group in north-west England (Cooper et al., in press) and the Ribband Group in south-east Ireland (McConnell et al., 1999). These all represent deposits formed on the continental margin of Avalonia, at the southern margin of the Iapetus Ocean. Although of broadly similar facies, the stratigraphy is different in detail in the three areas indicating deposition in localised sedimentary systems. The turbidite deposits of the Dalby Group are a fragment of a succession that was deposited in mid- to late Silurian times across both the Avalonian and Laurentian margins during the final stages of closure of the Iapetus Ocean. They are equivalent to the mid-Silurian part of the Windermere Group in north-west England and the Riccarton Group in southern Scotland (Barnes et al., 1999).

Deformation of the deposits formed at the northern margin of the Iapetus Ocean occurred progressively during the Ordovician and Silurian as the oceanic crust was subducted beneath Laurentia (e.g. Barnes et al., 1989; Barnes and Stone, 1999). The deposits on the southern margin were subjected to periodic upheaval, disrupting the succession and causing major unconformites (e.g. Stone et al., 1999). However, pervasive cleavage-forming deformation did not occur until the early Devonian when the Avalonian margin was eventually thrust beneath the leading edge of the Laurentian plate.

MANX GROUP

The term Manx Group was introduced by Simpson (1968) and is equivalent to the 'Manx Slate Series' of Lamplugh (1903). It was redefined by Woodcock et al. (1999c) to exclude rocks shown to be of Silurian age, and twelve component formations were defined, although an area in the north of the outcrop was not mapped. Work to redraw the geological map (BGS, 2001a) allowed rationalisation of this stratigraphy. The succession is disrupted by several strike-parallel faults. The oldest and youngest rocks, the Glen Dhoo Formation and the Lady Port Formation, respectively, crop out in close proximity in the north of the outcrop (Figure 3). Otherwise, the rocks occur in a north-west-younging succession across the Island, although this too is disrupted by faults which are interpreted to repeat parts of the succession.

Glen Dhoo Formation

This formation was originally distinguished by Simpson (1963) as the 'Glen Dhoo Flags', and partly recognised by Woodcock et al. (1999c) and Quirk and Burnett (1999) as the 'Glen Dhoo and Glion Cam units'. It is lithologically similar in many respects to the Lonan Formation and the two overlap substantially in age; they may therefore be equivalent.

The Glen Dhoo Formation is generally relatively poorly exposed. The type area is at the upper end of Glen Dhoo [around SC 3498 8995]. A small quarry [SC 2908 8761] and adjacent road cuttings at Glion Cam provide a subsidiary section through one of the sandstone-rich units. Volcanic rocks tentatively assigned to this formation are exposed in a disused

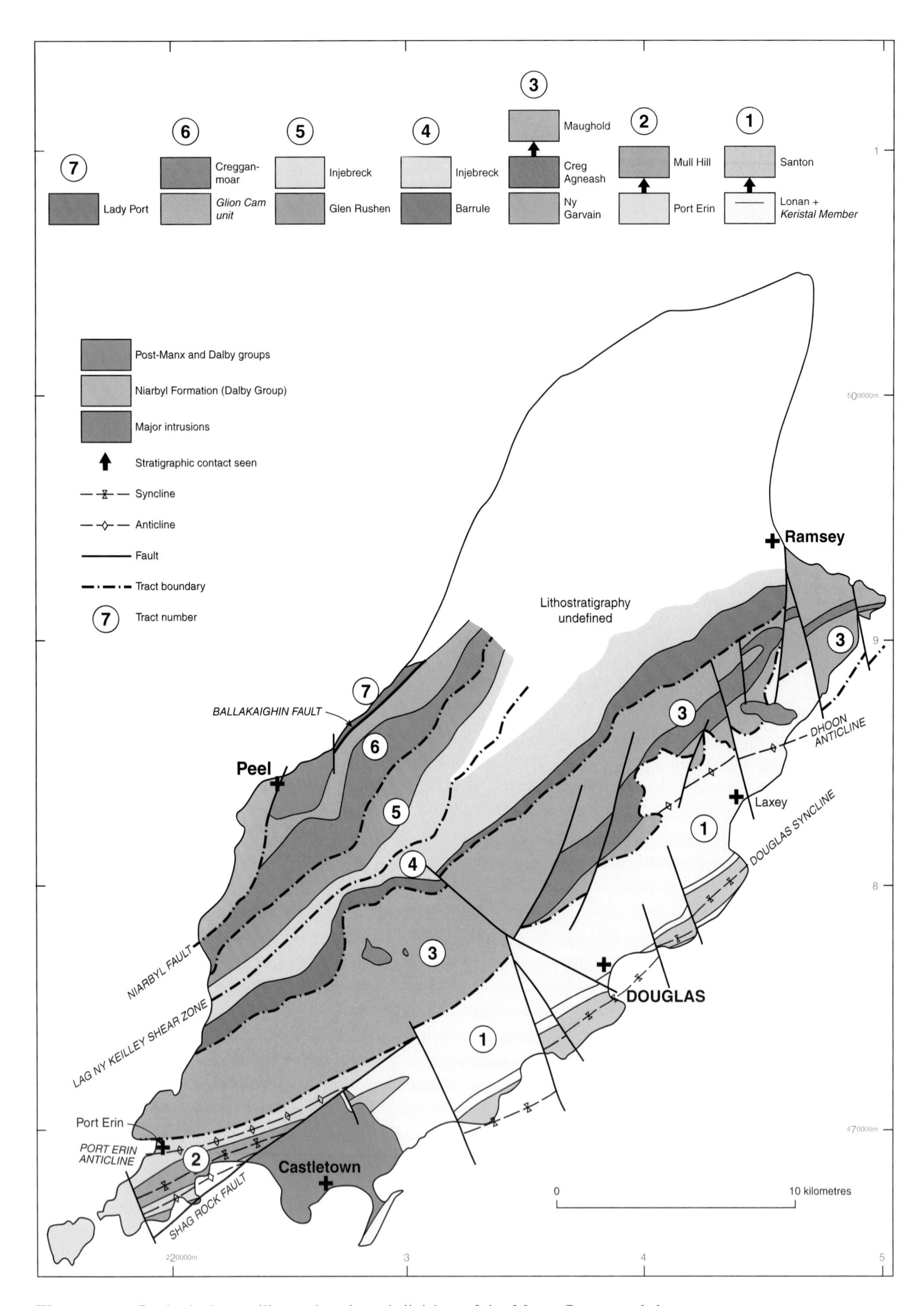

Figure 11 Geological map illustrating the subdivision of the Manx Group and the nature of the boundaries between structural tracts (after Woodcock et al., 1999c).

quarry south-west of Peel [SC 238 833] and in a structurally isolated outcrop at Ballaquane [SC 225 790].

The Glen Dhoo Formation is typically composed of mudstone with a variable proportion of pale grey to white siltstone in laminae to very thin beds (normally less than 0.5 cm thick). Mudstone generally dominates, with approximately 10 to 30 per cent siltstone, although some sections appear to be composed predominantly of poorly laminated or homogeneous green-grey siltstone. Thin beds of fine-grained, quartzitic sandstone also occur, some of which are planar to ripple cross-laminated. Locally, for example at Glion Cam and on the north flank of Slieau Dhoo [SC 3498 8995], grey, very fine- to fine-grained immature sandstone is dominant in successions that consist of thin to very thick (up to 2 m), massive to planar-laminated beds interbedded with laminated mudstone and siltstone.

Both of the occurrences of volcanic rocks included within the Glen Dhoo Formation were previously included within the Niarbyl Flags by Simpson (1963). However, Molyneux (1979) recovered an Arenig microflora from Peel quarry and they were therefore excluded from the Silurian Niarbyl Formation by Morris et al. (1999). Volcanic breccia intercalated with mudstone and siltstone in Peel quarry was first noted by Simpson (1963). There is little exposure at the present day but large blocks of andesite breccia within mudstone can be seen at the south end of the quarry [SC 2383 8333], and are interpreted as a syndepositional volcanic breccia. The microflora from this locality, first interpreted by Molyneux (1979) as late Arenig but now regarded as latest Tremadoc to early Arenig (Molyneux, 1999, 2001), is consistent with its inclusion in the Glen Dhoo Formation. A volcanic breccia composed of clasts of plagioclase-phyric andesite and glassy material in a fine-grained matrix including feldspar crystal debris had previously been noted at Ballaquane by Lamplugh (1903, p.163). Exposures are found in a small area [SC 225 790] close to the faulted contact between the Creggan Moar and Niarbyl formations, but no contact relationships are seen. Owing to similarities with the volcanic breccia exposed in the Peel quarry and the absence of other evidence of volcanic rocks in the adjacent formations, this outcrop is regarded as a sliver of the Glen Dhoo Formation within the Niarbyl Fault zone.

All of the exposed contacts of the Glen Dhoo Formation are faulted, and its internal structure is largely unknown due in part to the relatively poor exposure. The thickness of the Glen Dhoo Formation is thus difficult to determine, but it is likely to be at least several hundred metres.

The first constraints on the age of the rocks now attributed to the Glen Dhoo Formation were provided by latest Tremadoc to early Arenig acritarchs (Plate 2) obtained by Molyneux (1979, 1999) from Peel quarry and Slieau Curn. Supplemented by new collections (Molyneux, 2001), this age has been confirmed by acritarch assemblages from several localities extending along the length of the outcrop. The oldest floras may be those from the sandstone-rich facies at Glion Cam [SC 2908 8760], where an association of *Acanthodiacrodium*, *Cymatiogalea (C. cuvillierii?)* and *Timofeevia?* suggests a Tremadoc age. Mudstone intercalations with volcanic rocks in Peel quarry [SC 2386 8334] yielded abundant and reasonably well-preserved acritarchs originally interpreted as late Arenig to early Llanvirn age (Molyneux, 1979). However, based on subsequent work on comparable Lake District assemblages, Molyneux (1999) reinterpreted the assemblage as latest Tremadoc or earliest Arenig, equivalent to the upper part of the *messaoudensis–trifidum* Biozone or the *trifidum–bohemicum* Biozone (Cooper et al., in press). Reasonably diverse and abundant but poorly preserved acritarch assemblages from Slieau Curn [SC 3453 9157] and Bishop's Demesne [SC 3386 9181] (Molyneux, 2001) are early Arenig, either from the highest subzone of the *messaoudensis–trifidum* Biozone or the *trifidum–bohemicum* Biozone.

The acritarch assemblages from the Glen Dhoo Formation are closely comparable with assemblages from the Santon Member (Lonan Formation). They suggest correlation with the upper part of the *Araneograptus murrayi* Biozone, the *Tetragraptus phyllograptoides* Biozone, or the lower part of the *Didymograptus varicosus* Biozone.

Lonan Formation

Lamplugh (1903) designated much of the Manx Group outcrop on the south-eastern side of the Isle of Man as 'Lonan Flags' (Figure 9). Woodcock et al. (1999c), working mainly on the extensive coastal sections, divided this into four formations (Figure 11) which reflected lithological variations and uncertainty as to how parts of the exposure were related. However, resurvey work showed that the lithological variability extends inland and that distinction between the formations could not be supported. This has led to re-establishment of the term Lonan Formation for the whole outcrop, although the distinct units exposed at the coast are retained as members.

The Lonan Formation consists of mainly thin- to very thin-bedded or thickly laminated, fine-grained sandstone or siltstone and mudstone couplets (e.g. Plate 3). The proportion of sandstone varies from 25 to 80 per cent. Each sandstone bed typically has a sharp base and grades from light grey cross-laminated fine-grained wacke through parallel-laminated siltstone into dark grey mudstone, in some cases burrow-mottled. Convolute lamination is common in the cross-laminated divisions. Bedding surfaces commonly show straight-crested to undulatory, asymmetric current ripples. The graded beds of the type Lonan Formation are interpreted as the product of deposition from low-concentration turbidity currents in an oxygenated deep-marine environment.

The formation also contains sporadic units dominated by thin- to medium-bedded, fine-grained sandstone. Three relatively persistent, well-exposed units are distinguished as the Keristal, Santon and Ny Garvain members but this facies also occurs locally inland, for example in Ballaglass Glen [SC 4655 8974] and Crosby quarry [SC 3253 7920].

The base of the Lonan Formation does not occur at outcrop, but at least 2500 m of strata are exposed between the core of the Dhoon Anticline and the highest part of the Santon Member. The top of the Lonan Formation is best defined by the transition into the dominantly quartz arenite-bearing Creg Agneash and Mull Hill formations in the north-east and south of the Island, respectively. The boundary is more subtle in the area west of Douglas where these

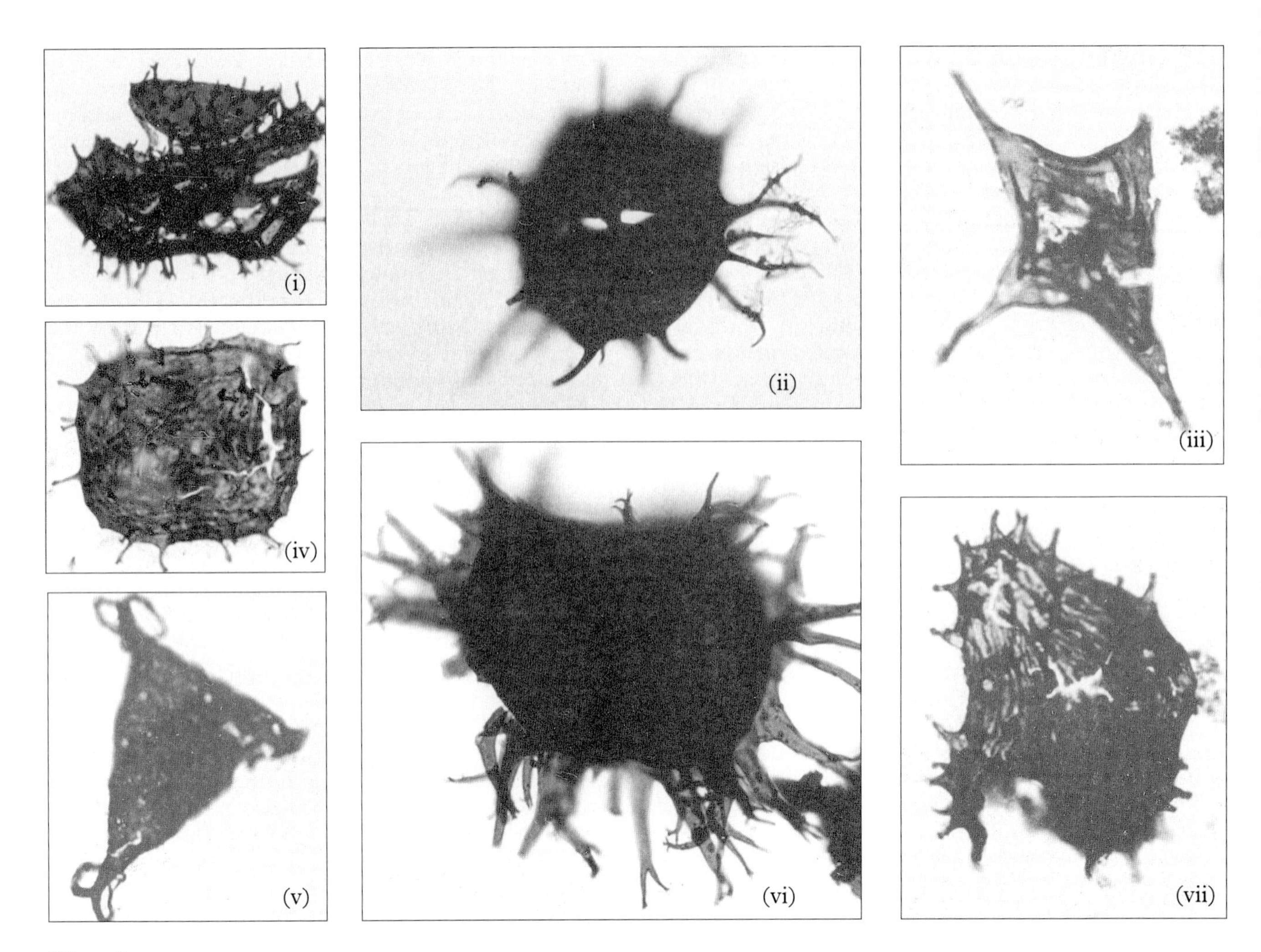

Plate 2a

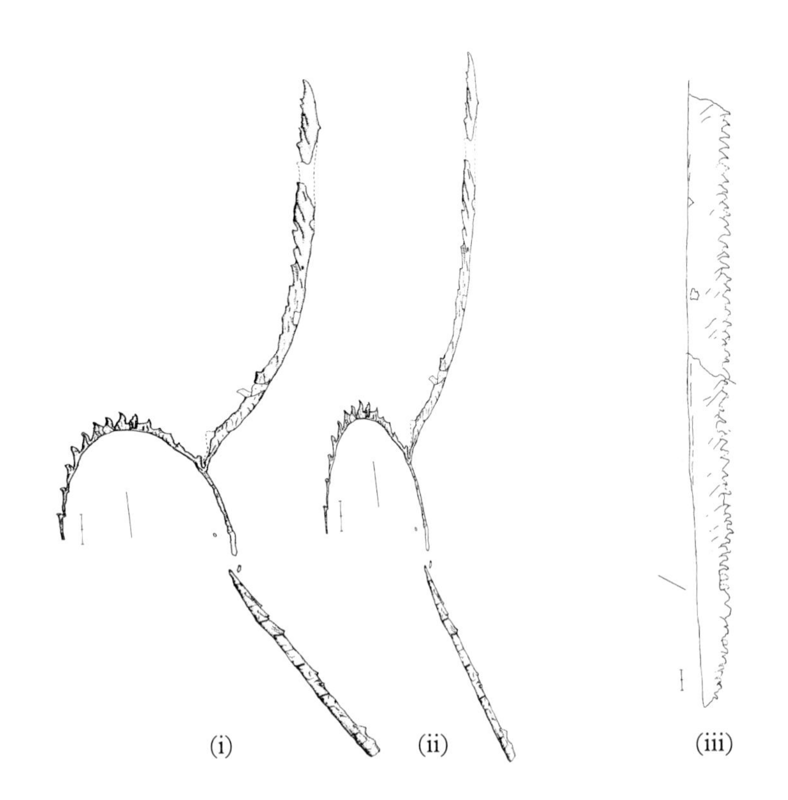

Plate 2b

Plate 3 Laminated to thinly bedded mudstone and siltstone typical of the Lonan Formation. Lenane, Maughold Head [SC 4943 9109] (P018662).

Plate 4 Thin- to medium-bedded sandstone typical of the Santon Member of the Lonan Formation Marine Drive, Douglas [SC 3778 7397] (P018605).

formations are absent and the Lonan Formation passes directly into the Maughold Formation.

The age of the Lonan Formation beneath the Santon Member is constrained by new acritarch floras from several localities (Molyneux, 2001), supplementing pre-existing data from the Santon Member (see below). Samples from Langness [around SC 2871 6571] yielded sparse and poorly preserved acritarchs, including *Stelliferidium trifidum?,* which suggest a possible late Tremadoc to early Arenig age. Material from Cass ny Hawin [around SC 2992 6925], directly beneath the Keristal Member, and Douglas Bay [about SC 3895 7700], also below the Keristal Member, yielded poorly preserved acritarchs. These include diacromorph acritarchs such as *Acanthodiacrodium,* and herkomorphs such as *Stelliferidium,* which are characteristic of Tremadoc assemblages although are not restricted to microfloras of that age. However, a Tremadoc age is likely from the absence of any post-Tremadoc forms in these assemblages and from the position of the sample localities below the Santon Member.

Plate 2 Ordovician acritarchs and Silurian graptolites from the Isle of Man.

a. Manx Group acritarchs.

i. *Stelliferidium trifidum* (Rasul) Fensome et al. MPK 10848, Glen Dhoo Formation, Slieau Curn.
ii. *Stellechinatum sicaforme contextum* Servais and Molyneux, MPK 12528, Glen Dhoo Formation, Peel.
iii. *Striatotheca rarirrugulata* (Cramer et al.) Eisenack et al., MPK 10852, Lady Port Formation, NE of Glion Cam.
iv. *Coryphidium* aff. *elegans* Cramer et al., MPK 12529, Glen Dhoo Formation, Peel.
v. *Frankea hamata* Burmann, MPK 10851, Lady Port Formation, SW of Ooig Mooar.
vi. *Cymatiogalea messaoudensis* Jardiné et al., MPK 12530, Glen Dhoo Formation, Peel.
vii. *Coryphidium* aff. *bohemicum* Vavrdová, Lady Port Formation, NE of Glion Cam.

All specimens are ×1200, and are housed in the micropalaeontological collections (MPK series) of the British Geological Survey, Keyworth, Nottingham.

b. Dalby Group graptolites.

i. *Cyrtograptus* cf. *lundgreni* Tullberg, IOMMM 98-140, Niarbyl Formation, Traie Dullish Quarry, near Peel. Specimen after computer processing to remove tectonic deformation.
ii. Same specimen as (i), prior to removal of tectonic deformation.
iii. *Monograptus flemingii* cf. *warreni* Burns and Rickards, IOMMM 98-142, Niarbyl Formation, Traie Dullish Quarry, near Peel.

Specimens are housed in the Manx Museum, Douglas, Isle of Man. Scale bars represent 2 mm. Direction of tectonic lineation indicated by lines adjacent to specimens.

Keristal Member

This distinctive unit was defined by Woodcock et al. (1999c) at the west side of Keristal Bay [SC 3505 7296], north-east of Port Soderick. It is only a few metres thick, but exposures at a number of other localities show that it is laterally persistent over 15 km beneath the Santon Member. A very similar unit is exposed near the base of the Ny Garvain Member in Port Cornaa [SC 4736 8786]. If the Ny Garvain and Santon members can be correlated then this too may be the Keristal Member.

The member comprises a discrete packet of between six and fourteen medium to very thick beds of distinctive pale, fine-grained quartz arenite or quartz wacke. The beds are ungraded or weakly graded, commonly massive or with parallel-lamination, but in some cases with ripple cross-lamination in thinner beds. They may be organised in either thinning-up or thickening-up sequences. In thinning-up sequences, the basal bed is commonly strongly erosional into underlying thin-bedded turbidites.

The Keristal Member was interpreted by Woodcock and Barnes (1999) as the product of a short-lived system of high- to medium-concentration turbidity flows, probably tapping a source of clean quartz sand that was distinct from the muddy sands more typical of the Lonan Formation.

The Keristal Member is probably Tremadoc or earliest Arenig in age, based on acritarch assemblages from the underlying Lonan Formation at Cass ny Hawin and Douglas Bay (see above) and early Arenig microfloras from the overlying Santon Member.

Santon Member

This member was originally named the Santon Formation by Woodcock et al. (1999c) and Woodcock and Barnes (1999) after coastal sections around Santon Head [SC 3328 7022]. It is well exposed in coastal sections from Onchan Head [SC 4026 7729] to Purt Veg [SC 3236 7030] where it crops out in the core of the Douglas Syncline. Although the top of the Santon Member is above the present erosion level, the exposed successions are up to about 600 m thick. It is characterised by medium- or thick-bedded, light grey or light greenish grey wacke (Plate 4) intercalated with a thin-bedded facies more typical of the Lonan Formation. Sandstone beds grade from fine- or very fine-grained sandstone into the intervening mudstone. Parallel- and ripple cross-lamination is common and some bed bases preserve flute marks and horizontal burrows. The graded beds are interpreted as deposits from high- to medium-concentration turbidity flows within the background of low-concentration events. An unusually thick-bedded, relatively coarse-grained sandstone succession about 50 m thick, which occurs in the Santon Member at Purt Veg [SC 3255 7037], was interpreted by Woodcock and Barnes (1999) as the fill of a trunk distributary channel in the turbidite system.

The wacke that dominates the member is particularly quartzose in places. Locally (e.g. at The Whing [SC 3603 7330]), isolated beds or packets of medium to thick beds of quartz arenite punctuate a less mature wacke succession.

Acritarchs were first recorded from the Santon Member at Wallberry Hill [SC 370 375] and on the Marine Drive [SC 3715 7353] by Downie and Ford (1966) and Molyneux (1979, 1999). In the absence of comparative empirical data, Molyneux (1979) concluded that the assemblage might occur close to the Tremadoc–Arenig series boundary. Subsequent work in the Lake District has produced more detailed information on acritarch ranges (Cooper et al., in press). The Santon Member assemblage is now considered to correlate with the *trifidum–bohemicum* or upper part of the *messaoudensis–trifidum* Biozone, indicating a probable early Arenig age (Molyneux, 1999). This is equivalent to some assemblages from the Glen Dhoo Formation (e.g. from Slieau Curn and Bishop's Demesne) and implies correlation with the earliest Arenig *Tetragraptus phyllograptoides* Biozone or a slightly higher level.

Rushton (1993) reported graptolites from the Santon Member at Baltic Rock [SC 3270 7023] but owing to their poor preservation they did not provide any information beyond indicating an Arenig age.

Ny Garvain Member

The name 'Ny Garvain Formation' was introduced by Woodcock et al. (1999c) for the north-eastern part of the Lonan Formation, in recognition of compositional and structural uncertainty over its correlation with the rest of the Lonan Formation (Barnes et al., 1999; Fitches et al., 1999; Woodcock and Barnes, 1999). In revision of the 1:50 000 map (BGS, 2001), the name is restricted to a package of relatively thickly bedded sandstone which crops out along the coast southwards from the headland of Gob ny Garvain [SC 4885 8986]. It is possible, however, that the Ny Garvain Member is equivalent to the Santon Member farther south.

The member is sandstone-dominated, with a high proportion of fine- to medium-grained wacke in medium to thick beds with very thin muddy partings in successions interspersed with packets of thin-bedded sandstone–mudstone couplets. Typical beds are sharp based, with a lower division of green-grey ripple cross-laminated fine-grained sandstone passing sharply up into interlaminated sand and dark grey mudstone. Convolute lamination is common in the cross-laminated divisions, which show current ripples on bedding surfaces. Thicker beds have a massive or weakly graded lower part. Most of the Ny Garvain Member was largely deposited from low- to medium-concentration turbidity currents.

Although the sandstone is generally quartz-rich, a discrete package a few metres thick of distinctive, thick to very thick irregular beds of pale quartz arenite occurs at the base of the member at Port Cornaa [SC 4728 8778], forming a unit similar to the Keristal Member. A few medium to thin beds of quartz arenite also occur west of Gob Ny Garvain [SC 4880 9015], although here they are interspersed with the wacke beds over a section about 10 m thick.

The member is incompletely exposed in a folded succession at the coast, thus making thickness determinations difficult. About 250 m of continuous succession are exposed in a steeply dipping limb near Port Cornaa. The base of the member is best exposed at Port Cornaa where bedding thickens upwards from the undifferentiated thin-bedded Lonan Formation to the west. The top of the member is not exposed or faulted, although an upward-thinning sequence along the south side of Port Mooar, west of Gob ny Garvain, may represent its transition back into more typical, thin-bedded strata of the Lonan Formation.

The age of the Ny Garvain Member is not constrained directly. A sample from Gob ny Garvain [SC 4881 8982] yielded a single possible acritarch fragment (Molyneux, 2001), but this is of no biostratigraphical significance. However, based on its stratigraphical position in the Lonan Formation, the member is likely to be of late Tremadoc or early Arenig age.

Creg Agneash Formation

The formation was named by Woodcock et al. (1999c) from Creg Agneash [SC 4295 8705] and equates to the north-eastern outcrop of 'Agneash Grits' mapped by Lamplugh (Figure 9). It is best exposed at Maughold Head [SC 4986 9142] where the gradational base and top of the formation are exposed, although there are many natural inland exposures of the formation (Lamplugh, 1903, pp.39–42) and there are quarry exposures at Dreemskerry [SC 4760 9112] and Windy Corner [SC 3900 8400].

The formation is characterised by white quartz arenite, typically thin or medium bedded, but in some localities includes thick or very thick beds. In the lower part of the formation, the quartz arenite beds occur within a background of laminated siltstone–mudstone that persists from the underlying Lonan Formation. This gives way upwards to very thin but persistent interbeds of a dark grey silty mudstone. The sandstone beds are massive or weakly graded from medium or fine sand to very fine sand or silt. Internal structure is typically a weakly defined, upward-thinning parallel-lamination (1–2 cm at base to millimetre-scale at top), in some cases with a thin ripple cross-laminated division at the top. Slump folding on a scale of tens of centimetres to metres is commonly developed, with close to tight disharmonic folds of widely varying orientation occurring within the same exposure. The Creg Agneash Formation was interpreted by Woodcock et al. (1999c) as the depositional product of medium-concentration turbidity currents punctuating a persistent background of low-concentration events.

The Creg Agneash Formation is about 180 m thick at Maughold Head, although the base is faulted. The outcrop width increases to the south-west where the formation may be as much as 750 m thick, although there may be some repetition caused by folding or faulting. The outcrop of the formation dies out north-west of Douglas, to the south-west of which it is absent. The Mull Hill Formation, which crops out along strike to the south-west, is lithologically similar and may be a lateral equivalent.

The base of the formation is a stratigraphical transition from the Lonan Formation. This is exposed in the River Laxey [SC 4183 8670] and on the coast south of Traie Foillan [SC 4983 9130] at Maughold Head, although the latter is complicated by faulting. At both localities, thin to medium quartz arenite beds gradually appear over several tens of metres or more within very thin-bedded or laminated sandstone/siltstone and mudstone typical of the Lonan Formation. At the base of the formation, the number of quartz arenite beds increases until they become the dominant lithology. The top of the formation, exposed at Traie Carn [SC 4970 9158], is transitional into the Maughold Formation with the sandstone beds progressively decreasing in number before abruptly giving way to laminated silty mudstone.

The Creg Agneash Formation is not dated other than by its situation above the Tremadoc to early Arenig Lonan Formation. Material from Windy Corner Quarry [SC 3901 8396] yielded a fragment of a possible sphaeromorph acritarch (Molyneux, 2001) but this is not diagnostic. However, sparse, low-diversity acritarch assemblages are a characteristic of the lower Arenig (*Didymograptus varicosus* Biozone) in the Lake District (Cooper et al., in press).

Mull Hill Formation

The formation was named after Mull Hill [SC 1897 6757] by Woodcock et al. (1999c). It is well exposed in coastal sections on the Cregneash peninsula. Lamplugh (1903, pp.42–43) used the term 'Mull Hill Grits' informally although he ultimately grouped these rocks with the other quartz arenite units as 'Agneash Grits'. Simpson (1963) separated two 'quartzite' outcrops, at Mull Hill and the Chasms, within his 'Maughold Banded Group' However, as originally interpreted by Lamplugh, these are fold repetitions of the same unit (Fitches et al., 1999). Quartzose arenite exposed at Spaldrick [SC 1940 6963], Port Erin, was also included within the Mull Hill Formation by Woodcock et al. (1999c), although there is some doubt about the structural continuity of this outcrop with the others.

The formation is characterised by light grey to white, medium- to very thick-bedded quartz arenite, contrasting strongly with the thin or very thin-bedded facies of the underlying Lonan Formation. Each sandstone bed grades up from medium-grained sandstone to very fine sandstone or siltstone, with thin or absent mudstone partings. A few beds have coarse- to very coarse-grained sandstone bases with mudstone rip-up clasts. Beds are typically massive to parallel-laminated at the base with an overlying cross-laminated division, interpreted as the product of deposition from high- and medium-concentration turbidity currents.

The Mull Hill Formation overlies the Lonan Formation with a gradational depositional contact over about 25 m. Woodcock et al. (1999c) estimated the thickness of the formation to be between 350 m and 400 m across Mull Hill. The quartzose sandstone packet at Spaldrick, interpreted as a lateral margin of the Mull Hill turbidite system, is about 40 m thick. However, the top of the formation is not exposed.

The Mull Hill Formation is not dated other than by its interpreted situation above the Tremadoc to early Arenig Lonan Formation. Two localities, north of Gansey Point [SC 2152 6843] and Cregneash quarry [SC 1909 6741], have yielded undiagnostic sphaeromorph acritarchs (Molyneux, 2001). Similarly sparse, low diversity acritarch assemblages are characteristic of the lower Arenig (*Didymograptus varicosus* Biozone) in the Lake District (Cooper et al., in press).

Maughold Formation

The unit was named by Woodcock et al. (1999c) following Simpson's (1963) term 'Maughold Banded Group'. Woodcock et al. (1999c) took the type section as the coast west of Port Lewaigue [SC 4630 9328 to 4682 9304], but this is now considered to lie within the Injebreck Formation. The Maughold Formation is exposed in largely inaccessible cliff sections from east of Port e Vullen [SC 4743 9284] to the contact with the Creg Agneash Formation at Traie Carn, and from north of Port Erin [SC 1916 6956] to the north flank of Gob ny Beinn [SC 2135 7320]. Most of the unit was mapped by Lamplugh (1903) as undivided 'Manx Slate Series', although parts of it containing significant amounts of quartz arenite were separated as 'Agneash Grits'. In the south-west of the Island, Lamplugh also distinguished horizons of 'crush-conglomerate'.

The Maughold Formation is dominated by dark grey mudstone in bedded or disrupted facies, but also includes significant amounts of quartz arenite. The laminated mudstone, typically with a millimetre-scale 'pinstripe' lamination, includes a variable proportion of pale grey siltstone in laminae to very thin beds and sporadic, thin to medium beds of fine-grained quartz arenite. Bioturbation is common as spots or as discordant silt-filled or mud-filled burrows. Pebbly mudstone is absent in the north-eastern part of the outcrop, but it becomes important to the south-west where it comprises about 65 per cent of the succession between Port Erin and Gob ny Beinn. Supported by the mudstone matrix, intraformational clasts are generally up to a few centimetres across and have a maximum size of 30 cm. They are mostly of shale, siltstone and fine-grained sandstone, with rare fragments of a fine-grained igneous rock. Bedded quartz arenite, locally dominant in packets up to about 25 m thick, resembles the Creg Agneash/Mull Hill facies. Pale or very pale greyish white, fine- to coarse-grained quartz arenite occurs in medium to thick beds. Pelitic interbeds include a few very thin beds of quartz arenite. The sandstone beds have sharp top and basal contacts. They are not discernibly graded and commonly contain tabular cross-sets through the thickness of each bed.

The mudstone in the Maughold Formation was interpreted by Woodcock et al. (1999c) as the product of hemipelagic fall-out and low-concentration turbidity flows into a deep-marine, periodically oxygenated basin. Owing to basin instability the bedded facies was locally resedimented as pebbly mudstone. Packets of quartzose sandstone accumulated by deposition from medium- to high-concentration turbidity flows.

Uncertainty about the structure precludes accurate thickness estimates of the Maughold Formation, although 500 to 600 m was suggested by Woodcock et al. (1999c). A gradational contact between the Maughold Formation and the underlying Creg Agneash Formation is exposed at Traie Carn [SC 4973 9158], and a similar relationship with the Mull Hill Formation is assumed although the contact at Port Erin is faulted. West of Douglas, where the overlying quartz arenite units are absent, a gradational contact with the Lonan Formation is interpreted. However, owing to the similarity of the facies in the two units this is difficult to define. The north-western contact of the Maughold Formation with the Barrule Formation is interpreted to be faulted (Figure 3), but an original stratigraphical relationship between the two formations seems likely.

The age of the Maughold Formation is poorly constrained other than by its interpreted position above the Tremadoc to early Arenig Lonan Formation. A sample from Port e Vullen [SC 4743 9275] yielded possible acritarchs that include an acanthomorph and a specimen of *V. trispinosum?* (Molyneux, 2001) which would indicate that it is not older than Arenig. Undiagnostic sphaeromorph acritarchs have also been recovered from Cregyn Doo [SC 2238 7375] and south-west of Cringle Reservoir [SC 2497 7395].

Barrule Formation

Lamplugh (1903) delimited several separate outcrops of black mudstone on the Isle of Man, calling the lithotype 'Barrule Slates'. Simpson (1963) retained this term for the most of the outcrops but separated those in the north as the 'Slieau Managh Slates'. In several areas Simpson combined separate strands of black mudstone that had been distinguished by Lamplugh, to produce the pattern of two parallel outcrops of 'Barrule Slates' with a third outcrop in the north (Slieau Managh Slates) that has appeared on most maps published subsequently (e.g. Woodcock et al., 1999c; Figure 11). The northern outcrop was outwith the area considered by Woodcock et al. (1999c) although the name 'Slieau Managh Slates' was retained by Quirk and Burnett (1999). Woodcock et al. (1999c) separated the other outcrops into the Barrule Formation in the south-east and the Glen Rushen Formation to the north-west (Figure 11) on the grounds that their equivalence could not be demonstrated.

Plate 5 Faintly laminated mudstone of the Barrule Formation close to the transition to the Injebreck Formation. Port Lewaigue [SC 4678 9300] (P018689).

This distinction between the Barrule and the Glen Rushen formations has been supported by the recent work, but the northern outcrops (previously the Slieau Managh Slates) are now recognised as the Barrule Formation (BGS, 2001). The two separate, parallel discontinuous strands of the Barrule Formation (Figure 3), correctly mapped by Lamplugh (Geological Survey, 1898), are interpreted as thrust repetitions of a single unit (Figure 3).

The outcrops of the Barrule Formation form the upland 'spine' of the Isle of Man, from the west coast north-east of Burroo Mooar [SC 216 735] to Port Lewaigue [SC 468 930] near Ramsey; along this line of hills the formation is relatively well exposed. Lithologically it is remarkably homogeneous, consisting of medium to dark grey and black pelite, which generally appears to be massive. However, in clean, smooth exposures a faint but persistent parallel, diffuse lamination can be seen, defined by slight colour variations and unaffected by bioturbation. The Barrule Formation is interpreted as hemipelagic mud deposited into anoxic bottom water.

The thickness of the formation is conjectural in the absence of evidence of way-up and internal structure and because the base is never seen. Simpson (1963) estimated a thickness of up to 1030 m whereas Woodcock et al. (1999c) calculated a thickness of 750 m by assuming that the succession is homoclinal. The maximum width of the outcrops is about 900 m, but the thickness may be substantially less if it is folded and/or internally thrust imbricated.

The boundaries of the Barrule Formation are commonly faulted or otherwise poorly exposed. The junction with the Maughold Formation was interpreted by Fitches et al. (1999) as a major fault. The south-eastern margin of the western strand is also a major fault, duplicating the outcrop of the Barrule Formation and the base of the Injebreck Formation. The top of the Barrule Formation is probably a gradational stratigraphical contact with the Injebreck Formation. This is best seen on the foreshore at Port Lewaigue [SC 4680 9300] (Plate 5), where faintly laminated black mudstone passes north into a few metres of a distinctive facies of laminated black mudstone with thin pale silty laminae at the base of the Injebreck Formation. A similar transitional facies is seen in discontinuous exposure at Injebreck [SC 3573 8423].

The age of the Barrule Formation is poorly constrained. A sample from Glen Auldyn [SC 4249 9243] yielded sparse acritarchs, in low diversity assemblages (Molyneux, 2001), including acanthomorph acritarchs, *Lophosphaeridium?*, sphaeromorph acritarchs and *Veryhachium? (V. lairdii?, V. trispinosum?)*. A sample from a quarry south of Round Table [SC 2469 7519] yielded a single, poorly preserved fragment of a possible acanthomorph acritarch. These are not diagnostic, although *Veryhachium trispinosum?*, if correctly determined, indicates that the sample from Glen Auldyn is not older than Arenig. Sparse, low-diversity acritarch assemblages, with similar forms, are characteristic of the lower Arenig (*Didymograptus varicosus* Biozone) in the Lake District (Cooper et al., in press). The interpreted stratigraphical position of the Barrule Formation, above the Tremadoc to lower Arenig Lonan Formation but below the middle Arenig Creggan Moar Formation, implies an early to mid-Arenig age.

Injebreck Formation

The Injebreck Formation was defined by Woodcock et al. (1999c) following use of the term 'Injebreck Banded Group' by Simpson (1963) for part of the succession which Lamplugh (1903) left as 'not separated'. It is well exposed on the west coast of the Isle of Man and in several stream sections inland. The lower part of the formation, along with a discontinuous sliver of the top of the Barrule Formation, is repeated by the Lag ny Keeilley Fault (see below).

The Injebreck Formation is similar to the Maughold Formation in many respects, being dominated by laminated dark mudstone with a variable proportion of thinly interbedded siltstone and fine-grained sandstone, but also contains units of quartz arenite and units of pebbly mudstone. A distinctive facies of finely laminated blue-grey mudstone and pale siltstone occurs over several metres at the base of the formation at the contact with the Barrule Formation. This passes up into the typical medium to dark grey, almost black, mudstone with dispersed, thin, pale grey silty laminae and a variable proportion of very thin beds of pale grey siltstone to very fine-grained sandstone. The latter typically have sharp tops and bases and are parallel- and ripple cross-laminated. Sporadic thin to medium beds of quartz arenite also occur.

A conspicuous sandstone-dominated unit, a few tens of metres to 100 m thick, some 200 to 300 m above the base of the formation, is well exposed on Mount Karin [SC 3802 9260], in stream sections at Injebreck and south of the Sulby reservoir, and also on the west coast south of Lag ny Keeilley. Typically, it consists of sandstone that is very fine to fine grained and thin to medium bedded, but with thick-beds in places. The sandstone is generally a quartzose arenite but also includes greenish grey, less mature sandstone in a background of laminated siltstone and mudstone. Beds tend to be weakly graded and are typically planar-laminated, although some ripple cross-lamination is apparent in thinner beds. Coarser grained sandstone occurs immediately south of the fault at Lag ny Keeilley. Here, the predominantly medium-bedded sandstone succession becomes dominated by thick- or very thick-bedded, amalgamated, medium- to coarse-grained quartz sandstone with pebbly layers up to 20 cm thick. These beds are interpreted as sandy debris flows.

Pebbly mudstone occurs locally as relatively thin units, typically less than 1 m thick, in the south-west of the outcrop. It consists of dispersed, intraformational clasts of pale laminated siltstone or sandstone up to 10 cm in diameter in a mudstone matrix. However, this lithology becomes dominant through much of the lower part of the formation in the north-east where it includes the 'Sulby Slump Breccia' of Simpson (1963). One unit, well exposed on the coast south of Ramsey, consists of clasts in the range 0.2 to 3 cm, some up to 35 cm, supported in a medium to dark grey mudstone matrix. The clasts, which could all be intrabasinal, are mostly of mudstone, siltstone, fine-grained sandstone or, rarely, a fine-grained igneous rock.

The Injebreck Formation is interpreted as an anoxic hemipelagic background facies, with occasional input of low-concentration turbidity flows. Sandstone-dominated facies record periods of medium- to high-concentration turbidity flows, some of which were highly quartzose. Debris flows are recorded in the south-west of the outcrop but are a much more significant feature in the lower part of the succession farther north-east.

The thickness of the Injebreck Formation is difficult to assess but must be at least several hundred metres with allowance for repetition by folding. The south-eastern boundary is a gradational contact at which the Injebreck Formation is assumed to overlie the Barrule Formation. At the northern boundary, a gradational contact with the faintly laminated black mudstone of the Glen Rushen Formation is exposed on the west coast just north of the Stack [SC 2160 7633]. Woodcock et al. (1999c) interpreted this as a south-younging succession, with the Glen Rushen Formation passing stratigraphically up into the Injebreck Formation. However, following the recent resurvey work, the succession at this locality is now thought to be north-younging.

The age of the Injebreck Formation is poorly constrained. Material from several localities has yielded sparse, low-diversity assemblages of sphaeromorph and acanthomorph acritarchs (Molyneux, 2001). One sample from Glen Auldyn [SC 4215 9111] also yielded *Polygonium?* and *Veryhachium trispinosum?* and a sample from Cronk Sumark [SC 3917 9411] yielded a single specimen of *Acanthodiacrodium*. These are insufficient to date the formation, although *Veryhachium trispinosum?*, if correctly determined, would indicate that the sample from Glen Auldyn is not older than Arenig. The interpreted stratigraphical position of the Injebreck Formation, above the Tremadoc to early Arenig Lonan Formation but below the middle Arenig Creggan Moar Formation, implies an early to mid-Arenig age. The sparse, low-diversity acritarch assemblages, characteristic of the lower Arenig (*Didymograptus varicosus* Biozone) in the Lake District (Cooper et al., in press), are consistent with this interpretation.

Graptolites were first recorded in the Manx Group by Bolton (1899) from a quarry on Cronk Sumark [SC 391 941], a locality now considered to lie within the Injebreck Formation, although close to the faulted contact with the Glen Dhoo Formation. The graptolites from Cronk Sumark have been viewed with some circumspection. Lamplugh (1903) found it difficult to believe that fossils could be preserved in what he considered to be severely deformed beds. Downie and Ford (1966, p.318) accepted that Bolton's specimens were genuine fossils, but questioned whether they had come from Cronk Sumark. Rushton (1993), however, recorded more graptoloid stipes, undeterminable but resembling those of *Dictyonema* or *Rhabdinopora*, on a loose block from Cronk Sumark, supporting Bolton's claim that his own graptolites had come from that locality. Rushton could not be certain about the identification of Bolton's specimens, given their state of preservation, but referred them to *Rhabdinopora flabelliformis?* or *Dictyonema*, and concluded that they could indicate either a Tremadoc or Arenig age.

Glen Rushen Formation

The Glen Rushen Formation is exposed in disused slate quarries in Glen Rushen [SC 2445 7845] and a short section of coastal exposure at Fheustal [SC 2173 7654]. It is also well exposed on Slieau Whallian [SC 2645 8040] and in Glen Helen [SC 2952 8432] in the northern part of the outcrop. Although defined by Woodcock et al. (1999c) to separate the north-western outcrops of mudstone from the eastern outcrops (with which they had previously been grouped as Barrule Slates by Lamplugh, 1903, and Simpson, 1963), they still considered it likely that the Glen Rushen and Barrule formations were equivalent. However, the recent recognition of the stratigraphical position of the Glen Rushen Formation between the Injebreck and Creggan Moar formations now precludes this possibility.

Lithologically, the Glen Rushen Formation is more akin to a muddy facies of the Injebreck Formation than the Barrule Formation. It is composed predominantly of laminated, medium to dark grey or bluish grey mudstone with a variable proportion of pale siltstone laminae generally less than 1 mm thick. Bioturbation is absent and the laminae are laterally persistent. Thin quartzose sandstone beds and pebbly mudstone occur rarely. The Glen Rushen Formation was interpreted by Woodcock et al. (1999c) as an anoxic hemipelagic facies, with occasional input of low-concentration turbidity flows.

Woodcock et al. (1999c) suggested a maximum thickness of no more than 250 to 500 m for the Glen Rushen Formation, although this is poorly constrained in the absence of evidence for internal structure. Repetition of the boundary with the Creggan Moar Formation suggests tectonic thickening of the south-western part of the outcrop (BGS, 2001).

As noted above, the Injebreck Formation can be seen to pass stratigraphically up into the Glen Rushen Formation at the Stack [SC 2162 7632], a relationship which has been interpreted along the length of the outcrop (Figure 3). About 250 m to the north-west [SC 2173 7654] the Glen Rushen Formation is juxtaposed against the Creggan Moar Formation by a north-west-trending fault. Woodcock et al. (1999c) noted an increase in the proportion of silt laminae in the Glen Rushen Formation towards this fault and suggested that it may obscure an originally gradational stratigraphical contact. About 200 m to the north, a few tens of metres of laminated mudstone, exposed in the foreshore [SC 2173 7670], are interpreted to be a faulted repetition of the top of the Glen Rushen Formation. Here, there is a clear gradational transition into the Creggan Moar Formation. Very thin manganiferous ironstone beds occur within the mudstone and become more common as the siltstone laminae become thicker at the boundary.

Most samples taken from the Glen Rushen Formation for palynological analysis yielded sparse, low-diversity acritarch assemblages, including sphaeromorph and acanthomorph acritarchs. A slightly more diverse assemblage from Laurel Bank [SC 2842 8347] includes common *Striatotheca principalis parva*, *Polygonium*, acanthomorph acritarchs (Molyneux, 2001), *Micrhystridium* aff. *acuminosum?* and *Coryphidium*, indicating an Arenig age.

Two samples from one of the Glen Rushen Slate quarries [about SC 2433 7885] yielded sparse acritarchs. These samples may be from the top of the Glen Rushen Formation or the base of the Creggan Moar Formation. One sample yielded an assemblage comprising *Stelliferidium* aff. *pseudoornatum* and a possible sphaeromorph acritarch. The second sample, collected about 5 m towards the south and therefore inferred to be lower in the succession, yielded a single acanthomorph acritarch, possibly *Polygonium*, and a possible sphaeromorph acritarch. *Stelliferidium* aff. *pseudoornatum* is a common component of assemblages from the Creggan Moar Formation, and is diagnostic of a mid-Arenig biozone in the Lake District (Cooper et al., in press). Its presence in one of the samples may indicate that the base of the *S.* aff. *pseudoornatum* Biozone lies at or just below the base of the Creggan Moar Formation, and implies that the top of the Glen Rushen Formation is of mid-Arenig age. The relatively sparse assemblages from other samples of the Glen Rushen Formation are more typical of material beneath the *S.* aff. *pseudoornatum* Biozone in the Lake District.

Creggan Moar Formation

In strata left unseparated by Lamplugh (Geological Survey, 1898) or included in the Maughold Banded

Plate 6 Laminated siltstone and mudstone with thin sandstone beds and very thin beds of manganiferous ironstone typical of the Creggan Moar Formation. Shore at Creggan Moar [SC 2166 7680] (P104235).

Group by Simpson (1963), this formation was defined by Woodcock et al. (1999c) to separate rocks containing distinctive very thin beds of manganiferous ironstone. It is well exposed in the coastal section from north of the Stack [SC 2173 7654] to Niarbyl [SC 2118 7758] and was fully described by Kennan and Morris (1999).

The Creggan Moar Formation is dominated by sandstone or siltstone and dark grey mudstone, with very thin beds of distinctive manganiferous ironstone (Plate 6). The sandstone/siltstone beds are very thin or thin bedded, very fine grained and pale or greenish grey, or exceptionally reddish brown, in colour. Typically, they are parallel-laminated (rarely cross-laminated) and pass gradationally into the intervening mudstone, commonly with conspicuously bioturbated tops. The manganiferous beds weather to a bright reddish brown or dark brown to black colour, and occur singly or are clustered. This facies is intercalated with pale, greenish or brownish grey, parallel-laminated siltstone in thick, monotonous successions, although very thin bedding can be discerned where siltstone–mudstone couplets or rare manganiferous beds occur. Quartz arenite is also present as sporadic, pale grey, faintly laminated, thin to medium beds.

Volcanic rocks, noted at Ballaquane by Lamplugh (1903), are regarded (BGS, 2001) as a sliver within the fault zone between the Creggan Moar Formation and the Dalby Group, and have been included within the Glen Dhoo Formation described above. It is possible, however, that they lie within the Creggan Moar Formation.

The Creggan Moar Formation is interpreted mostly as the product of low-concentration turbidity flows and chemical deposits into oxygenated bottom waters.

The preserved thickness of the Creggan Moar Formation is likely to be of the order of several hundred metres from its gradational contact with the Glen Rushen Formation, but internal deformation precludes a more accurate estimate. The top of the formation is not seen; in the north the Glen Dhoo Formation has been thrust above it and in the south it is faulted into juxtaposition with Silurian rocks of the Dalby Group.

The age of the Creggan Moar Formation was previously unconstrained. One sample, from a roadside exposure in Glen Rushen [SC 2413 7929], dated as possibly mid-Arenig by Molyneux (1979, 1999) was previously attributed to the Glen Rushen Formation, but the locality is now considered to lie near the base of the Creggan Moar Formation. However, new work (Molyneux, 2001) suggests that the formation is one of the most consistently fossiliferous units in the Lower Palaeozoic rocks which crop out on the Isle of Man, and ranges in age from mid- to late Arenig.

Samples from near the base of the succession at Gob ny Gameran [SC 2168 7675 and 2171 7654] and in Glen Rushen [close to SC 2412 7928], and higher in the succession at Niarbyl [SC 2118 7759], all yielded *Stelliferidium* aff. *pseudoornatum*, commonly in otherwise sparse assemblages. The material from Glen Rushen also included acanthomorph acritarchs, *Cymatiogalea?*, *Dictyotidium?*, *Polygonium?* and sphaeromorph acritarchs. Material from Niarbyl included more abundant and more varied acritarchs, including *Acanthodiacrodium?*, acanthomorph acritarchs, *Coryphidium bohemicum?*, *Polygonium*, sphaeromorph acritarchs, *Stelliferidium* aff. *pseudoornatum*, *Striatotheca principalis parva?*, *Vavrdovella?*, *Veryhachium lairdii* and *Veryhachium trispinosum*. One sample collected from either the base of the Creggan Moar Formation or the top of the Glen Rushen Formation in one of the Glen Rushen slate quarries also yielded *Stelliferidium* aff. *pseudoornatum* (see above).

The *Stelliferidium* aff. *pseudoornatum* Biozone is indicated by the zonal fossil. Other aspects of the assemblage from the Isle of Man, including the low diversity and the predominance of morphologically simple acanthomorph acritarchs (including *Polygonium?*) and sphaeromorph acritarchs, are also characteristic of the biozone in the Lake District. Correlation with graptolite biostratigraphy in the Lake District indicates that the *Stelliferidium* aff. *pseudoornatum* Biozone spans the mid-Arenig *Didymograptus simulans* Biozone. Its base is thought to lie near the top of the underlying *Didymogratus varicosus* Biozone and its top extends above the base of the overlying *Isograptus victoriae* Biozone (Cooper et al., in press). The record of *S.* aff. *pseudoornatum* from the Glen Rushen slate quarry suggests that the base *S.* aff. *pseudoornatum* Biozone may lie close to the base of the Creggan Moar Formation or possibly in the highest beds of the Glen Rushen Formation.

A somewhat different acritarch assemblage was obtained from Creggan Moar [SC 2152 7711] where there is no indication of *S.* aff. *pseudoornatum*. Instead, the sample yielded a variety of forms, including acanthomorph acritarchs, *Coryphidium* aff. *bohemicum?*, *Frankea hamata?* (fragment), *Micrhystridium?*, sphaeromorph acritarchs, *Striatotheca rarirrugulata?*, *Veryhachium lairdii* s.l. and *Veryhachium trispinosum?*. Preservation is poor, and consequently many determinations are tentative. Nevertheless, the occurrence of *Striatotheca rarirrugulata?*, *Frankea hamata?* and *Coryphidium* aff. *bohemicum?* suggests the *hamata–rarirrugulata* Biozone. This biozone succeeds the *Stelliferidium* aff. *pseudoornatum* Biozone in the Lake District. Its base is inferred to lie within either the upper part of the *Isograptus victoriae* Biozone or the overlying *Isograptus caduceus gibberulus* Biozone, and it extends through the latest Arenig *Aulograptus cucullus* Biozone (Cooper et al., in press). Its top may lie close to the Arenig–Llanvirn boundary in the Lake District. The *hamata–rarirrugulata* Biozone is thus late Arenig in age. Previous records of the *hamata–rarirrugulata* Biozone on the Isle of Man are from the Lady Port Formation (see below). The microflora from Creggan Moar is younger than that from samples collected to the south, from close to the base of the succession, near Gob ny Gameran. It is, however, also younger than that from Niarbyl to the north (see above), suggesting either thrust repetition or folding of the Creggan Moar Formation in the coastal section.

Lady Port Formation

Originally distinguished by Simpson (1963) as the Lady Port Banded Group and Ballanayre Slump Breccia, the Lady Port Formation was defined by Woodcock et al. (1999c) to include a range of lithofacies which crop out in a narrow strip along the coast near Lady Port [SC 2882 8786]. The formation was described in detail by Woodcock and Morris (1999).

The formation is heterogeneous, with major olistostrome deposits. The most common lithology is medium grey to black mudstone with thin to thick siltstone laminae, which may be sharp based and graded or more diffuse. Light grey quartzose sandstone punctuates the mudstone succession in places, typically in thin or very thin beds. Distinctive buff to black manganiferous ironstone beds a few millimetres thick occur north of Ballanayre [SC 2810 8710], in association with siltstone and fine-grained quartzose sandstone, in a facies similar to that of the Creggan Moar Formation (Kennan and Morris, 1999). Thin- to medium-bedded, light grey to greenish grey wacke occurs at Ballanayre Strand [SC 2763 8678] and below Buggane Mooar [SC 2747 8663]. Beds fine upwards from fine- or very fine-grained sandstone to mudstone. Parallel- and ripple cross-lamination is preserved, although beds are commonly conspicuously bioturbated. In places, bedding is strongly disrupted, due at least in part to soft-sediment slumping.

Pebbly mudstone is very well exposed along Ballanayre Strand and displays a gradual passage from bedded sandstone into the disrupted succession [at SC 2759 8677]. The deposit is supported by the mudstone matrix. Clasts are typically 1 to 5 cm in diameter, but are commonly up to 20 cm in size. Rafts of bedded sediment also occur within the succession; one example is around 50 m in length [at SC 2778 8693]. However, the similarity of some of the larger stratified sections to other formations, such as the distinctive manganiferous ironstone-bearing facies of the Creggan Moar Formation, suggests that even these sections may be blocks within the mélange.

The Lady Port Formation was interpreted by Woodcock and Morris (1999) as the product of deposition in a mudstone-prone deep-marine subbasin that was subject to repeated slumping and debris flows. An early phase of muddy sand turbidite deposition predated major disruption of sediments within the basin and episodic medium-concentration turbidity flows deposited quartzose sandstone.

The Lady Port Formation is structurally isolated, internally complex and incompletely exposed, providing little information as to its thickness. Woodcock et al. (1999c) estimated that the Lady Port section could be no thicker than a few hundreds of metres.

Dark grey and blue-grey mudstone with pale grey siltstone laminae, exposed between Lady Port [SC 2883 8785] and north of Ooig Mooar [SC 2919 8825], yielded poorly preserved acritarchs considered to be late Arenig by Molyneux (1979, 1999). The presence of *Coryphidium* aff. *bohemicum*, *Frankea hamata* and *Striatotheca rarirrugulata* provides a clear indication of the *hamata–rarirrugulata* assemblage, equivalent to the youngest part of the Creggan Moar Formation. On this evidence, Molyneux (1999) concluded that the Lady Port Formation is late Arenig in age. However, the complex nature of the unit and the presence of rafts that may have been derived from underlying formations means that this age should be considered only as a maximum age for the formation.

DALBY GROUP (NIARBYL FORMATION)

Lamplugh (1903) named the sandstone-rich succession which is well exposed between Peel Castle and The Niarbyl, on the western side of the Isle of Man, as 'Niarbyl Flags' (Figure 9). This term was retained by Simpson (1963), although he extended the outcrop to include sandstone-bearing units that crop out north of Peel. Both authors regarded this succession as part of the 'Manx Slate Series', possibly equivalent to the Lonan Flags which crop out on the south-eastern side of the Island. Cooper et al. (1995) included volcanic rocks exposed at Ballaquane and Peel within a Niarbyl Formation which was considered to be early Arenig, based on acritarchs from Peel quarry (Molyneux, 1979). Recently, however, Howe (1999) reported new palaeontological evidence which shows that the succession south of Peel is Silurian (late Wenlock) in age and hence this was distinguished by Morris et al. (1999) as the Niarbyl Formation of the Dalby Group. Following these authors, the volcanic rocks are considered to lie within the adjacent Manx Group.

The Niarbyl Formation is dominantly composed of fine- to medium-grained sandstone and silty mudstone, but includes very thinly laminated hemipelagite

Plate 7 Thin- to medium-bedded sandstone of the Niarbyl Formation folded by a D_1 syncline. Coastal exposure south of Glen Maye [SC 2237 7987] (P 104 236).

and rare metabentonite beds. Five facies were described by Morris et al. (1999). Most of the succession comprises thin-, medium- or thick-bedded, pale grey (weathering to a greenish buff) sandstone with thin mudstone partings (Plate 7). Bouma sequences, characteristic of turbidite deposits, are well developed within the sandstone beds, which occur in thinning- and thickening-upwards successions up to 15 m thick. Short sequences of thick to very thick beds of massive sandstone occur sporadically. Sole marks are common on sandstone beds, indicating palaeocurrent directions that were dominantly from the north-west, with some from the south-west. The sandstone-dominated successions are interspersed with packets, up to 10 m thick, of thin- to very thin-bedded, parallel- and cross-laminated, very fine-grained sandstone or siltstone and mudstone. The hemipelagite is grey- or brown-weathering and comprises very thinly interlaminated siltstone and carbonaceous pelite. It is rare in the southern part of the outcrop, being best developed within the interlobe facies from Contrary Head northwards, where it forms units generally from a few millimetres to 10 cm in thickness, and ranging up to 2 m in thickness. Thin metabentonite beds were first recorded by Lamplugh (1903) from Contrary Head and three occurrences were described by Morris et al. (1999) from Dalby Point and a quarry on Peel Hill [SC 2370 8401].

The sandstone sequences are interpreted as sandstone lobe deposits (Pickering et al., 1986, facies C2.1–2.3) within which the massive sandstone units probably represent channel fill deposits. The very thin- to thin-bedded facies may represent material deposited between or at the fringes of the sandstone lobes. The hemipelagite, which comprises alternate layers of organic material and siltstone, was probably deposited from suspension (Morris et al., 1999, but also see Rickards, 1965, Kemp, 1991).

The age of the Niarbyl Formation is constrained by a graptolite and orthocone nautiloid fauna from a quarry above Traie Dullish on the west side of Peel Hill [SC 2370 8401]. The graptolites were identified by Howe (1999) as *Cyrtograptus* cf. *lundgreni*, *Monograptus flemingii* cf. *Warreni* and *Monograptus* ex gr. *flemingii*, and were considered to suggest a mid-Silurian, Wenlock (*lundgreni* Biozone) age.

The Niarbyl Formation is incompletely exposed and all of its contacts with units of the Manx Group are faulted. At the southern end of the outcrop it is juxtaposed, by a late brittle fault, against a broad high strain zone (see below) within the Creggan Moar Formation just south of the Niarbyl. The boundary with the Creggan Moar Formation along the south-east of the outcrop is also interpreted to be faulted, as is the contact with the Glen Dhoo Formation at Peel. Folding and faulting within the succession preclude an accurate estimate of the thickness of the exposed succession, but Morris et al. (1999) suggested that it might be of the order of 1250 m.

The distinctive, very thinly laminated hemipelagite facies is typical of middle Silurian successions in north-west England, south-west Scotland and Ireland (e.g. Rickards, 1965; Kemp, 1991). The Niarbyl Formation is similar sedimentologically to the Ross Formation of the Hawick Group in the Southern Uplands but the latter is significantly older and the sandstone is of different composition (Barnes et al., 1999).

Plate 8 Tight to isoclinal D_1 folds refolded by recumbent open D_2 folds in laminated to thinly bedded mudstone and siltstone of the Lonan Formation. Port Erin [SC 1959 6929] (P 104237).

Biostratigraphically the Niarbyl Formation is equivalent to the Birk Riggs Formation of the Windermere Group in the southern Lake District (e.g. Kneller et al., 1994). In this case the sandstones show marked compositional similarity, supporting a close relationship between these units.

STRUCTURE

The predominantly steep dip imposes a relatively simple outcrop pattern on the Lower Palaeozoic succession of the Isle of Man, which, together with much of the detail of the outcrop-scale structure, was recognised by Lamplugh (1903) and Simpson (1963). Evidence of three phases of ductile deformation is preserved in folds and cleavages (e.g. Plate 8) and localised high strain zones, and brittle deformation is evident as a variety of faults. Interpretation of the larger scale structure, however, has always been more conjectural, having been based on lithological correlation in the absence of good biostratigraphical control. Lamplugh (1903) linked the two main outcrops of his 'Barrule Slates' (Figure 9) and the sandstone-dominated rocks exposed to the north-west and south-east around a synclinorium of upright D_1 folds. Recognising way-up indicators, Simpson (1963) identified major D_1 fold structures in the south-west and south-east of the Island (Figure 10). He invoked a major D_1 syncline along the axis of the Island with superimposed, large-scale D_2 folds to explain the outcrop pattern. However, such large-scale fold models have not been supported by biostratigraphical data. Molyneux (1979) showed that both the lithostratigraphy and the structural model of Simpson (1963) were untenable, although all of the rocks were still considered to be of late Cambrian or early Ordovician (Arenig) age. Howe (1999) established that the Niarbyl Formation is Silurian (probably Wenlock), removing any possible correlation with the Arenig Lonan Formation which crops out over much of the south-east of the Island. Uncertainty remained over the possible equivalence of the black mudstone units (e.g. Woodcock et al., 1999c), but this has been resolved following more recent work.

Fitches et al. (1999) corroborated Simpson's interpretation of the three-fold structural succession apparent in exposure and some of his major D_1 structures, but they also considered the possible significance of major strike-parallel faults. They tried not to impose a model which could not be supported by the stratigraphical evidence, and a series of tracts was identified (Figure 11). Within each tract a reasonably coherent stratigraphy could be recognised, but correlation between tracts remained speculative (e.g. Woodcock et al., 1999c, fig. 8) and faulted contacts were possible. Building on this, the recent work has allowed the resolution of some of the remaining uncertainties and presents a stratigraphical and structural model supported by better biostratigraphical control (Molyneux, 2001). Two successions are recognised (BGS, 2001):

- in the south-east, the Lonan Formation passes up through the quartz arenite units of the Mull Hill and Creg Agneash formations into the Maughold Formation
- in the centre of the Island, the Barrule, Injebreck, Glen Rushen and Creggan Moar formations form a north-westerly younging succession

Thrust imbrication duplicating the Barrule Formation and the base of the Injebreck Formation is demonstrated by repetition of the distinctive sandstone-dominated packet 200 to 300 m above the boundary (Figure 3). The fault is exposed as a high strain zone on the shore at Lag ny Keeilley (see below). This supports the interpreted tectonic boundary between the Barrule and Maughold formations, although there may not be much, if any, stratigraphy missing. Similar imbrication is interpreted to duplicate the top of the Glen Rushen Formation and the base of the Creggan Moar Formation in Glen Rushen and to the south-west.

The significance of high strain zones exposed on the west coast of the Island was discussed in some detail by Fitches et al. (1999). The 'Niarbyl shear zone' has long been known (e.g. Lamplugh, 1903; Morrison, 1989; Roberts et al., 1990) and may have particular significance because of its proximity to the base of the Silurian Niarbyl Formation. A narrower zone of high strain, at Lag ny Keilley, is now thought to be associated with the fault that imbricates the top of the Barrule Formation and the base of the Injebreck Formation (Figure 3).

The first two phases of deformation in the Isle of Man affected both the Ordovician Manx Group and the Silurian Niarbyl Formation. The early deformation affected many of the minor intrusions and the Dhoon granite (Power and Barnes, 1999) and possibly metamorphic phases in the aureole of the early Devonian Foxdale granite, although not the granite itself (Simpson, 1965). The deformation is therefore considered to be late Silurian or early Devonian in age, equivalent to the 'Acadian' deformation of north-west England (Soper et al., 1987). D_1 and D_2 are associated with low grade regional metamorphism although the pattern is strongly influenced by the original composition of the various units (Power and Barnes, 1999) and possibly granite batholiths at depth (Roberts et al., 1990). The third tectonic phase is evident only locally and comparable with structures in the Carboniferous rocks and therefore may be Variscan in age (Fitches et al., 1999).

D_1 structures

Open to isoclinal F_1 folds are common on a wide range of scales, their wavelength varying from a few millimetres to several kilometres. Axial surfaces are generally steep north-west- or south-east-dipping and hinge zones are typically gently plunging to horizontal, although locally (e.g. in the northern part of Langness) they plunge more steeply east. Fold preservation is relatively poor in the mudstone-rich units, although folds can be interpreted locally by the recognition of changes in younging direction or cleavage vergence. Small to intermediate size folds are locally abundant in thinly bedded units (e.g. at Port Erin), but folds on a range of sizes are best preserved in the medium- to thick-bedded sandstone successions. Continuous trains of folds occur in the Ny Garvain Member and the overlying part of the Lonan Formation and throughout the outcrop of the Niarbyl Formation (Fitches et al., 1999, figs 8, 9, 10). Larger structures can be mapped in the Mull Hill Formation (e.g. Fitches et al., 1999, figs 3, 4). The Douglas syncline and the Dhoon anticline in the Lonan Formation (Figure 11) are the largest folds that can be recognised.

Boudinage, generally of sandstone beds, early veins and igneous sheets, is commonly associated with the D_1 deformation, and produces boudins of various forms and orientations (Fitches et al., 1999).

S_1 cleavage is the dominant tectonic fabric in most parts of the Manx Group, although locally, particularly in mud-rich layers or units, it may be overprinted by S_2. In pelitic rocks it is defined mainly by aligned flakes of white mica and chlorite. Locally it may become phyllitic and is marked by pressure solution striping. In sandstone, the S_1 cleavage is commonly a weak, spaced pressure solution fabric (with spacing of a few millimetres), but in places it comprises aligned, flattened detrital grains. The S_1 cleavage commonly lies virtually parallel to bedding. In fold hinge zones it is axial planar or fans and refracts from bed to bed through the fold profile. However, it may transect the F_1 folds by a few degrees, usually clockwise but locally anticlockwise.

D_2 structures

D_2 structures occur throughout the Manx and Dalby groups, but they are only weakly developed in the sandstone-rich formations. The gently dipping S_2 cleavage, particularly well developed in finer grained lithologies, is generally the most obvious evidence of D_2. It is a crenulation cleavage but is associated with pressure solution striping in some pelitic rocks. Usually it is easily distinguished from S_1 because the latter is steeply dipping and commonly penetrative while S_2 is flat-lying and clearly spaced. However, where the D_2 vertical flattening was particularly intense and S_1 was rotated to a near horizontal attitude, a combined S_1–S_2 fabric has been produced.

Visible F_2 folds are only sporadically developed and generally of small size, with wavelengths typically up to a few tens of centimetres and, rarely, a few metres. Axial surfaces are gently north-west- or south-east-dipping with gently plunging hinges. Small F_2 folds have a close to tight chevron profile and they typically verge down-dip. Larger folds are more open and rounded, causing changes in the dip direction either side of vertical. F_2 folds are usually clearly distinguishable from the co-axial but much steeper F_1 folds, particularly where they are superimposed. Where D_2 deformation was particularly intense, F_1 axial surfaces and S_1 have been rotated into alignment with F_2 axial surfaces and the two generations of structures are almost indistinguishable.

High strain zones

D_1 and D_2 strain was distributed unevenly in the mudstone-dominated parts of the Manx Group and zones of relatively intense deformation occur locally (e.g. in the Lady Port Formation at Lynague Strand [SC 2801 8705]). These 'high strain zones' may not necessarily be associated with major structures, although two examples described in detail by Fitches et al. (1999) are of particular significance.

A zone of high strain exposed on the foreshore below Lag ny Keeilley [SC 215 745] occurs within the Injebreck Formation. It occurs at the northern margin of the sandstone-rich package situated 200 to 300 m above the base of the formation. These northernmost sandstone beds contain patches of intraformational conglomerate that have been strongly flattened. The most intensely deformed rocks occur in a 5 m-wide zone of pelite in which an intense fabric with disrupted quartz veins is deformed by variably orientated shear bands or extensional crenulation fabrics showing a predominantly sinistral sense of displacement. This zone passes northwards into a strongly foliated zone and then into less disturbed boudinaged bedding, including a pre-S_1 sill, cut by F_2 folds and cleavage. While it is possible that this marks a major D_1 shear zone, its location immediately adjacent to the thick sandstone package led Fitches et al. (1999) to interpret the high strain zone as the result of strain partitioning at the boundary between rheologically different packages of rock. The location of the high strain zone, however, correlates closely with the fault that duplicates the top of the Barrule Formation and the base of the Injebreck Formation (Figure 3).

A broader zone of high strain exposed directly south of The Niarbyl was recognised by Lamplugh (1903). Often termed the 'Niarbyl shear zone', it has been discussed by many subsequent authors (e.g. Simpson, 1963; Morrison, 1989; Roberts et al., 1990; Morris et al., 1999), but its significance remains enigmatic. The most intensely deformed part of the zone comprises phyllonite with abundant quartz and carbonate augen, tightly folded quartz veins, well-developed S–C fabrics and shear bands (predominantly indicating sinistral shear) in various orientations. The phyllonitic fabric is deformed by S_2 and thus was formed during or shortly after D_1, but is unusual in that it is north-east-dipping, perpendicular to the regional strike of S_1. The high strain zone is cut by several steep brittle faults, one of which (named the Niarbyl Thrust by Fitches et al., 1999) juxtaposes it against relatively weakly deformed bedded sandstone of the Niarbyl Formation to the north. To the south, the zone of high strain dies out over several tens of metres within the Creggan Moar Formation, although narrow zones of disrupted and transposed bedding alternating with wide zones of coherent rocks persist over several hundred metres. The high strain zone clearly affects the Creggan Moar Formation and basic intrusions therein, but it is unclear to what extent the Niarbyl Formation was involved. Fitches (*in* Fitches et al., 1999) considered that the high strain zone is essentially contained within the Creggan Moar Formation and juxtaposed against the Niarbyl Formation by the Niarbyl Thrust. By considering the orientation of the fabric perpendicular to the contact, he decided that it was unlikely that the zone was related to the emplacement of the Niarbyl Formation into its present situation. On the other hand, Morris (*in* Morris et al., 1999 and *in* Fitches et al., 1999) suggested that the high strain zone involves rocks of the Niarbyl Formation and is associated with its tectonic emplacement.

Post D_2 structures

Late south-east-directed thrust faults, which are scattered throughout the Lower Palaeozoic rocks of the Isle of Man, were regarded as late Caledonian in age by Fitches et al. (1999), possibly equivalent to similar structures in the early Devonian Peel Sandstone Group.

D_1 and D_2 structures and fabrics in the Manx Group are sporadically deformed by a broadly north-trending, steeply dipping crenulation cleavage associated with upright folds. These are commonly north-west-striking, although they vary with similar structures being north- or north-east-striking in south-western parts of the Isle of Man. They probably mark the presence of conjugate sets of structures, but may be a result of more than one phase of deformation. Most of these folds are open, with rounded hinges and wavelengths in the 0.10 to 10 m range, although chevron and kink folds also occur. The age of these structures is uncertain. Some may have been formed at the same time as late Caledonian thrusts. Those with north–south strike may be equivalent to similarly orientated Variscan folds and cleavage in the Dinantian rocks in the south of the Isle of Man.

INTRUSIVE IGNEOUS ROCKS

A range of intrusive rocks occur at outcrop on the Isle of Man, ranging in age from pre-S_1 or syn-S_1 to Carboniferous. Granite may underlie much of the Island at depth (Cornwell, 1972; Chapter 2), but it crops out as three relatively small granitic bodies and a suite of acid sheets along the central spine of the Island. Other minor intrusions of a range of compositions are abundant in the Manx Group and occur locally within the Niarbyl Formation.

Granitic rocks

The two larger intrusions, the Dhoon granodiorite in the north-east and the Foxdale granite in the central part of the Island, both crop out over an area of about 2 km^2. A third, smaller outcrop of granitic rocks, the Oatlands Complex, is known in the south-east of the Island (Lamplugh, 1903; Taylor and Gamba, 1933) but exposure is poor. In addition, a series of acid sheets occur along the central spine of the Island (Lamplugh, 1903; Simpson, 1964).

The two larger granitic bodies are of different ages and provide useful event markers. The Dhoon granodiorite was intruded early in the history of the Manx Group and has a minimum age of syn-S_1 (Power and Barnes, 1999) while the Foxdale granite, with an isotopic age of around 400 Ma (personal communication, S F Crowley and P S Kennan), postdates the formation of the S_2 cleavage.

DHOON GRANODIORITE The Dhoon granodiorite [SC 450 870] forms the high ground of Slieau Ouyr and Slieau Lhean to the west of the Douglas–Ramsey road and Barony Hill to the east. There is a large disused quarry [SC 459 872] in the granodiorite on the south-west flank of Barony Hill at Dhoon. A granitic mylonite, dipping 45° to the south in the north side of the quarry, forms the northern margin of the granodiorite at this location.

The granodiorite is a fine- to medium-grained grey rock. In thin section, it is composed of subhedral plagioclase with subordinate quartz and rare potassium feldspar, together with biotite as discrete flakes and as clusters containing titanite and epidote. Some isolated phenocrysts of plagioclase and quartz may also be seen. In some cases, where biotite is present as small flakes it defines a poor foliation. Biotite also forms clot-like aggregates which, together with evidence from partly adsorbed xenoliths of country rock, were interpreted by Nockolds (1931) as suggesting contamination of the magma by assimilation. The most striking feature is the state of alteration; zoisite and muscovite grains have extensively replaced the plagioclase, and quartz grains are commonly recrystallised to form polygonal aggregates around the margins of relict grains. The granodiorite has undergone greenschist facies metamorphism. Chemically the metagranodiorite is sodic (with Na_2O/K_2O values of about 2) and now has higher Fe, Mg, and Ca than a true granite. Trace element chemistry suggests a volcanic arc origin for the granite.

No age determination work has been published on the Dhoon granodiorite, possibly because of the potential problems of the alteration and contamination by assimilation. However, geological relationships in the contact aureole indicate that the granodiorite was emplaced into the Manx Group at an early stage. Simpson (1964) suggested that this was post-S_1 but pre-S_2. Power and Barnes (1999) showed that contact metamorphic spotting is flattened in S_1. This, together with the evidence that the granodiorite underwent the regional greenschist facies metamorphism, indicates that the Dhoon granodiorite could not have been emplaced later than syn-D_1 but most probably was pre-D_1 in origin.

OATLANDS COMPLEX Lamplugh (1903) described the occurrence of a small area of granitic rocks at Oatlands [SC 323 725] in the south-east of the Island. The thin sections described by Watts (*in* Lamplugh, 1903) range in composition from diorite through granodiorite to granite. There is now little in situ exposure as the old quarries have been filled, but a variety of igneous rock types may be observed in walls in the neighbourhood. A more detailed description of the complex was provided by Taylor and Gamba (1933). They described an elliptical area of igneous rocks, 0.6 km long and 0.2 km wide, the major part of which is gabbroic in composition and into which a central area of granite has been intruded. The boundary between the two rock types is gradational and is marked by a diorite that was interpreted as a hybrid rock formed by intrusion of the granite into the solid gabbro. Taylor and Gamba (1933) noted that the contact aureole, in the form of hornfelsed and spotted rocks, seems large for the exposed size of the complex. They concluded that the Oatlands Complex has more in common with the Dhoon granodiorite than the Foxdale granite.

FOXDALE GRANITE The Foxdale granite crops out on Stoney Mountain [SC 286 772], but is relatively poorly exposed other than in two quarries [SC 288 773 and 292 771] so the boundaries have been taken from Lamplugh's mapping (Lamplugh, 1903). Simpson (1965) also provided a detailed description of the granite.

The granite is a fine- to medium-grained white rock with obvious muscovite. Although generally undeformed, it is locally highly deformed in small-scale shear zones. The main part of the granite in Stoney Mountain quarry [292 771] is medium grained with roughly equal amounts of quartz and feldspar, rather less potassium feldspar, and up to 10 per cent muscovite. Accessory minerals include apatite, zircon, monazite and garnet. A finer grained, porphyritic microgranite, which occurs locally, is considered to be intruded into the more common variety (personal communication, S F Crowley and P S Kennan). This variant has a distinctive texture of feldspar, muscovite and quartz phenocrysts in a fine-grained matrix. Although its mineralogy is similar to that of the main granite, the microgranite also contains accessory spodumene. Pegmatitic veins of various types also occur. The most common are vertical, north-west-trending veins with centimetre-scale quartz, microcline, muscovite, and may be seen in the upper quarry [SC 288 773] at Stoney Mountain. Other veins are near vertical and east–west trending, and may contain beryl as well as quartz, microcline and muscovite. The granites have a crust-dominated geochemistry and are silicic, peraluminous and high in Rb, U and Th (personal communication, S F Crowley and P S Kennan).

Published age determinations on the Foxdale granite are limited. A granite muscovite separate gave a K–Ar age of 381 ± 7 Ma (Brown et al., 1968) and a sample of potassium feldspar from a pegmatite gave a K–Ar age of 322 ± 5 Ma (Ineson and Mitchell, 1979). A recent Rb–Sr whole rock isochron age of 383 ± 11 Ma (MSWD = 0.805) with an initial Sr isotope ratio of 0.71489 (personal communication, S F Crowley and P S Kennan) agrees closely with the age obtained by Brown et al. (1968). However, a model age of around 400 Ma from muscovite in a pegmatite suggests that these ages may have been reset, and is considered more likely to approximate to the age of emplacement of the Foxdale granite (personal communication, S F Crowley and P S Kennan).

Simpson (1965) described the development of chlorite, biotite, staurolite and garnet porphyroblasts in the contact aureole of the Foxdale granite and in a nearby area of thermal alteration at Archallagan to the north of Foxdale. He interpreted these minerals as static overgrowths on D_2 crenulations and argued that the strong quartz, muscovite and chlorite foliation that encloses these porphyroblasts is a 'renewed development of S_2'. However, Power and Barnes

(1999) envisaged this foliation as a later event, possibly due to localised shearing, which may have contributed to the resetting of some of the isotopic systems in the Foxdale granite.

Minor intrusions

Minor intrusions of a range of compositions are abundant in the Manx Group and occur sporadically within the Silurian Niarbyl Formation. Their age is uncertain but many are deformed and/or metamorphosed and thus predate emplacement of the post-D_2 Foxdale granite in the early Devonian. A few undeformed dolerite dykes may be of Carboniferous age, and a conspicuous suite of Palaeogene olivine dolerite dykes cuts the Carboniferous and, offshore, the Permo–Triassic rocks (Chapter 8).

Lamplugh's field maps and the detailed account given in the memoir (Lamplugh, 1903, including some petrographical descriptions made by W W Watts) remain the primary source of information on the minor intrusions as little systematic work appears to have been carried out subsequently. Lamplugh recorded almost 2000 minor intrusions and most were attributed a rock name in the field. Apart from the olivine dolerite suite, considered by Lamplugh (1903, p.327) to be Tertiary (i.e. Palaeogene) in age, the majority of the dykes were recognised as being pre-Carboniferous. More than half of these were classified as 'diabase' or 'greenstone', a large proportion of which are sheared or otherwise altered. The others were classified as dolerite, diorite, camptonite, mica trap or microgranite. However, from re-examination of Lamplugh's thin section collection, housed at BGS, some of the rock names used by Lamplugh prove to have been applied to more than one rock type. For example, a number of the 'diabase' samples are actually sheared granodiorite. Reasonable caution thus needs to be exercised when using Lamplugh's maps to identify a particular dyke rock. In practice, as noted by Lamplugh (1903, p.297), it is often difficult to determine the original nature of the dyke rocks because of the effects of deformation, metamorphism and metasomatism. Even in thin section, many of the rocks can only be classified as chlorite-, actinolite- or calc-schist. As a consequence, the majority of the dykes represented on the new geological map (BGS, 2001) are classified as metabasite.

As in other parts of the British Caledonides (e.g. Barnes et al., 1986), it is evident in the Isle of Man that a range of magma types were available and were emplaced periodically throughout the deformation history of the host sedimentary rocks. Many of the dykes were emplaced early in the tectonic history of the Manx Group as they are commonly cleaved (some containing two or three cleavages) and some examples are folded or boudinaged.

Basic intrusions

The basic intrusions typically range from a few centimetres to a few metres in thickness and commonly lie parallel to the steeply dipping bedding in the host rocks. They are generally cleaved, commonly by both S_1 and S_2, causing loss of the original igneous minerals and textures. The rocks are now greenschist with a mineral assemblage of chlorite, albite, quartz and calcite.

Some basic dykes that intrude the Manx Group have very complex contacts and may have been intruded into unconsolidated sediments, and hence would be the earliest dykes that have been preserved. Examples occur at Lady Port [SC 288 878] and Cass ny Hawin [SC 292 683]. However, in both cases the rocks have been strongly deformed and an unambiguous conclusion cannot be drawn.

A series of inclined sills at Poortown [SC 270 833], 3 km east of Peel, range in composition from olivine basalt to basaltic andesite (Power and Crowley, 1999). Some are pyroxene-rich dolerite and others plagioclase-phyric andesite. They have been metamorphosed to greenschist facies and the only primary igneous mineral partly preserved is augite. Alignment of metamorphic chlorite is parallel to the S_1 cleavage in the country rocks. The geochemistry of the more immobile elements suggests a volcanic arc origin in an active continental margin environment. There is uncertainty over the age of the Poortown Complex but it could be equivalent to the Caradoc volcanic rocks in the Lake District. Several sills or more irregular intrusions crop out to the north and north-west of Poortown (e.g. on the coast at the north end of Will's Strand [SC 269 859]). These are very similar to the Poortown rocks and are probably part of the same suite.

A few basic dykes cut the Silurian Niarbyl Formation, indicating that at least some were emplaced in the late Silurian. However it is possible that many of the metabasite dykes in the Manx Group may also have been emplaced at this time, during the main phase of tectonic deformation. This is consistent with field evidence that some dykes are clearly folded by D_1 folds, and others were emplaced parallel to the S_1 cleavage and/or cross-cut and postdate D_1 folds and the S_1 cleavage. Other examples may have been emplaced syn- or post-D_2. For example, a dyke exposed at Black Hut [SC 402 885] was interpreted by Power and Barnes (1999) as syn-D_2. Watts (*in* Lamplugh, 1903) recognised a group of sheared basic rocks termed 'actinolitic trap', also from central parts of the Island, which show similar characteristics to the Black Hut dyke and may have a similar origin.

Dolerite dykes with no sign of foliation and with well-preserved igneous textures occur at widely scattered localities throughout the outcrop of the Lower Palaeozoic rocks. They are fine to medium grained and composed of augite, plagioclase and opaque minerals. They generally show at least some secondary alteration with the development of chlorite, epidote, calcite and titanite. They were described as 'ophitic dolerite' or 'porphyritic diabase' by Lamplugh (1903). They clearly postdate deformation and metamorphism of the Lower Palaeozoic rocks, but otherwise their age is unknown. It is conceivable that, as suggested by Lamplugh, they are of Carboniferous age.

Dioritic dykes

These mica-poor rocks were often classified as camptonite by Lamplugh (1903) although there are no indications that they are rich in alkali elements. A series of these dykes occurs at Langness where they clearly predate the Carboniferous rocks. They are fine to medium grained and are composed of euhedral brown hornblende, plagioclase, quartz and opaque oxides. One sample contains augite as well as hornblende.

Some alteration of hornblende to chlorite is common but they are commonly quite fresh and unaltered.

Granitic dykes

A suite of sheared granodiorite dykes is apparent from Lamplugh's thin section collection. These dykes were originally classified as diabase or other rock types so it has not been possible to fully separate them from the metabasite suite on the map. They tend to be medium grained but their original texture has been almost entirely lost due to the effects of alteration and deformation. It is clear, however, that the granodiorite dykes were emplaced before or during D_1 deformation. They probably show the same field relationships as the metabasite dykes.

A suite of microgranite dykes, restricted to the central spine of the Island, was accurately mapped by Lamplugh (1903) who referred to them as 'Dhoon granite elvans'. A detailed account of them was also given by Simpson (1964). Generally they strike north-east with a steep dip and vary in thickness from less than a metre to about 5 m. They may be lenticular in form because they cannot be traced for more than a few tens of metres. Simpson (1964), like Lamplugh, associated them with the Dhoon granodiorite although they are never seen in actual contact with the granodiorite. Simpson (1964) stated that they commonly appear to be intruded along S_1 and must therefore postdate S_1, although he did not describe examples cross-cutting S_1. These dykes commonly have a strong foliation defined by shape orientation of quartz and muscovite, ascribed by Simpson (1964) to flexural slip at the beginning of D_2. Watts (*in* Lamplugh, 1903) and Simpson (1964) described samples from acid sheets at the top of Greeba Mountain [SC 318 816] as having euhedral porphyroblasts of chloritoid up to two millimetres in size overgrowing the strong foliation. One of Lamplugh's samples from this locality (L2798) [SC 315 807] is fine grained with a strong cleavage defined by muscovite anastomosing around elongate quartz and plagioclase grains. Subhedral chloritoid, up to 2 mm in size, with marked relief and colourless to blue-green pleochroism, has overgrown the cleavage. Power and Barnes (1999) found that chloritoid overgrew S_1 but always predated S_2 in the metasedimentary rocks so the cleavage in the dykes must be S_1 and the dykes are almost certainly pre- or syn-D_1.

Lamplugh (1903) named one group of dykes as the 'Foxdale Elvans' as he associated them with the Foxdale granite. One of the larger examples of this rock type is the Crosby dyke [SC 325 791] which is a medium-grained leucocratic granite. It has a chemistry that is more evolved than that of the Foxdale granite (personal communication, S F Crowley) but could be related to the Foxdale intrusion. It is intruded into the core of a D_2 fold and contact metamorphic biotite has overgrown D_2 crenulations.

4 Post-Caledonian structure

This chapter describes the structure and evolution of the relatively weakly deformed sedimentary cover rocks that rest with strong unconformity on the Caledonian basement. These cover strata, in places more that 9000 m thick, can be split into two main units (Figure 12). A Carboniferous succession is cut by predominantly normal faults with only localised reverse faulting and folding. This is overlain unconformably by rocks of Permian to Jurassic age, which are cut by dominantly normal faults, but are also characterised by widespread salt-related structural effects.

CARBONIFEROUS STRUCTURE

Following the Caledonian Orogeny, regional uplift and erosion led to near peneplanation of the basement surface before the resumption of deposition in latest Devonian or earliest Carboniferous times.

Regional lithospheric extension directed roughly north–south (Leeder, 1982) or north-north-west–south-south-east (Lee, 1988), provided the main drive for Carboniferous basin development in the Manx region. Basin subsidence occurred in two distinct phases. In early Carboniferous (Dinantian) times a synextensional 'rift' phase was characterised by fault-controlled extensional basins subsiding rapidly between structurally elevated and periodically emergent blocks. Structural trends were strongly influenced by the grain of the underlying Caledonian basement (Chapter 2). In later Carboniferous (Namurian and Westphalian) times, postextensional 'sag' subsidence of a more regional nature was characterised by a lack of major fault-control, and led to submergence and depositional onlap of the earlier structural highs (e.g. Kirby et al., 2000).

Development of the Variscan Foldbelt culminated in latest Carboniferous times, with large-scale thrust and nappe emplacement in northern France, Belgium, southern England, south Wales and southern Ireland. The Manx region lies north of the Variscan Foldbelt, on the Variscan Foreland. Here, Variscan deformation was much less pervasive, being largely restricted to the partial reversal of pre-existing Dinantian normal faults and associated basin inversion.

Carboniferous rocks occur at the northern and southern ends of the Isle of Man (Chapter 5), and are present over much of the offshore region where they are largely concealed beneath the Permo-Triassic basin system. The Carboniferous succession, though identifiable on seismic reflection data, is commonly buried to considerable depth, and details of basin margin faulting are not well resolved. In addition, none of the available deep wells penetrates a reasonably complete Carboniferous succession (Figure 13), so its total thickness is not known. Consequently, knowledge of Carboniferous basin structure in the region is rather sketchy, though broad aspects can be discussed.

EARLY CARBONIFEROUS 'RIFT' PHASE

The main areas of Dinantian rifting preserved in the Manx region (Figure 12a) appear to be strongly influenced by basement structure. In the west and north of the region, the Peel and Solway basins rest on basement rocks of the Iapetus Convergence Zone (Chapter 2). They show dominantly Caledonoid structural trends and may have formed by reactivation of Acadian basement thrusts (Chapter 2). Extending from south-west of the Isle of Man, north-eastwards through the central part of the region, the Manx–Lakeland Ridge forms a major elongated basement high, interpreted as a rigid structural buttress close to the north-west margin of Avalonian crust (Chapter 2). This feature has long been recognised; parts of it have been variously termed the Isle of Man Massif, the Manx Massif, and the Ramsey– Whitehaven Ridge (e.g. Bott, 1964; Jackson et al., 1995). In early Carboniferous times it formed a major Dinantian structural high, characterised by platform carbonate deposition, linking eastward to the Lake District and Alston blocks of northern England. In the southern part of the region the Eubonia Basin and Central Province Trough rest on Avalonian basement. Structural trends in these latter basins are not well understood, in part because of their greater depth and poor well control.

Solway Basin

Only the westernmost part of the Solway Basin lies within the Manx region (Figure 12); it continues eastwards across northern England as the Solway–Northumberland Basin (Chadwick et al., 1995), to die out beneath the North Sea. It formed as a major Dinantian rift, over 200 km in length, parallel to the underlying Iapetus Convergence Zone. In the Manx region it is a roughly symmetrical feature, bounded to the north by the east-north-east-trending North Solway Fault and to the south by the near parallel Maryport Fault which separates the basin from the elevated Manx–Lakeland Ridge (Figure 14a). The Maryport Fault passes *en échelon* into the major Stublick–Ninety Fathom Fault System which continues eastwards across northern England at the southern margin of the Solway–Northumberland Basin. There is uncertainty over the thickness of Dinantian strata in the Solway Basin owing to a lack of deep borehole control, but they are likely to be at least 2000 m thick. Along strike beneath northern England the Dinantian succession exceeds 4000 m in thickness (Chadwick et al., 1995; Ward, 1997).

Manx–Lakeland Ridge

The Manx–Lakeland Ridge formed a major, elevated Dinantian tilt block, bounded to the north-west by the Maryport Fault and to the south-east by the Lagman and Eubonia faults (Figure 12). Over much of the

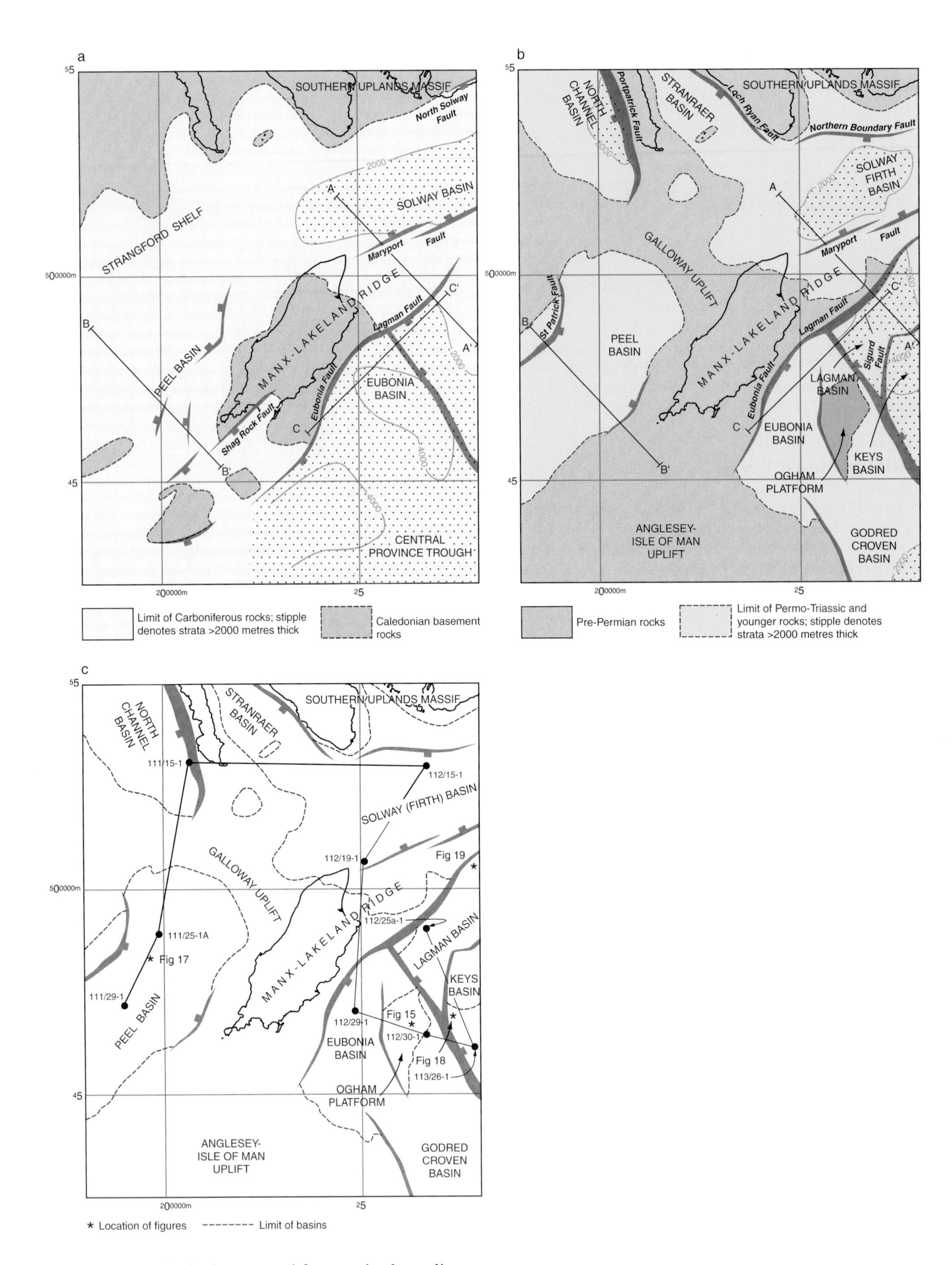

Figure 12 Principal structural features in the sedimentary cover.

a. Carboniferous structures.
b. Permo-Triassic structures.
c. Map to show location of well correlation line (see Figure 13).

ridge, Dinantian strata are either thin or absent and it is clear that parts of the ridge crest (for example, over the Isle of Man) remained subaerial for some considerable time in the early Dinantian. Dinantian occurrences at the northern and southern ends of the Isle of Man, though of contrasting facies (Chapter 5), typify the relatively thin, platform strata of the Manx–Lakeland Ridge. The Dinantian succession thickens gradually north-eastwards on the tilt block towards the Maryport Fault, across which it thickens abruptly into the Solway Basin (Figure 14a). Early Carboniferous oblique–normal displacements on the Maryport Fault have been estimated as up to 2000 m (Chadwick et al., 1993).

Peel Basin

The oldest sedimentary rocks of the Peel Basin may be the red-bed strata of the Peel Group (Chapter 5). These occur at the eastern margin of the basin, within a fault-bounded outlier on the west coast of the Isle of Man (Piper and Crowley, 1999). There is uncertainty over the age of these beds; they may represent very early syn-rift deposits of Devonian age, or alternatively, molasse-type deposits of late Carboniferous age (see below). The main rift deposits of the Peel Basin lie offshore, concealed beneath Permo–Jurassic cover, (Figures 12a, 13), where Dinantian strata are preserved in a series of tilt blocks bounded by normal faults (Figure 14b). Structural trends are difficult to establish from the available seismic data, but are assumed to be dominantly north-north-east, parallel to the local basement trend (Chapter 2; Quirk et al., 1999a; Newman, 1999). The tilt blocks lie within the hanging wall block of the west-north-west-dipping Barrule Thrust Zone and may have been formed by extensional reactivation of this structure (Chapter 2).

Eubonia Basin and Central Province Trough

A third area of early Carboniferous basin development is in the south of the region, concealed by Permo–Triassic cover rocks, where a very thick Carboniferous succession is developed in the Eubonia Basin and the area to the south (Quirk et al., 1999a). The Eubonia Fault formed the north-west margin of the basin, separating it from the Manx–Lakeland Ridge (Figure 14c). Dinantian thicknesses are poorly constrained, but appear to increase south-westwards towards the fault, indicating syndepositional normal displacement. Carboniferous rocks around the Keys Fault are more deeply buried and structural details are less well resolved, so the extent to which the Keys Fault controlled early Carboniferous basin development is uncertain. There is evidence of minor Dinantian thickening across the fault (Figure 14c), but this is poorly constrained. Elsewhere, deep beneath the Permo–Triassic cover of the Godred Croven Basin, Dinantian basin structure is generally not well understood. In broad terms it is likely to constitute north-trending embayments of the Central Province Trough (Jackson et al., 1995), a major Dinantian depocentre forming the offshore westward continuation of the Craven Basin (Kirby et al., 2000). There is uncertainty over Dinantian thicknesses in the Central Province Trough, but they are generally believed to be around 2000 m (e.g. BGS, 1994; Jackson and Mulholland, 1993).

LATE CARBONIFEROUS 'SAG' PHASE

In late Carboniferous times active crustal extension gave way to regional post-rift subsidence, with a much reduced structural demarcation between the elevated blocks and the rift basins. Namurian and Westphalian strata were deposited in a regime of regional sedimentation, with little syndepositional normal faulting, and tended to onlap previously exposed massifs. This is well illustrated by a substantial post-rift succession on parts of the Manx–Lakeland Ridge (subcropping beneath Quaternary deposits at the northern end of the Isle of Man, Chapter 5), which tends to onlap the syn-rift (Dinantian) rocks (Figure 14a). Depositional thickness trends of the post-rift succession are not tightly constrained; in most areas the upper part of the sequence is not preserved and in some areas, notably north of the Manx–Lakeland Ridge, most of the post-rift succession was removed by Variscan events (see below). However comparison of preserved strata indicates a general southward thickening trend, towards the Central Province Trough (Figure 12a, Jackson et al., 1995), where maximum Upper Carboniferous thicknesses in the 'Quadrant 109 Syncline' are perhaps locally in excess of 5000 m (Jackson and Mulholland, 1993; Jackson and Johnson, 1996).

LATE CARBONIFEROUS (VARISCAN) BASIN INVERSION

Towards the end of the Carboniferous, basin subsidence gave way to regional uplift as Variscan compression initiated the process of basin inversion. This appeared to involve both north–south and east–west directed components of shortening, and was accomplished both by regional basin upwarping and also by localised, partial reversal of basin margin faults, the latter reducing net displacements on the basin-controlling syn-rift normal faults.

Basin inversion appears to have been most pronounced north of the Manx–Lakeland Ridge, where Dinantian and, locally, Namurian strata subcrop beneath the Permo–Triassic cover (Newman, 1999). The Solway Basin suffered strong inversion with uplift of the basin fill and erosion of much of the Westphalian and Namurian successions (Jackson et al., 1995). Variscan reversal of the Maryport Fault (Figure 14a) is demonstrated by the preservation of a much more complete post-rift sequence on its footwall block (the Manx–Lakeland Ridge) than on its hanging wall block (the Solway Basin). Perhaps the best evidence for Variscan inversion of the Solway Basin lies to the east, just outside the Manx region, where high quality seismic reflection data show anticlinal folding of the Carboniferous basin fill (Akhurst et al., 1997; Newman, 1999), and also reversal of the Maryport Fault, with reverse 'short-cut' faults splaying into its footwall block, the Manx–Lakeland Ridge (Chadwick et al., 1993). The Peel Basin also appears to have been strongly inverted, its post-rift succession having been largely removed (Figure 14b) and with Dinantian

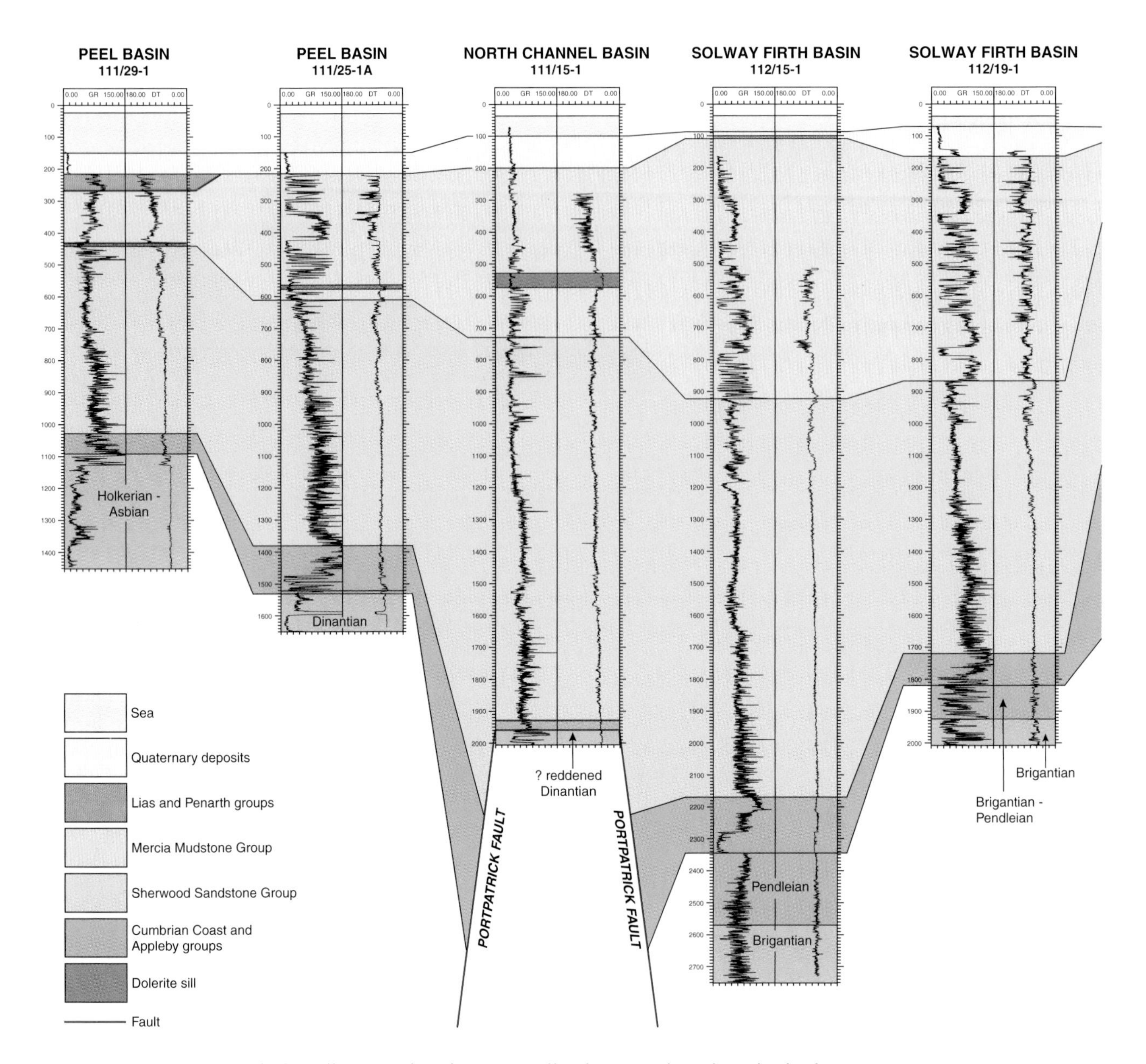

Figure 13 Well correlation diagram showing generalised successions in principal basins and blocks.

rocks now forming much of the base Permian subcrop (Newman, 1999).

South of the Manx–Lakeland Ridge, the effects of Variscan basin inversion were less marked, with relatively younger Carboniferous strata preserved, to the extent that Westphalian rocks form the dominant subcrop in the Eubonia Basin (Figure 14c). Nevertheless, here too there is ample evidence of Variscan movements. In the Carboniferous inlier of the Ogham Platform, a steep pre-Permian reverse fault is clearly imaged on the seismic data (Figure 15), with associated hanging wall folding affecting Namurian and Westphalian strata. The possible presence of an intra-Westphalian unconformity hereabouts (Figure 15) provides striking evidence of several episodes of basin inversion. Here a folded Westphalian A–C (Langsettian to Bolsovian) succession is unconformably overlain by a distinctive package of younger strata which is, in turn, overlain by the Permian Appleby Group (see below). The package of strata is tentatively assigned a Bolsovian (Westphalian C) to Stephanian age. The strata occupy a synclinal area termed the Onchan Depression and were interpreted by Quirk and Kimbell (1997) as synorogenic deposits shed from contemporaneously developing Variscan folds. A further suggestion (Quirk and Kimbell, (1997) is that the red-bed strata of the Peel Group, formally assigned to the Devonian (Chapter 5), may in fact be a similar, roughly coeval, molasse-type deposit.

More widely, the intra-Westphalian unconformity may correlate with the unconformable base of the Whitehaven Sandstone Formation in west Cumbria (Eastwood et al., 1937; Akhurst et al., 1997). It may perhaps also be associated with the Symon Unconformity (Ramsbottom et al., 1978; Tubb et al., 1986; Leeder and Hardman, 1990), seen in the Lancashire Coalfield and beneath the southern North Sea where it marks the base of primary red beds above grey Westphalian coal measures.

At the north-west end of the seismic section in Figure 15, the base of the Permo–Triassic can be seen to cut progressively deeper into the Carboniferous succession. This pattern continues north-westwards towards the

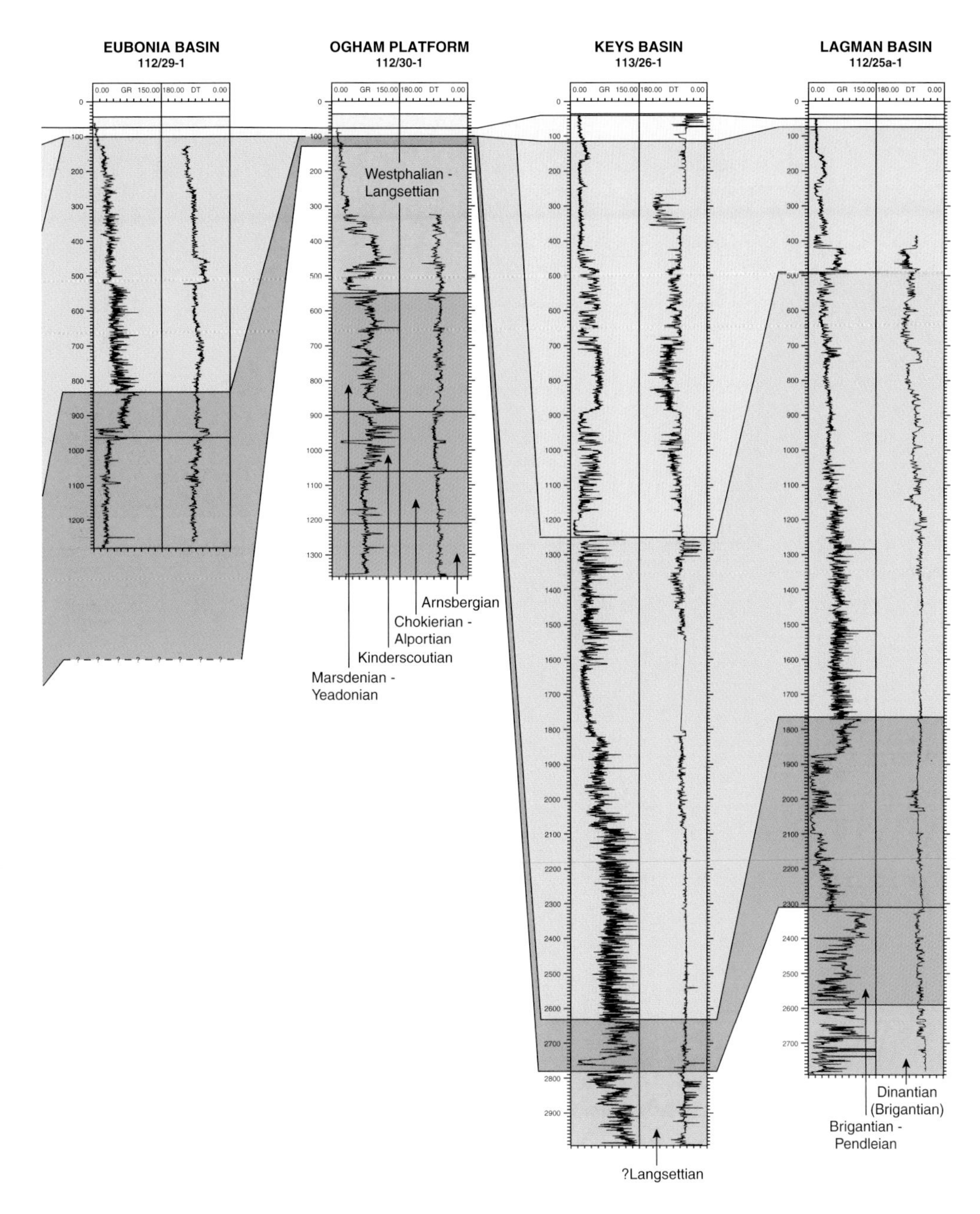

Figure 13 *continued* (For location see Figure 12c)

Eubonia Fault, whose hanging wall block shows Permo–Triassic rocks resting upon lowest Westphalian or Namurian strata. This indicates that the Eubonia Fault underwent pronounced Variscan reversal with development of a major hanging wall anticline.

Elsewhere, a generally less complete preservation of the post-rift succession on the hanging wall block of the Keys Fault (Figure 14c) attests to a significant element of Variscan reverse displacement here also. The Keys Fault is parallel to the Lake District Boundary and Pennine faults of northern England and may be comparable to these features which also show evidence of Variscan reverse movement (Akhurst et al., 1997). However, it is uncertain whether all of these faults were reactivating pre-existing, Dinantian structures, or were new Variscan 'transfer' features (Chapter 2).

The latest Variscan movements postdated the youngest preserved Westphalian rocks in the Manx region, Westphalian D to Stephanian strata being preserved in the core of the 'Quadrant 109 Syncline' of the Central Province Trough (Jackson and Mulholland, 1993; Jackson and Johnson, 1996). This is consistent with apatite fission-track analysis which indicates that a major cooling episode (interpreted as signifying Variscan uplift), occurred around the Isle of Man at about 300 Ma (Green et al., 1997).

The amount of strata removed by Variscan erosion in the Manx region is not known for certain. In northern England where the Carboniferous succession is much better documented, the thickness of eroded strata varies between about 1000 m from the southern part of the Lake District Block and over 4000 m from the Ribblesdale Foldbelt, along the inversion axis of the Craven Basin (Fraser and Gawthorpe, 1990; Kirby et al., 2000). The overall degree of erosion in the Manx region was probably of the same order. In the north, in the Peel and Solway basins, considerably more than 1000 m of dominantly Upper Carboniferous rocks were probably removed. In the south, however, where Westphalian strata are still

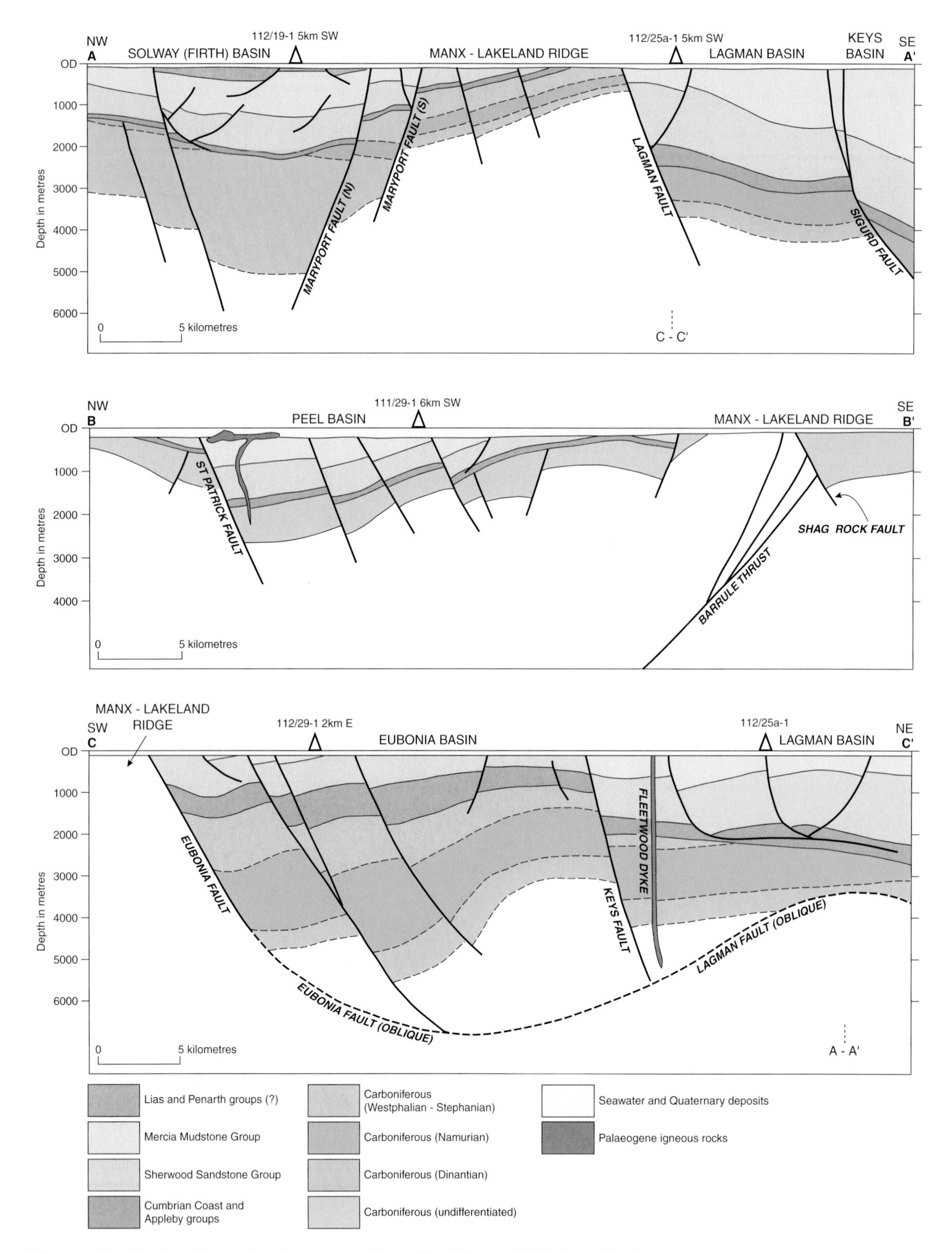

Figure 14 Regional geoseismic cross-sections. (See Figure 12 for location.)

a. Solway Basin–Manx-Lakeland Ridge–Lagman Basin–Keys Basin.
b. Peel Basin–Manx-Lakeland Ridge.
c. Manx-Lakeland Ridge–Eubonia Basin–Lagman Basin.

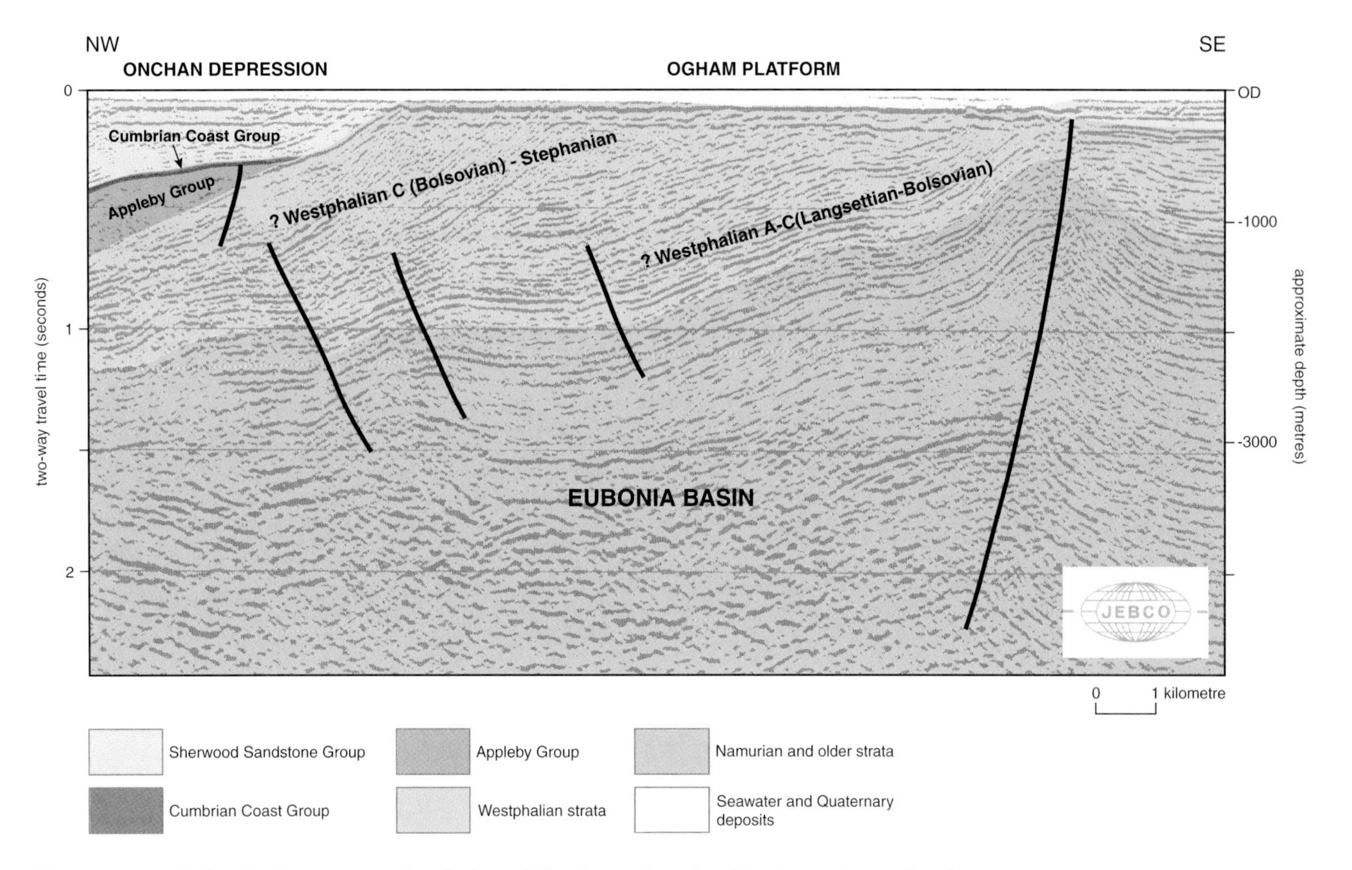

Figure 15 Seismic line across the Ogham Platform showing Variscan inversion in the Eubonia Basin and thick Permian strata in the Onchan Depression. (See Figure 12 for location.)

preserved, erosion may have removed only a few hundred metres of Carboniferous strata.

Variscan erosion notwithstanding, owing to subsequent burial beneath the Permo–Triassic cover, the base of the Carboniferous in the Manx region now lies at a considerable depth over large areas. Beneath the deeper parts of the Solway Basin, the base of the Carboniferous is likely to lie at depths of at least 5000 m (Figure 14a). Similar, or greater depths are probably reached in the south of the region in the Central Province Trough (Jackson and Mulholland, 1993). The most extreme burial is close to the eastern edge of the region, where a substantial Carboniferous succession, identified from seismic reflection data, lies beneath the very thick Permo–Triassic cover of the Keys Basin. Here, the base of the Carboniferous may be as deep as 9000 m.

PERMIAN TO EARLY JURASSIC STRUCTURE

Following Variscan basin inversion and regional uplift, the Carboniferous succession in the Manx region underwent progressive erosion and peneplanation, before the resumption of rifting and, subsequently, deposition in late Permian times.

The tectonic framework of late Permian and, particularly, early Triassic times, found the north-west European region forming an isthmus between the rapidly developing Arctic–North Atlantic rift system to the north and the Tethys–Central Atlantic–Gulf of Mexico rift-wrench system to the south (Coward, 1995). Regional extension, directed roughly east–west, became established as the dominant tectonic process (Chadwick and Evans, 1995). The Manx region formed part of a Permo–Triassic rift system that extended from the English Channel Basin in the south to the western Scottish offshore basins in the north.

The Permian to Lower Jurassic succession is well imaged by the seismic reflection data and is fully penetrated by several deep wells (Figure 13); consequently, basin configuration is well understood and fairly detailed structure-contour maps of the succession can be constructed (Figures 16a, b, c).

As in early Carboniferous times, major basin trends were strongly influenced by basement structure and structural grain, and some aspects of basin configuration were broadly similar to those of the Carboniferous rift system. In particular the Manx–Lakeland Ridge still formed a rigid basement buttress, remaining structurally elevated more-or-less throughout. More generally, however, the roughly east–west directed Permo–Triassic extension reactivated the basement structural template somewhat differently than had the early Carboniferous north–south or north-north-west–south-south-east directed extension. The main difference lay in the reactivation of basement fractures with the Caledonian, or Variscan, 'transfer' direction (Chapter 2), and the consequent development of major basin-margin normal faults with north-north-west or north-west trends. Thus the North Channel, Stranraer and Keys basins were all principally controlled by major, roughly dip-slip, north-north-west- or north-west-trending, basin-margin normal faults which had been relatively unimportant in the Carboniferous. In northern England, similarly trending faults, such as the Lake District Boundary and Pennine faults also underwent renewed activity at this time. Above the Iapetus Convergence Zone (Chapter 2),

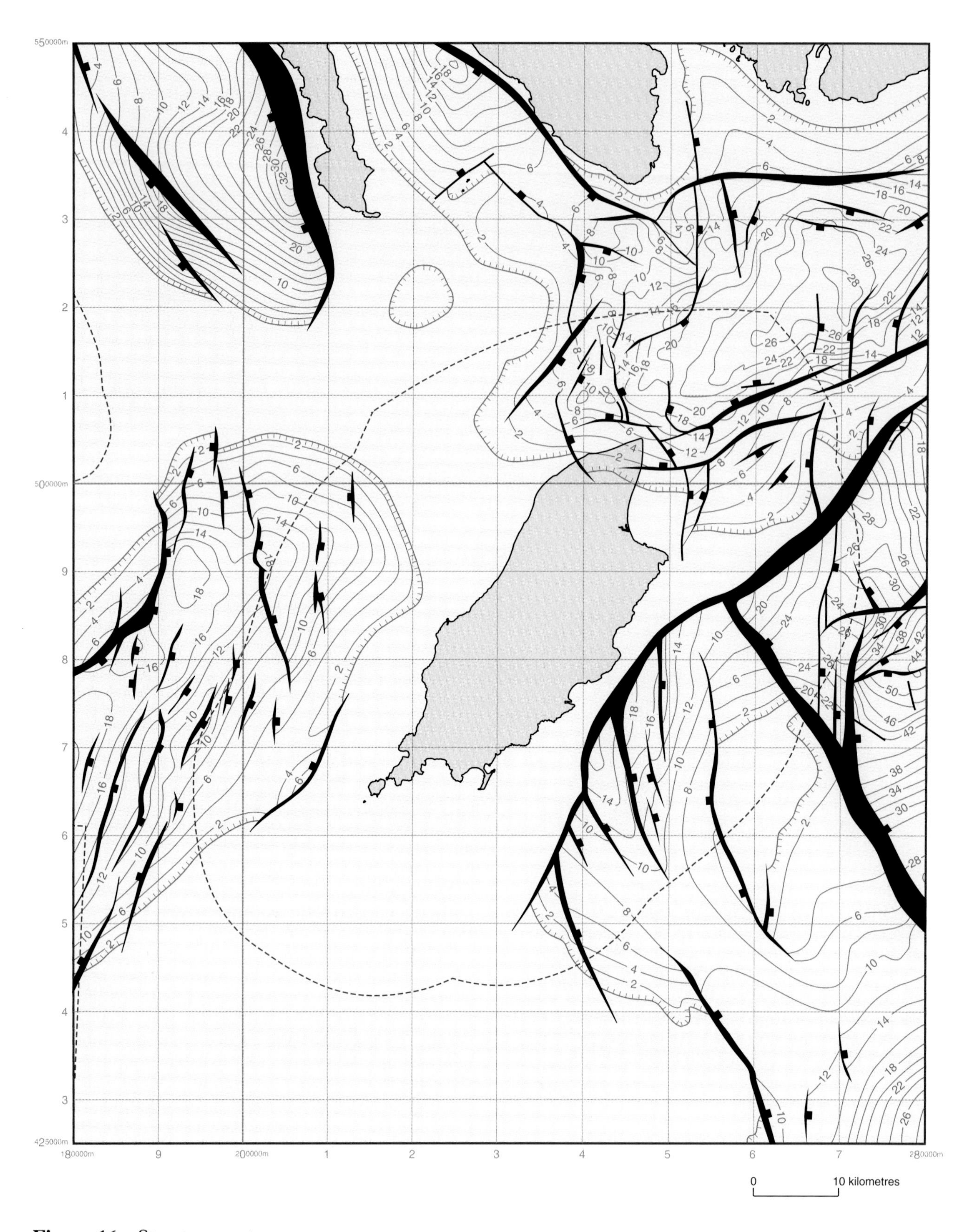

Figure 16 Structure contour maps.

a. Structure contours on the base of the Permo-Triassic (metres × 100).

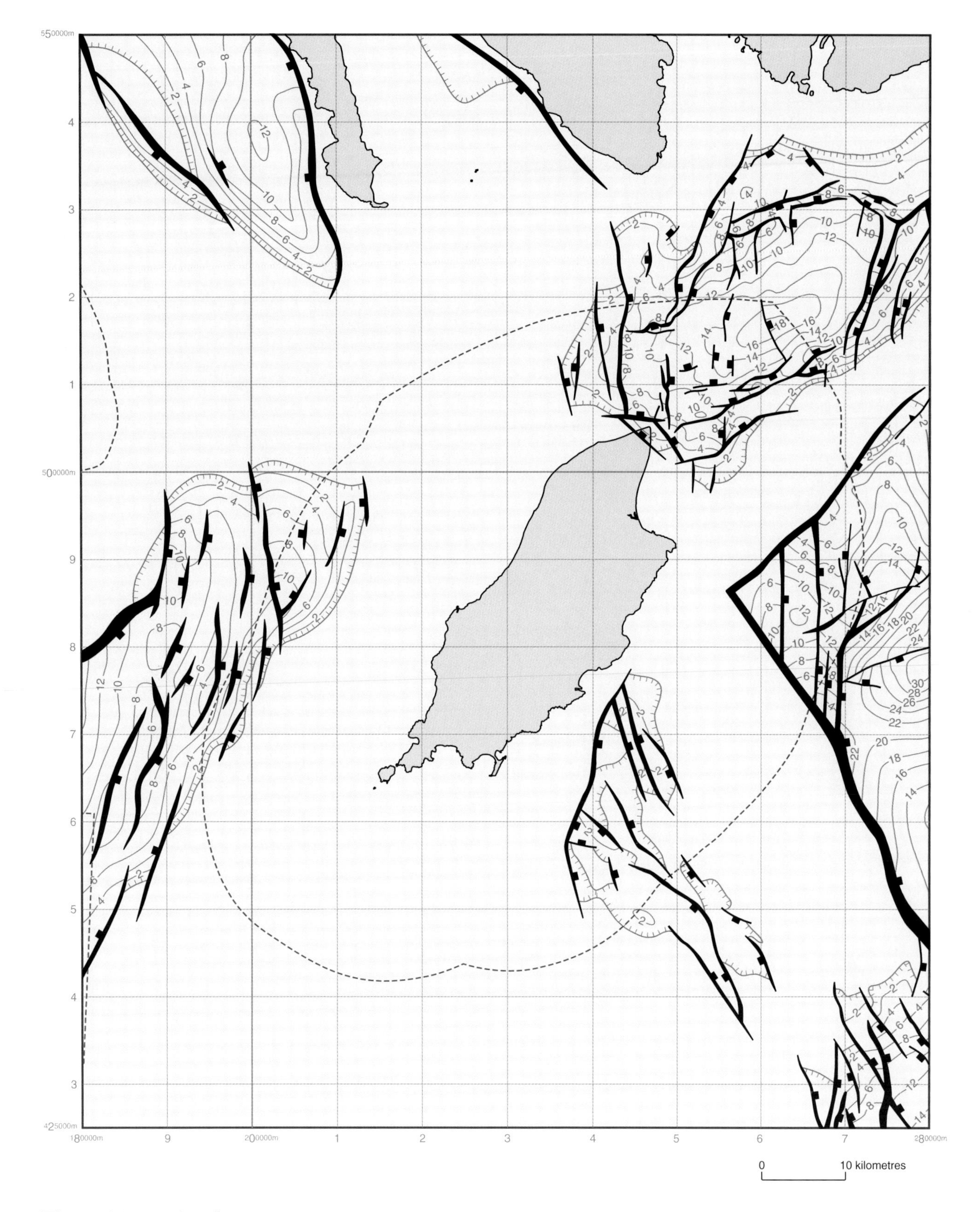

Figure 16 *continued*

b. Structure contours on the base of the Mercia Mudstone Group (metres × 100).

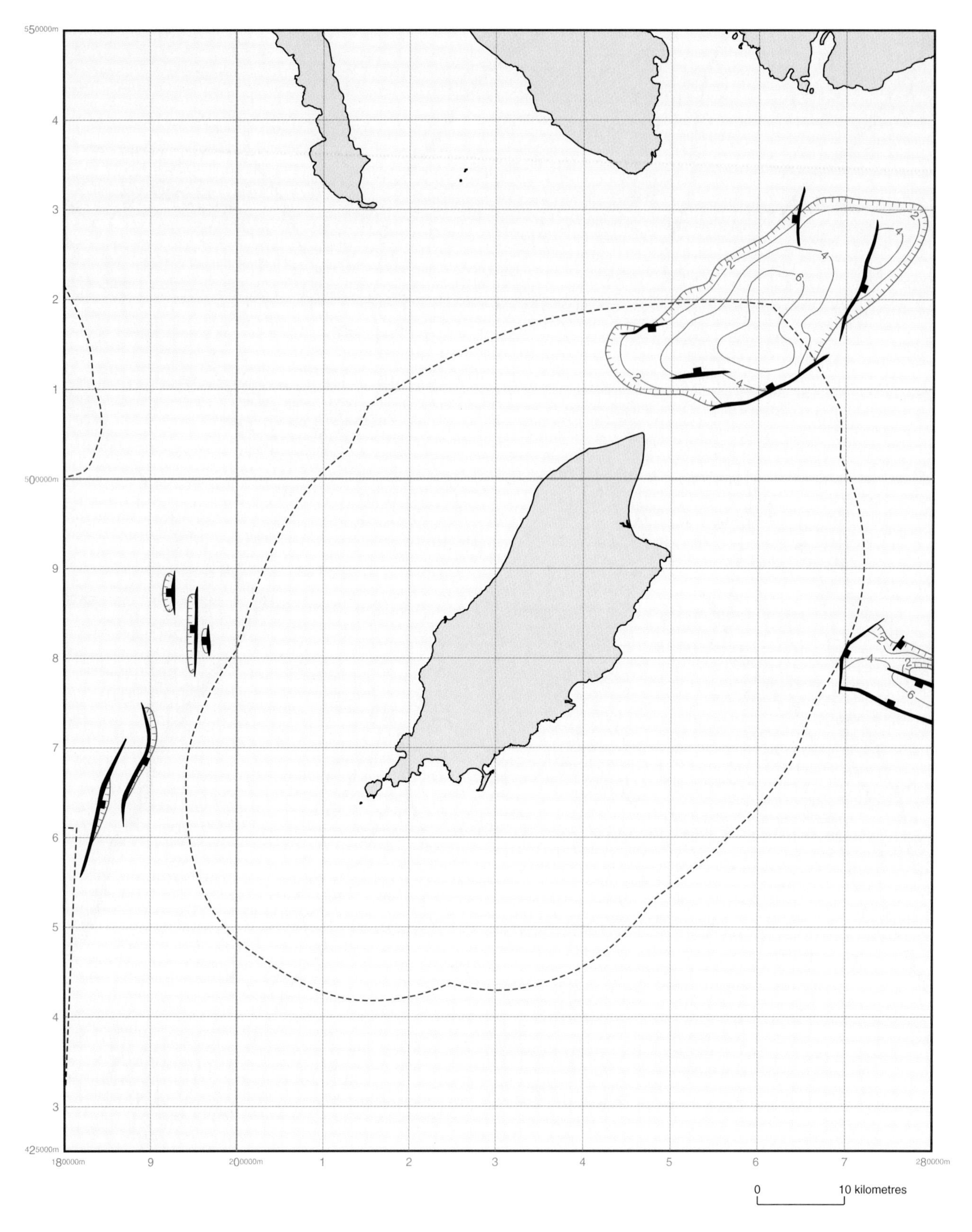

Figure 16 *continued*

c. Structure contours on the base of the ?Penarth Group (metres × 100).

however, the north-east–south-west 'Caledonoid' trend remained dominant, controlling development of the Solway and Peel basins and the southern margin of the Manx–Lakeland Ridge. Thus the important early Carboniferous Eubonia and Maryport faults were reactivated as major Permo–Triassic structures. A third structural trend, manifest in most of the basinal areas, is a pervasive north to north-north-west strike in the majority of small to medium sized intrabasin faults (Figure 16a). Analysis of similar fault trends in the Cheshire basin (Chadwick, 1997) indicated that these faults were new Permo–Triassic structures which formed perpendicular to the contemporary east-north-east-directed extension. This is supported by the development of east or east-north-east-trending transfer faults (parallel to the extension direction), exemplified by offsets in the Sigurd Fault Zone (Figure 16a) of the Keys Basin.

LATE PERMIAN BASIN DEVELOPMENT

Permian rocks in the Manx region are of late Permian age and belong to the Appleby and Cumbrian Coast groups (Chapter 6). They rest with marked angular unconformity on eroded Carboniferous strata, overlapping locally onto Caledonian basement massifs. The Permian strata are cut by normal faults which pass down into underlying Carboniferous rocks and commonly show greater displacements in the latter (Akhurst et al., 1997). This has been interpreted by some workers as signifying an episode of faulting in latest Carboniferous (late Westphalian) times, a scenario difficult to reconcile with the dominantly compressive Variscan tectonic regime. It is more likely that the normal faults are much younger than this. They were initiated during early Permian subaerial rifting, whilst the area was still in a post-Variscan erosional regime (compare with Quirk et al., 1999a), and prior to the onset of deposition in late Permian times.

Sandstones of the Appleby Group vary quite markedly in thickness, show evidence of syndepositional normal faulting and were considered by Quirk et al. (1999a) as a late syn-rift deposit. The North Channel Basin (see below) appears to have been a particular locus of Permian rifting. Judging by the seismic data, thick Appleby Group sedimentary rocks (or their lateral equivalents) are likely to occur, and the presence of Permian volcanic rocks, such as these proved in the Larne Borehole (Penn et al., 1983), cannot be ruled out. A marked depocentre is also evident in the Eubonia Basin (Figures 13, 14c), with sedimentary strata of the Appleby Group infilling a pronounced topographical depression (Figure 15). This latter feature may be just an accident of erosion, or it may signify an area of enhanced Permian rifting.

After deposition of the Appleby Group, thickness changes within the Cumbrian Coast Group were more gradual (Chapter 6), signifying the transition to a depositional regime of more regional post-rift or 'sag' subsidence.

TRIASSIC BASIN SUBSIDENCE

In early Triassic times, rates of basin subsidence increased markedly as rifting recommenced (Cowan et al., 1999). Deposition of the Sherwood Sandstone Group marked the onset of major rift-basin development which was to continue through later Triassic times with deposition of the Mercia Mudstone Group, the latter characterised by an increasing component of regional thermal subsidence. The deposition of salt in the Cumbrian Coast Group (in late Permian times), and, more particularly, within the Mercia Mudstone Group led to the development of salt-related detachment faulting and folding in the larger basins. Of particular importance was the migration of salt up major normal faults, some reaching as far as the sea bed. The resultant salt loss led to the development of major collapse graben in the hanging wall blocks of the faults (Newman, 1999).

North Channel Basin

The southern part of the North Channel Basin (e.g. Hall et al., 1984), termed the Portpatrick Basin (Maddox et al., 1997) or the Portpatrick Sub-basin, encroaches into the far north-west of the Manx region. It forms a pair of eastward deepening tilt blocks, with a dominant north-north-west structural trend, exemplified by the basin-controlling Portpatrick Fault (Figure 12b). This is perpendicular to the east-north-east–west-south-west regional Caledonoid grain of the Lower Palaeozoic basement in the Southern Uplands (Stone, 1995), but is roughly parallel to the putative basement 'transfer' trend (Chapter 2), which was particularly susceptible to reactivation during the Permo–Triassic. The Permo–Triassic succession in the basin is not fully understood, but seismic data suggest that it is very thick. Permo–Triassic strata thicken stratigraphically towards the Portpatrick Fault, where thicknesses of more than 3000 m are likely (Figure 16a). The key well, 111/15-1, does not penetrate the full Permo–Triassic succession before passing through the Portpatrick Fault into Lower Palaeozoic basement rocks (Figure 13). The favoured interpretation of this well actually requires at least two closely spaced major fault strands, both penetrated by the well (Chapters 6 and 7).

Stranraer Basin

As with the North Channel Basin, reactivation of the basement 'transfer' trend appears to have been the dominant influence on basin formation, rather than the east-north-east trends of the regional Caledonian basement grain. The Stranraer Basin has the form of a simple easterly deepening half graben, bounded by the basin-controlling Loch Ryan Fault (Kelling and Welsh, 1970). There is uncertainty about the sedimentary thicknesses within the basin owing to a lack of deep well or seismic control. Gravity modelling (Stone, 1995) suggests that the basin is perhaps two thirds as deep as the North Channel Basin, so the Permo–Triassic succession may well approach or even exceed a thickness of 2000 m at its eastern margin (Figure 16a). Bearing in mind the lack of preserved Permo–Triassic strata on its footwall block, these thicknesses are fully consistent with the work of Kelling and Welsh (1970) who estimated a throw of 1525 to 1700 m for the Loch Ryan Fault onshore. The fact that only a small and putative outlier of Mercia Mudstone Group is now preserved in the basin (BGS, 1994; Jackson et al., 1995) suggests that it was formerly considerably deeper.

As discussed above, both the North Channel and Stranraer basins show dominant north-west or north-north-west structural trends as shown by their basin-controlling faults. It is notable however, that both basins are terminated to the south-east by a prominent north-east-trending gravity lineament (Figure 7). This appears to be an important Caledonian basement feature (Chapter 2), and seems to mark the northern limit of dominantly east-north-east or north-east 'Caledonoid' fault trends in the sedimentary cover structure of the Manx region, as exemplified by the Solway and Peel basins.

Solway Firth Basin

The Permo–Triassic Solway Firth Basin overlaid and developed something of the structural form of the early Carboniferous Solway Basin. Lying above the Iapetus Convergence Zone, the basin is elongated west-south-west–east-north-east along the Caledonian trend. It is a roughly symmetrical feature whose nature varies somewhat along its length. In the east of the region it forms a graben bounded to the north by down-to-the-south normal faults, the largest of which is here termed the Northern Boundary Fault, and to the south by the Maryport Fault (Figure 12b). Both of these faults are major structures with basinward downthrows which locally exceed 1000 m at base Permo–Triassic level (Figure 16a). To the west, the throws on these basin-bounding faults are lower, and the basin has more the form of a faulted sag (Figure 14a). As discussed above, a distinction can be drawn between the Caledonoid trends of the major basin margin faults and the dominantly north–south trends of the smaller intrabasin structures (Figures 16a, b). A full Permo–Triassic succession, with halite in the Cumbrian Coast and Mercia Mudstone groups, is preserved in the middle of the basin with locally more than 2500 m of Permo–Triassic strata (depending on the thickness of any overlying Jurassic strata, see below). In the basin centre, salt-related structures are mainly restricted to local swells and listric faulting within the Mercia Mudstone Group, commonly associated with the development of minor angular unconformities. However, close to the basin margins, and more generally in the western part of the basin, larger salt-related structures are evident. In the Mercia Mudstone Group local collapse graben have low-angle listric bounding faults which detach on to presumed salt layers within the Cumbrian Coast Group (Jackson et al., 1995). Adjacent to the Maryport Fault, salt-related collapse structures and pop-ups are locally developed, buttressed against the Manx–Lakeland Ridge (Newman, 1999).

Peel Basin

The Peel Basin (Quirk et al., 1999a; Newman, 1999) lies roughly along strike from the Solway Firth Basin, elongated north-east–south-west along the Caledonian trend. As with the Solway Firth Basin, north-east–south-west Caledonoid trends of the basin margin faults contrast with the dominantly north to north-north-west trends of the intrabasin faults. The structure of the basin is quite complex; an abundance of small- to medium-sized normal faults dissects the basin into a mosaic of tilt blocks and its cross-sectional geometry varies markedly. In the north-east it forms a fairly symmetrical faulted sag, whereas a little way south, around Well 111/25-1A, two west-dipping half-graben are present. Farther south still, the basin becomes generally asymmetrical, forming a west-dipping half-graben, internally faulted, with the basin fill thickening towards the St Patrick Fault which forms the north-western basin margin (Figures 12b, 14b). A full Permo–Triassic sequence is preserved in the deepest parts of the basin, and is comparable to, though thinner than, that of the Solway Firth Basin (Figure 13). Within the Manx region the base of the Permo–Triassic in the Peel Basin reaches a depth of about 2000 m (Figure 16a), but this is likely to be exceeded farther south-west. Salt-related structures are also widespread, particularly in the Mercia Mudstone Group where numerous low-angle listric normal faults detach at various levels, some in association with minor halokinetic swells (Quirk et al., 1999a). Over large areas of the basin the Mercia Mudstone Group is structurally detached from the underlying Sherwood Sandstone Group (Figure 17). Deeper detachments are also present, providing a good example of 'rift–raft' tectonics (Penge et al., 1999), where listric normal faults root into the Permian evaporites and control deep collapse graben full of Mercia Mudstone Group strata (Newman, 1999). These structures result in severe structural attenuation of the Sherwood Sandstone Group, in a manner reminiscent of the better documented Tynwald and Crosh Vusta fault complexes of the East Irish Sea Basin (Jackson and Mulholland, 1993; Arter and Fagin, 1993; Akhurst et al., 1997). The Peel Basin is also notable for its abundance of shallow dolerite sills and dykes of Palaeogene age (Chapter 8).

Manx–Lakeland Ridge

In Permo–Triassic times the Manx–Lakeland Ridge had a structural role similar to that of its early Carboniferous precursor, separating the Solway Firth and Peel basins to the north-west from the main East Irish Sea Basin to the south and east (Figure 12b). The ridge is particularly well defined in the east, where its north-west margin is marked by the Maryport Fault, and its south-east margin by the Lagman and Eubonia faults. These latter structures form the north-west boundary of the major East Irish Sea Basin, of which the Keys and Lagman basins (see below) form constituent parts. Though in places quite symmetrical, for the most part the Manx–Lakeland Ridge forms a gentle north-west-tilted fault block (Figure 14a). Depositional rates over the ridge were much lower than in the adjacent basins to the north and south and the Permo–Triassic succession is correspondingly stratigraphically thin. Owing to post-Triassic erosion (see below) the succession is only partially preserved, and is wholly absent on parts of the ridge crest, notably on the Isle of Man.

Ogham Platform

The Ogham Platform (Figure 12b; Jackson et al., 1995; Quirk and Kimbell, 1997), lies to the south of the Manx–Lakeland Ridge. There is some evidence that the area was platformal in early Carboniferous times, Dinantian strata being relatively thin (Figure 14c), but the Ogham Platform *sensu stricto* did not

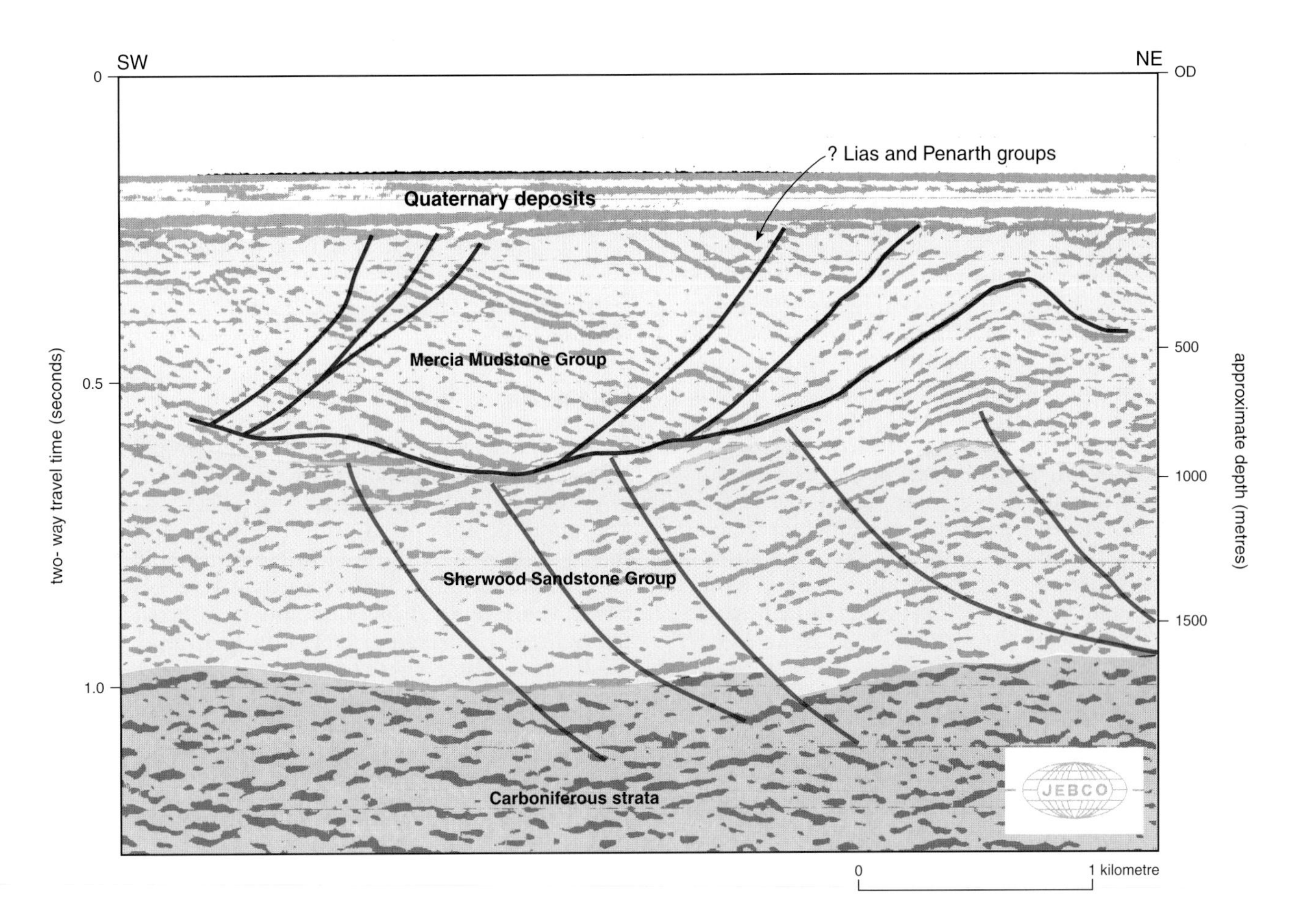

Figure 17 Detachment faulting in the Peel Basin. West-dipping listric normal faults (red) in the Mercia Mudstone Group are detached from steeper east-dipping normal faults (blue) in the Sherwood Sandstone Group. The latter may themselves detach on to Permian evaporites. (See Figure 12 for location.)

attain its full structural expression until the Triassic. This followed from the development of the Keys Fault as a major Triassic structure, the Ogham Platform forming its uplifted footwall block (Figure 14c). Permo–Triassic strata on the Ogham Platform are generally thin and only partially preserved. In places they are entirely absent (Figure 15), with the central part of the structure, termed the Ogham Inlier, comprising a partly fault-bounded area of Carboniferous strata (Figure 1).

Lagman Basin

The Lagman Basin forms the northernmost component of the major East Irish Sea Basin (Jackson et al., 1987). The western part of the basin falls within the Manx region, where it is bounded to the north and west by the Lagman and Keys faults respectively (Figures 14a, c). The Lagman Fault is a major normal fault which is subplanar and dips to the south-east at about 50°. It has a southerly downthrow which, at base Permo–Triassic level, locally approaches 3000 m (Figure 16a). Judging by the displacement of the base Mercia Mudstone Group, a significant proportion of this movement occurred in late or post-Triassic times. The Lagman Basin is markedly asymmetrical in the north, where Permo-Triassic strata dip obliquely towards the Lagman Fault, but is more flat-bottomed farther south. On the whole there appear to be relatively few faults within the Lagman Basin, except for a zone of north-trending intrabasin faults which step the basin fill up to the west, towards the Manx–Lakeland Ridge, in a series of terraces (Figure 16a). A fairly complete Permo–Triassic sequence up to 3000 m thick is preserved locally, but more generally a less complete succession is the norm.

The Lagman Basin is demarcated on the south-east by the Sigurd Fault, a roughly north-trending intrabasin feature (Figures 12b, 16a). Unlike the basin margin faults, which appear to follow basement trends, the Sigurd Fault is interpreted as a 'new' fault which formed in Permo–Triassic times, perpendicular to the extension direction. It is a complex structure, of variable geometry and throw, and is offset in a number of places by east- to east-north-east-trending cross-faults (Figure 16a; Akhurst et al., 1997). These latter structures are near vertical, have the appearance on seismic data of 'flower structures' and are interpreted as transfer faults, formed parallel to the east to east-north-east extension direction.

Keys Basin

Separated from the Ogham Platform by the Keys Fault and from the Lagman Basin by the Sigurd Fault, the Keys Basin is one of the deepest Permo–Triassic rift basins in UK waters. Only the westernmost part of the basin lies within the Manx region, but some of its salient features can be illustrated. The Keys Fault (Figure 18) is a major subplanar normal fault, dipping east-north-east at between 50° and 65°. The present-day throw on the fault at base Permo–Triassic level is locally up to 4000 m (Figure 16a), but this decreases markedly to less than 1500 m at its intersection with the Lagman Fault. The Permo–Triassic succession within the basin is locally fully preserved and extremely thick, approaching 5000 m in the basin centre (Figure 16a). This is principally the result of an extremely thick development of the Mercia Mudstone Group (Jackson and Johnson, 1996), driven by continued or possibly accelerated movement on the Keys Fault.

Within the basin, at the level of the base of the Permo–Triassic, faults are relatively small and scarce, with the more deeply buried basin sedimentary rocks relatively undeformed. At higher structural levels however the situation is more complex. The Mercia Mudstone Group reaches a maximum thickness of nearly 3000 m beneath the eastern edge of the Manx region, comprising nearly two thirds of the entire Permo–Triassic succession (Jackson and Johnson, 1996). The presence of thick salt units within the sequence (Chapter 7) has resulted in the development of complex salt-related structure and the best examples of salt diapirism within the entire East Irish Sea Basin (Figure 18). Low angle listric faults detach at various levels within the Mercia Mudstone Group and in places large 'rafts' of strata several kilometres across appear to 'float' on the weak salt layers (Figure 18). The most dramatic examples of salt-related tectonics, however, lie outside the Manx region, to the east, and are described more fully elsewhere (e.g. Jackson et al., 1987; Arter and Fagin, 1993; Akhurst et al., 1997).

Eubonia Basin

The Eubonia Basin forms a shallow, asymmetrical graben over much of its extent, bounded to the north-west by the Eubonia Fault, the south-westerly continuation of the Lagman Fault (Figures 12b, 14c). Intrabasin faults splaying southwards from the Eubonia Fault (Figures 16a, b) are interpreted as 'new' features forming perpendicular to the extension direction. Preserved Triassic rocks, mostly belonging to the Sherwood Sandstone Group, locally exceed 1000 m in thickness. Although this thickness is similar to equivalent strata in the Peel Basin (Figure 13), the Eubonia Basin has suffered greater subsequent erosion with removal of much of the Mercia Mudstone Group (Figure 16b).

Godred Croven Basin

The Godred Croven Basin (Jackson et al., 1995), forms an easterly tilted asymmetrical graben bounded to the east by the Godred Croven Fault (BGS, 1994). Its structural polarity contrasts therefore with that of the Keys and Eubonia basins which tilt and thicken towards their western bounding faults. The Permo–Triassic succession in the basin is moderately thick, with perhaps more than 3000 m preserved outwith the Manx region to the south (BGS, 1994).

EARLY JURASSIC BASIN SUBSIDENCE

Rapid basin subsidence characteristic of the late Triassic continued into early Jurassic times with probable deposition of a thick and widespread Jurassic succession (e.g. Warrington, 1997; Cope, 1997). However, owing to subsequent erosion (see below) only scattered outliers of lower Jurassic strata (Lias Group) are now preserved in the Manx region (Chapter 7). These are restricted to three areas (Figure 16c).

Peel Basin

In the Peel Basin, grey shales interpreted as lower Jurassic strata have been proved in the uppermost part of Well 111/29-1 (Chapter 7). This occurrence appears to comprise a thin sliver of strata preserved in the hanging wall block of a listric normal fault. Similar narrow outliers are likely to exist elsewhere in the basin where marked block rotations on listric normal faults allow preservation of relatively young strata in the hanging wall blocks (Figure 17). The possibility of more widespread preservation of lower Jurassic rocks in the deeper, western part of the basin cannot be ruled out.

Keys Basin

A small outlier of the Lias Group is present in the central part of the Keys Basin (BGS, 1994), proven by shallow Borehole 89/11A (Chapter 7; Warrington, 1997). The rocks are mostly, but not entirely, restricted to a small graben bounded by listric normal faults which detach within the Mercia Mudstone Group (Figure 18). A strong seismic reflector seen at between 0.5 and 0.6 seconds two-way travel time (Figure 18) is interpreted as corresponding roughly with the base of the Penarth Group. Thus a package of strata comprising Penarth and Lias groups may locally be up to 700 m thick (compare with Jackson et al., 1995). However, the interpretation is unconstrained so the Jurassic succession may be much thinner than this. This faulted outlier containing Jurassic beds is typical of the numerous 'rafts' which formed in the highly mobilised strata of the Mercia Mudstone Group hereabouts (see above). The fact that it involves Jurassic rocks indicates that salt tectonics within the Mercia Mudstone Group were active well into Jurassic times and possibly even later.

Solway Firth Basin

The largest putative outcrop of Jurassic strata in the Manx region is, paradoxically, the least well founded. In the central part of the Solway Firth Basin, a strong seismic reflector is present, marking a slight unconformity above a thick succession of Mercia Mudstone Group (Newman, 1999). The general appearance of the reflector is similar to the event chosen as the base Penarth Group in the Keys Basin and on this basis has been tentatively interpreted in a like manner. Mapped structure contours (Figure 16c) indicate that the total thickness of this package of strata, comprising presumed Penarth and Lias groups, is in excess of 600 m. However, two shallow boreholes, 73/51 and 73/48 prove red-brown and grey-green lithologies which

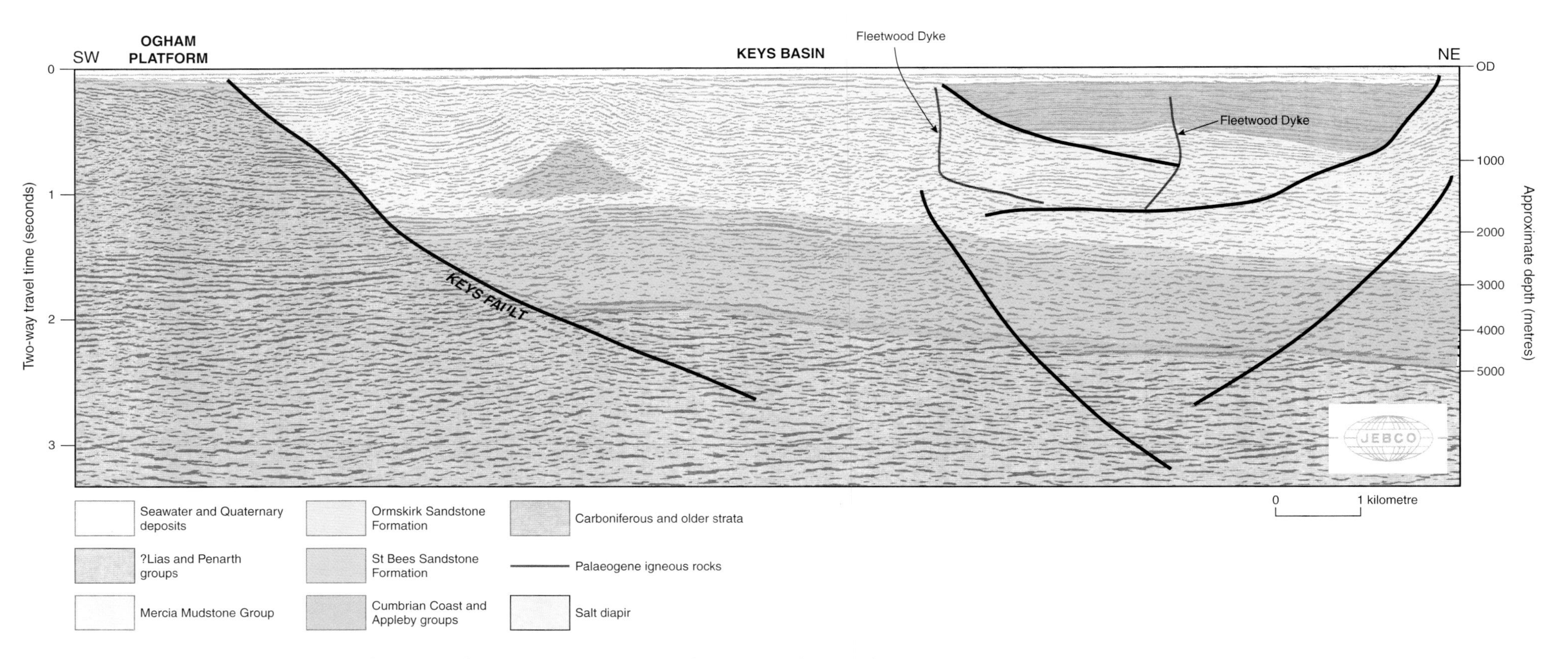

Figure 18 Keys Fault. Note the thick Carboniferous succession on the Ogham Platform, salt tectonics in the Keys Basin, faulted outlier of ?Jurassic strata and intrusions associated with the Fleetwood Dyke. See Figure 12 for location.

are more suggestive of the Mercia Mudstone Group (see Chapter 7 and Jackson et al., 1995). All in all, the stratigraphical affinity of this outlier is conjectural and should be viewed with caution.

POST-EARLY JURASSIC STRUCTURE

With the exception of scattered basic intrusive rocks of Palaeogene age (Chapter 8), the rock record of the period from the early Jurassic to the Pleistocene has been removed by erosion. However, several lines of indirect evidence can be used to assess the Mesozoic and Cainozoic structural development of the region. Comparisons can be made with neighbouring areas where a more complete stratigraphical sequence has been preserved, and depth of burial studies provide quantitative estimates of the thickness of the former cover sequence.

JURASSIC TO EARLY CRETACEOUS BASIN SUBSIDENCE

Before the onset of North Atlantic sea floor spreading in mid-Cretaceous times, the Jurassic to early Cretaceous development of the Manx region was characterised by episodes of regional crustal extension. Comparison with more complete sequences in basins elsewhere in the UK (e.g. Whittaker, 1985; Kirby and Swallow, 1987; Badley et al., 1989) indicates that extension occurred principally in the early Jurassic and again in late Jurassic to early Cretaceous times. The existing Permo–Triassic structural template is likely to have exerted a strong control over structural development, with the main basins continuing to subside and the Manx–Lakeland Ridge and Ogham Platform remaining as elevated features (compare with Akhurst et al., 1997).

The principal post-Triassic extensional structures were probably the major basin margin structures established during the Permo–Triassic. The Lagman and Keys faults throw down the base of the Mercia Mudstone Group by more than 500 m and up to 2200 m, respectively (Figure 16b). Some of this displacement undoubtedly accompanied deposition of the Mercia Mudstone Group, but the remainder was post-Triassic. Because of the lack of younger strata adjacent to these faults, the amount of post-Triassic displacement is difficult to assess, but Jackson and Mulholland (1993) suggested that it could account for about one third of the total displacement on the Keys Fault. Other major Permo–Triassic basin-controlling structures, such as the Maryport, Portpatrick, Loch Ryan and St Patrick faults are also likely to have suffered significant post-Triassic normal movements. Jurassic listric or detached normal faulting also occurred, as indicated by the fault-bounded outliers of Lower Jurassic strata in the Keys Basin (Figure 18).

The scattered Lower Jurassic outliers are undoubtedly remnants of a much thicker, more widespread sequence (Chapter 7) which probably once covered the entire Manx region (e.g. Warrington 1997). The depositional history from mid-Jurassic to early Cretaceous times is more difficult to assess because of the remoteness of the nearest preserved strata of this age. It is likely that widespread deposition continued well into the late Jurassic and possibly into earliest Cretaceous times. Apatite fission-track analysis suggests that some areas of the Manx– Lakeland Ridge reached their maximum post-Variscan depth of burial in the early Cretaceous (Green et al., 1997). Directly after this, deposition probably ceased, certainly away from the deeper basinal areas, when a fall in relative sea level led to development of the regional Late Cimmerian unconformity (Whittaker, 1985). Late Cimmerian erosion was most severe on the block areas, and any Jurassic rocks deposited on the Manx–Lakeland Ridge may well have been removed at this time (compare with Chadwick et al., 1994).

MID-CRETACEOUS TO END CRETACEOUS REGIONAL SHELF SUBSIDENCE

Crustal extension had effectively ceased by mid-Cretaceous times (e.g. Whittaker, 1985) as sea floor spreading propagated northwards into the North Atlantic region. Post-extensional shelf subsidence became established over the Manx region, with structural demarcation between blocks and basins much diminished. Interpolation of the rather uniform Upper Cretaceous sequence preserved both in eastern England and also Northern Ireland implies deposition of Chalk across the entire Manx region. The maximum post-Variscan burial of most of the region was probably attained at or around the end of Cretaceous times.

PALEOCENE TO PLEISTOCENE REGIONAL UPLIFT AND BASIN INVERSION

In Paleocene times uplift of the Manx region triggered a period of erosion which probably continued with relatively minor interruptions to the Pleistocene. It was caused by a combination of two distinct tectonic processes: regional uplift and basin inversion. Regional epeirogenic uplift, a putative side effect of the formation of the Icelandic Plume (e.g. Brodie and White, 1994; Nadin and Kuznir, 1995), was associated with development of the North Atlantic Igneous Province and widespread igneous activity in the Manx region (Chapter 8). Apatite fission-track data from wells in the Solway Firth and Peel basins (Newman, 1999) indicate a phase of rapid cooling (uplift) at about this time (60 Ma). Superimposed upon this regional uplift were basin inversion phenomena associated with crustal shortening. These included basin upwarping and partial reversal of numerous earlier normal faults with associated minor folding (e.g. Knipe et al., 1993). Inversion of the Solway Firth Basin led to the development of a major anticlinal structure in the hanging wall block of the Maryport Fault (Chadwick et al., 1993), whilst at the southern margin of the Manx–Lakeland Ridge, reversal of the Lagman Fault led to development of small hanging wall anticlines (Figure 19a). Similar hanging-wall folding occurred above the Portpatrick Fault (e.g. Shelton, 1997) and oblique reversal of the Sigurd Fault led to the development of complex 'pop-ups' and flower structures. The dating of these basin inversion structures is uncertain, but outcrops on the Isle of

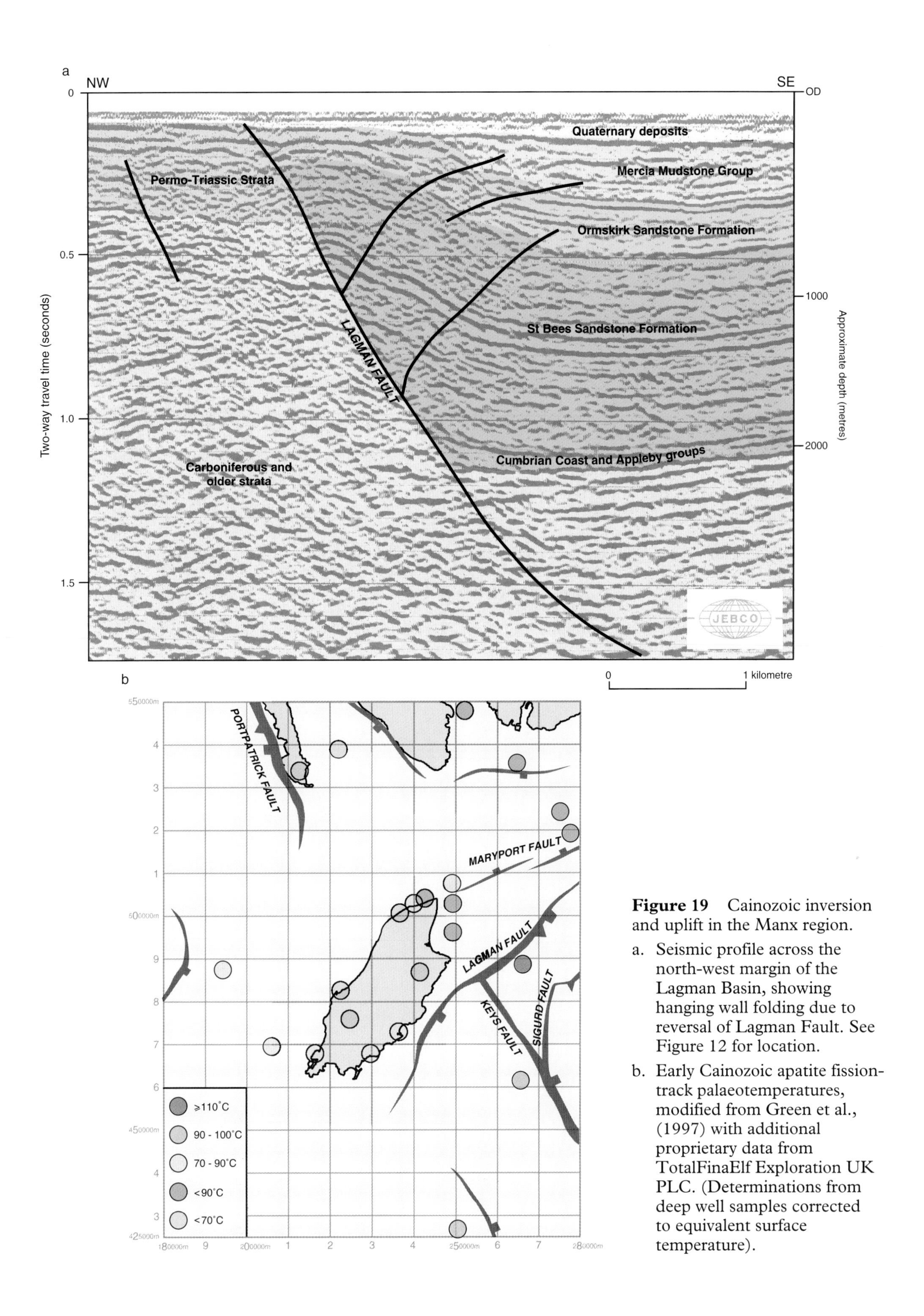

Figure 19 Cainozoic inversion and uplift in the Manx region.

a. Seismic profile across the north-west margin of the Lagman Basin, showing hanging wall folding due to reversal of Lagman Fault. See Figure 12 for location.

b. Early Cainozoic apatite fission-track palaeotemperatures, modified from Green et al., (1997) with additional proprietary data from TotalFinaElf Exploration UK PLC. (Determinations from deep well samples corrected to equivalent surface temperature).

Man show minor reverse faults which displace and hence postdate the Paleocene dykes (Quirk and Kimbell, 1997). In addition, apatite fission-track data (Newman, 1999) indicate that a second Cainozoic phase of cooling occurred at about 25 to 20 Ma. This is consistent with basin inversion in the Manx region forming part of the main Oligo–Miocene inversion of southern Britain and the southern North Sea (Van Hoorn, 1987; Badley et al., 1989; Chadwick, 1993).

DEPTH OF BURIAL STUDIES

The amount of Mesozoic extension-related subsidence and subsequent Cainozoic uplift in the Manx region and adjacent areas has been the subject of recent vigorous debate (e.g. Lewis et al., 1992; Holliday, 1993; Chadwick et al., 1994; Cope, 1997). Perhaps the most effective means of obtaining burial depths is by the inversion of palaeotemperatures obtained from apatite fission-track analysis (e.g. Green et al., 1997). On and closely adjacent to the Isle of Man and also around the Southern Uplands of Scotland, early Cainozoic apatite fission-track palaeotemperatures range from less than 70° to 90°C (Figure 19b). Higher palaeotemperatures, typically 90°C to greater than 110°C, characterise the Lagman and Keys basins (Figure 19b). A conductive heatflow model, incorporating a likely combination of overburden lithologies, was used by Chadwick et al. (1994) to compute burial depths from fission-track palaeotemperatures in northern England. Similar modelling for the Manx region, assuming a sedimentary overburden, a Paleocene heatflow of 70 mWm^{-2}, and a surface palaeotemperature of 20°C, yields overburden estimates of 900, 1450 and 2150 m from fission-track temperatures of 70°, 90° and 110°C respectively. Clearly, palaeoheatflow estimates are subject to uncertainty and the assumption of purely conductive heat transfer is likely to be an oversimplification, particularly close to basin margins where hydrothermal effects are likely to be significant. Nevertheless, calculated amounts of removed overburden are broadly consistent with estimates based on regional stratigraphical criteria (e.g. Holliday, 1993; Chadwick et al., 1994). Moreover, systematic regional variations suggest that the Isle of Man and Southern Uplands had significantly less overburden removed during Cainozoic times, than did the Lagman and Keys basins. This is consistent with the hypothesis (Chadwick et al., 1994) that the massifs suffered only the Paleocene epeirogenic component of uplift whereas the basins underwent an additional (Miocene) component of structural inversion.

An additional possibility, proposed by Green et al. (1997), is that early Cainozoic geothermal gradients were significantly higher than those at the present-day; either a consequence of elevated basal heatflow, or regional hydrothermal activity. Neither supposition is unreasonable in view of the widespread igneous activity at the time (Chapter 8). If such were the case, then estimates of overburden would be reduced in direct proportion.

5 Devonian and Carboniferous

DEVONIAN

Peel Sandstone Group

The Peel Sandstone Group consists of an interbedded succession of red sandstone and conglomerate, with minor siltstone, claystone and calcrete palaeosol horizons. The group crops out in the area around the town of Peel, where it is thought to occupy a north–south-trending graben that extends offshore into the west Irish Sea (Boyd Dawkins, 1902). Estimates of its thickness range from at least 519 m (Boyd Dawkins, 1902) to 1000 m, possibly rising to 1500 to 2000 m onshore (Crowley, 1985), but neither the base nor the top is preserved. The best exposures of the group form discontinuous outcrops along a 2.5 km-long coastal strip north-east of Peel. Inland, the group is concealed beneath Quaternary deposits, and hence its extent is difficult to prove, although early workers suggested that it does not extend inland for more than 1.5 km. To the south two small outliers have been recorded at Glenfaba Bridge, 1 km to the south of Peel (Boyd Dawkins, 1902).

The Peel Sandstone Group is bounded to the east and west by two north–south-trending normal faults. At the north-eastern limit of the exposure, the Will's Strand Fault crops out in coastal cliffs where it can be seen to juxtapose the Manx Group against the Peel Sandstone Group. The Peel Harbour Fault, on the western margin, is not exposed, but its presence has been inferred by Boyd Dawkins (1902) and Quirk et al. (1999a). The Peel Harbour Fault was thought by Quirk et al. (1999a) to be cross-cut by the major Central Valley Lineament fault zone, which trends west-north-west–east-south-east to north-west–south-east across the Isle of Man, and may act as the southern limit to the Peel Sandstone Group (Quirk et al., 1999a). The succession is generally tilted, dipping northwards at angles of between 10° and 50°, but shows little evidence of complex deformation and cleavage formation. Deformation, where present, is generally restricted to fold structures adjacent to normal or thrust faults (Piper and Crowley, 1999).

A number of synsedimentary deformational features are present within the highest part of the exposed succession and these are well exposed along the coast at Will's Strand. They have been described by Ford (1972, 1993) and Ford et al. (2001) and include slumped beds, folds and faults. Slumped beds are typically steeply inclined and overlie subhorizontal extensional glide planes. These can be observed, stacked vertically on top of each other. Compressive structures are commonly developed, at the toe of these structures and include thrust faults, small duplex-like structures and folds, some of which are overturned. Extensional faults in the hanging walls of thrust faults trend north-north-west–south-south-east, and the axial planes of the slump folds trend north-east–south-west and north–south, indicating movement towards the south-east and east, respectively.

The synsedimentary deformation features at Will's Strand indicate that these deposits were unstable and periodically dislodged (Ford, 1993; Ford et al., 2001). This would require the development of an inclined palaeoslope, with slump movement possibly triggered by a seismic source. The orientation of slump structures indicates that the palaeoslope dipped to the east or south-east; this is consistent with the palaeocurrent trend measured for the fluvial facies within the group. The localised nature of these disturbances might indicate that movement was linked to movement on a nearby active fault.

Sandstone and conglomerate within the group contain a highly varied clast suite including quartz, quartzite, agate, porphyritic igneous rock, unaltered acidic lava, pyroclastic rock, altered volcaniclastic rock, sandstone, limestone clasts of Wenlock and Ashgill age, and purple shale (Boyd Dawkins, 1902; Lamplugh, 1903; Crowley, 1985; Ford, 1993). Manx Group clasts are absent. Crowley (1985) described an inverted clast stratigraphy and suggested that the conglomerates exposed at Whitestrand in the north-east are stratigraphically younger than those to the south-west. This is in keeping with the regional younging direction mapped for the group.

The age of the Peel Sandstone Group has proved historically contentious owing to the lack of indigenous fossils. Clasts of limestone containing a shelly fauna of Ordovician and/or Silurian age within the succession put a lower limit on the age. Early workers were divided as to whether the group was Permian (Boyd Dawkins, 1902) or Early Carboniferous (Lamplugh, 1903) in age, with Berger (1814) suggesting that it was the lateral equivalent of the Langness Conglomerate. Neves (in Ford, 1972) proposed a possible Early Carboniferous age for the group based on palynological evidence. The lack of significant structural deformation within the group means that it must postdate the main Caledonian deformation phase. The group lacks Manx Group clasts, which are present in the Lower Carboniferous Langness Conglomerate Formation (Lamplugh, 1903). Hence Crowley (1985) proposed that the group must predate the Carboniferous (possibly rift-related) uplift phase that led to unroofing of Manx Group material. In addition, the group has a significantly higher regional dip than the Carboniferous succession of the Castletown area, suggesting that it probably predates Carboniferous deposition. Crowley (1985) thus proposed a late Early Devonian (Siegenian to Emsian) age for the group. More recently, Quirk and Kimbell (1997) suggested that the group might be Late Carboniferous in age and equivalent to red beds of Bolsovian (Westphalian C)/ Westphalian D to early Stephanian age from onshore UK. This is more speculative and does not appear to fit with the evidence outlined above.

The most recent work to address this subject was that of Piper and Crowley (1999). Their palaeomagnetic study identified a postdepositional detrital

Table 1 Comparison of the stratigraphical subdivisions established by various workers for the Peel Sandstone Group (Boyd Dawkins, 1902; Crowley, 1985). These terms have now been discontinued.

Boyd Dawkins (1902)		**Crowley (1985)**		
	(Thickness in metres)	**Formation**	**Member**	**Lithological and sedimentological features**
			Will's Strand	sandstone-dominated low sinuosity streams, intense synsedimentary deformation
Upper or Stack Series	130	Whitestrand	Whitestrand Conglomerate	distal alluvial fan conglomerates and pebbly sandstones
			Whitestrand	distal alluvial fan conglomerates, sandstones and siltstones; abundant desiccation features, sparse pedogenic profiles
			Cain's Strand	sandstone-dominated low sinuosity streams
Bright red sandstones	24		The Stack	medial alluvial fan conglomerates, pebbly sandstones and sandstones; abundant pedogenic carbonate profiles
Dull red sandstones of the Gob and Traie Fogog	99		Traie Fogog	distal to medial alluvial fan conglomerates, sandstones and mudstones; abundant desiccation features, sparse pedogenic carbonate profiles
Ballaquane and Creg-Malin Beds	117	Peel Sandstone	Creg Malin	stacked upwards-fining cycles, low sinuosity streams
			Ballaquane	conglomerate and sandstone-dominated low sinuosity channels, sheetflood sandstones
Drift covered sandstones	149			
Total	519			

remanence which gave a palaeolatitude of 29° south of the equator for the group, corresponding to the position of Britain during late Silurian to early Devonian times. This was used to infer that the Peel Sandstone Group forms part of the Lower Old Red Sandstone and a date of between 410 and 400 Ma has been proposed for the group (Piper and Crowley, 1999).

Two stratigraphical schemes have previously been proposed for the Peel Sandstone Group (Table 1), with the most recent, that of Crowley (1985), recognising two formations and eight members. However, the inconsistencies in stratigraphical terminology used (e.g. the name Whitestrand has both formation and member status) and the paucity of inland exposures, which makes mapping even to formation level impossible, means that it has been decided to discontinue the use of this nomenclature.

The sedimentology of the group has been described by Crowley (1981, 1985) who interpreted it as a garnet-rich, sandstone-dominated succession representing continental braided river and distal alluvial fan deposits with flow directions towards the south-east. Fauna found within clasts from the succession indicate a progressive unroofing of a Silurian limestone shelf succession which is not presently found in the Southern Uplands. This source was thought to be fairly local, perhaps only 5–10 km to the north-west (Crowley, 1981).

The work presented in this account agrees in general terms with the overall sedimentary environmental interpretations of Crowley (1981, 1985), but provides more facies details, and recognises a minor but significant aeolian component (Table 2). The aeolian dune facies dominantly comprises medium-grained, cross-bedded sandstone that lacks any of the coarser grained detritus that is characteristic of the fluvial facies. The aeolian association forms some of the oldest rocks in the group and is well exposed at the northern end of the Promenade at Peel where it forms steeply dipping, well-bedded sandstone (Plate 10). Measured azimuths from cross-bedding foresets for the dune facies indicate winds that blew from the present-day east or north-east.

The aeolian facies association is cut by an erosively based channel sandstone (Plate 9). Aeolian deposition ceased at this point and fluvial complexes became dominant. Channel systems were highly variable in size and lithological fill, and they show much poorer sorting characteristics than the aeolian facies. Most channels were fairly shallow (1–2 m in depth) and were probably of low sinuosity, although a small percentage show evidence for more sinuous channel forms (Table 2). Measured palaeocurrent readings for this association indicate that flow directions towards the south-east were dominant. Interbedded with the channels are parallel-bedded sheetflood sandstones and conglomerates. Deposition was probably quite episodic, with flash floods a common feature during periods of intense rainfall. An alluvial plain or distal alluvial fan is the likely depositional setting for these facies.

Following these flood events, temporary lakes formed and mud was deposited from suspension. Numerous beds of desiccation-cracked mudstone indicate that these lakes were ephemeral features and that the climate must have been at least semi-arid at times. Some of these mudstone beds are preserved in

Table 2 Description of the main types of sedimentary facies present within the Peel Sandstone Group.

Facies Association	Facies	Description	Interpretation	Locality example
Aeolian	Aeolian dune	fine- to medium-grained, pinkish brown sandstone, in well-defined tabular beds that lack erosive relief. Low-angle asymptotic trough cross-bedding common in small sets up to 1 m in thickness. Restored foresets dip to west/ south-west. Foresets comprise alternations of bimodally sorted fine- to medium-grained and medium- or medium to coarse-grained laminae. Finer foresets comprise approximately 60 per cent of the facies, in moderate to well-sorted laminae up to 10 mm thick. Coarser foresets laminae less common and form poorer sorted laminae up to 5 mm in thickness. Grains are typically subrounded and transparent, although coarser grains are well rounded and frosted. Ripple-form sets sometimes present on tops of sets. Rare bioturbation, inclined U-shaped burrow with retrusive meniscate back-fill — ?*Beaconites* affinity	preservation of the lower parts of small aeolian dunes. Tabular bounding surfaces formed by planing off dune tops below water table. Predominant wind direction thought to have been from the east–north-east. Aeolian grainfall forms dominant foreset lamina type, with some of the coarser foresets representing grainflows. *Beaconites* probably represents a back-filled arthropod burrow	outcrops at northern end of Peel promenade, on eastern side of face
	Dry sandsheet	this facies is uncommon, but occurs interbedded with aeolian dune and wet sandsheet facies. Forms beds of pinkish to reddish brown sandstone, generally as thin beds a few centimetres in thickness, rarely in beds up to 0.3 m. Comprises a well defined parallel pinstripe lamination, defined by millimetre-thick alternations of very fine- to fine- and fine to medium-grained sandstone. Rare aeolian rippleform sets; asymmetrical with a wavelength of 20 mm and a height of approximately 4 mm	deposition by aeolian processes on a flat-lying plain that lacks relief. Migration of wind ripples gives rise to pinstripe lamination	outcrops at northern end of Peel promenade, on eastern side of face
	Wet sandsheet	this facies is very uncommon, but forms beds a few cm in thickness, interbedded with aeolian dune and dry sandsheet facies. It comprises pinkish brown, poorly sorted, muddy, fine-grained sandstone. Mud is present as darker, irregular wavy to crinkly and convoluted laminae. Discontinuous sandy lenses are common; bioturbation is present locally	deposition of sand and mud by wind, with sediment adhering to an irregular damp sediment surface. Periods of drying result in migration of wind ripples and deposition of pinstripe lamination	outcrops at northern end of Peel promenade, on eastern side of face
Fluvial	Channel	reddish to pinkish brown pebbly sandstone and conglomerate, in erosively based units from 2 to 3.5 m in thickness. They occur interbedded with other fluvial facies. Poorly sorted sandstones dominate and vary from fine, medium and coarse grained, in upwards-fining successions. Medium to large intra- and extra-formational pebbles are common and comprise abundant mudstone and some limestone and sandstone clasts, chert, common granules of quartz and sparser frosted grains. Coarse more common and pebbly layers are overlying channel bases and can be up to 1 m in thickness. Laterally discontinuous scoured surfaces common. Rare lateral accretion bedding defined by low-angle inclined beds that pass through the entire thickness of individual channel units; these taper in their top part and thicken downwards. The dominant sedimentary structure is trough cross-bedding, in small sets generally less than 0.3 m in thickness. Rare current ripple cross-lamination. Cross-bedding foresets dip to the south-east	the recognition of thick sandstone units bounded by erosion surfaces suggests they represent deposition in fluvial channel systems. Orientation of cross-beds suggest flows to the south-east. Poor sorting and numerous scours points to deposition from rapid, sediment-loaded flood events. Braided channel systems more likely, although the presence of lateral accretion bedding suggests some of the channels were sinuous in form. Vertical stacking of fluvialfacies creates multistorey deposits. Floodplain or distal alluvial fan setting likely	common within the group, good examples at northern end of Peel promenade, on western side of face, at The Gob and on south side of Traie Fogog Bay

Table 2 *continued*

Facies Association	Facies	Description	Interpretation	Locality example
Fluvial (*continued*)	Sheetflood	comprises reddish to pinkish brown, fine- to medium-grained, locally coarse and pebbly sandstones and minor conglomerates in well-bedded, tabular units up to 1 m in thickness, sometimes upwards-fining. Beds can be wedge-shaped or have undulatory tops in places. Bed bases vary from sharply planar to gently erosive in form. Typified by its poor sorting and bed thickness. Intra- and extra-formational clasts common, especially overlying bed bases. Dominant sedimentary structure is unidirectional trough cross-bedding, rare cross-lamination and primary current lineation. Sheetflood sandstones mainly interbedded with channel and sheet-flood facies in south-west, with mudstone and calcrete palaeosols more common to north-east	deposition from individual high-energy unconfined flash floods. These would probably flow down the regional palaeoslope. Floodplain or distal alluvial fan setting likely	good examples at The Gob, on south side of Traie Fogog Bay, Cain's Strand to Will's Strand
Ephemeral Lake	Ephemeral lake sandy Ephemeral lake muddy	both facies types contain similar features with differentiation between the two based on sand-mud ratio, with >50% sand taken as cut-off between the two facies. Facies characterised by intimate thin (cm scale) interlayering of pinkish to reddish brown claystone, siltstone and very fine to fine-grained sandstone of varying percentages. Mudstones can locally be up to 1 m in thickness. Sandstones are typically current and wave ripple cross-laminated and mudstones often laminated. Sand-filled desiccation cracks are abundant and ubiquitous. These are often associated with dewatering structures and upturned crack margins. Bioturbation can be locally common, including ?*Beaconites*. Minor pebbly sandstone, fine conglomerate and weakly-developed calcrete also occur interbedded with these facies	lake formation indicated by the presence of wave rippled sandstones. These probably represent individual weak flood events, with ponding of flood waters responsible for lake formation. Muds were deposited by low-energy settling from suspension. Ephemeral lake conditions indicated by numerous desiccation cracked horizons. Dewatering structures probably intrinsically linked to desiccation process	good examples between White Strand and Will's Strand
Palaeosol	Calcrete	beds of reddish brown destratified siltstone or sandstone up to 3 m in thickness, with common occurrence of irregular hard, white calcareous nodules (glaebules). These glaebules generally have an irregular, subrounded appearance and occur individually or slightly coalesced. In the lower parts of soil profiles glaebules are typically elongate with a vertical fabric. Rarely glaebules form thin sheets (up to 0.2 m in thickness) of more amalgamated nodules	carbonate nodules are pedogenic features formed by the precipitation and displacive growth of carbonate in a soil profile; represent fairly immature stage 2 to 3 calcretes of Machette (1985). High rates of evapo-transpiration are favoured with carbonate rich ground-waters. A semi-arid climate is likely with very low aggradation rates	good examples at The Stack and between White Strand and Will's Strand

situ but, in general, they would have been preferentially reworked during successive floods, leading to an abundance of mudstone clasts within fluvial facies. A semi-arid climate is also suggested by the presence of calcrete-bearing soil horizons within the succession. These formed during periods of low sediment aggradation on the floodplain.

This work is in keeping with the palaeogeographical setting proposed by Allen and Crowley (1983) and Jackson et al. (1995), who suggested that the Peel Sandstone Group forms part of a post-Caledonian continental facies termed the 'Old Red Sandstone' which was deposited in a warm, semi-arid climate with a markedly seasonal rainfall that could support major rivers. The region was thought to lie between 15° and 20° south of the equator, on the margin of a major continent, with open sea to the south. Jackson et al. (1995) suggested that the Old Red Sandstone facies may have been deposited along a north-west–south-east-trending belt, 50 to 80 km in width, that stretched from the Isle of Man in the north and may have connected southwards with the Anglo-Welsh Basin.

ONSHORE CARBONIFEROUS

In western Europe, the Carboniferous is divided into two subsystems: the Dinantian (older) and the Silesian

Plate 9 Photograph to illustrate the differences between the aeolian and fluvial facies associations of the Peel Sandstone Group. Aeolian (mainly dune) facies are present in the lower right of the photograph, just above the rucksack and form parallel, well-bedded sandstones that dip steeply to the left. The upper left part of the photograph illustrates the coarser, cross-bedded and erosive nature of the fluvial channel facies. Photograph taken at the north-eastern end of Peel promenade, where the steps descend down to the beach (GS 1037).

(younger). These in turn are subdivided into 'time-rock' intervals known as stages. Classification for the British Dinantian is based on the work of George et al. (1976), later modified by Riley (1993). For the Silesian, the work of Ramsbottom et al. (1978) has been followed. A historical overview of previous research on the Carboniferous of the Island has been summarised by Dickson et al. (1987). Their classification scheme is given in Table 3, together with a revised scheme produced during the recent resurvey. Detailed remapping was not undertaken, but all the available type localities and key reference sections of Dickson et al. (1987) were re-examined.

The onshore Carboniferous rocks are restricted to the northern and southern tips of the Isle of Man. Only the southern area is exposed, between Port St Mary and eastwards to Cass ny Hawin. The north-west margin of this outcrop is defined by the south-west–north-east-trending trending Boundary Fault, which downthrows Carboniferous rocks against Lower Palaeozoic basement. The eastern margin coincides with the unconformable contact of Carboniferous (and possibly Devonian) rocks on Lower Palaeozoic basement. The intersection of the Boundary Fault with the unconformity, which defines the northernmost outcrop, occurs just south-east of Silver Burn. In the northern part of the Island, Carboniferous rocks are concealed by Permo–Triassic strata and Quaternary deposits. This is also the case offshore, except adjacent to the coastal outcrops of Carboniferous rocks in the southern part of the Island.

The general tectonosedimentary setting for Carboniferous rocks in the Manx area is similar to that in the Republic of Ireland, Northern Ireland and England; thus synrift sedimentary rocks characterise much of the Dinantian sequence and post-rift sedimentary rocks characterise the Silesian sequence. The base of the synrift succession is either of late Devonian or early Carboniferous age; precise dating is not possible owing to lack of biostratigraphical control. (In a regional context the Peel Sandstone Group could also belong to this same synrift sequence as it unconformably overlies cleaved Caledonian basement, but this stratigraphical age relationship conflicts with the recent interpretation of an early Devonian age based on palaeomagnetic evidence for the Peel Sandstone.) These early synrift sedimentary rocks are terrestrial/fluvial deposits. In the mid-Dinantian, a marine transgression produced a predominantly carbonate sequence, initiated as a ramp, but later evolving into a platform as glacio-eustacy took effect. In the late Dinantian, the platform was overlain progressively by hemipelagic clay, limestone turbidites, debris flows and volcanic rocks in the south and 'Yoredale-type' cyclothemic mixed carbonate and clastic sediments in the north. The Silesian sedimentary rocks are incompletely proved and restricted to the northern part of the Isle of Man and adjacent offshore area, where they are concealed beneath Permo–Triassic rocks. They comprise fluviodeltaic sandstone and marine claystone. The youngest proven Silesian strata are of basal Langsettian (Westphalian A) age. Apart from the volcanic rocks, there are strong parallels with the transition northwards from the Craven Basin to the Southern Lake District High of the adjacent English mainland. Indeed, much of the mainland lithostratigraphy has probable lateral continuity with the Isle of Man, especially the hemipelagic intervals. For this reason the hemipelagic lithostratigraphical classification follows that of the Craven Basin (Riley, 1990). The BGS has recently reviewed the lithostratigraphical classification of the Carboniferous rocks of the United Kingdom. This new terminology is used where appropriate. Details of this classification will be available through the BGS website.

DINANTIAN ROCKS IN THE SOUTHERN PART OF THE ISLE OF MAN

Langness Conglomerate Formation (Devonian?–Courceyan)

This formation has a thickness of about 30 m, according to Dickson et al. (1987). It is essentially a red-bed succession composed of conglomerate, breccia and sandstone. The lower part is dominated by debris flow/fan breccia, fluvial conglomerate and sandstone. These facies suggest deposition during ephemeral runoff from high ground, in a seasonally arid environment, close to the sediment source. The formation rests on an uneven and weathered surface of Lower Palaeozoic rocks, and infills local topography (Plate 10). The best exposures can be found at the type locality [SC 281 652] and on the foreshore at Derbyhaven [SC 293 680]. The upper 10 m of the formation at Derbyhaven are separated from the lower part by an armoured breccia horizon which appears to be an omission surface. It may have regional stratigraphical significance. Above this horizon, red beds give way successively to grey beds. The uppermost part of the formation at Derbyhaven comprises clean, cross-bedded littoral sandstone formed by marine reworking of the underlying terrestrial clastic deposits.

Table 3 Comparison of stratigraphical schemes for the exposed Carboniferous succession of onshore Isle of Man.

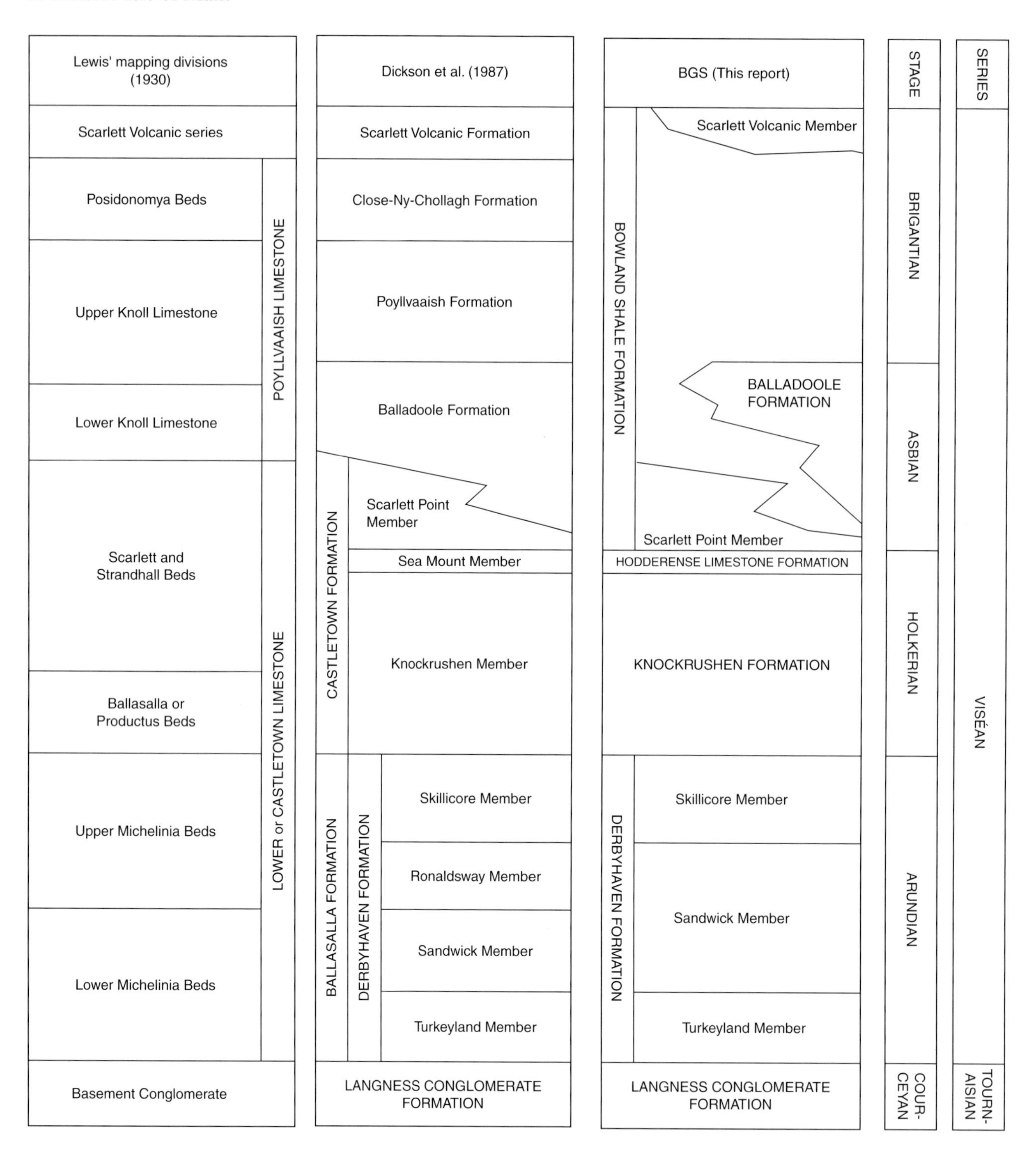

The sandstone is, in turn, overlain by marine carbonate rocks of the Derbyhaven Formation.

Great Scar Limestone Group

Derbyhaven Formation (Arundian)

The recent work on the Carboniferous of the Isle of Man has called into question the definition of the contiguous Ballasalla Formation of Dickson et al. (1987) and we recommend that this term be abandoned. The newly defined Derbyhaven Formation records a marine transgression and the initiation and growth of a carbonate ramp. It is over 90 m in thickness and comprises three members.

TURKEYLAND MEMBER The Turkeyland Member, the lowest of the three members, was formerly exposed in the now infilled Turkeyland quarry [SC 294 694] where Dickson et al. (1987) observed up to 18 m of ooidal and bioclastic grainstone, with rare claystone partings, 'resting on a sharply defined surface of the Langness Conglomerate'. The member is currently exposed on the foreshore at Derbyhaven, but unfortunately dolomitisation has destroyed much of the primary rock fabric (and its microfossils) at this

Plate 10 Langness Conglomerate Formation lying unconformably on Lower Palaeozoic strata. Langness Peninsula [SC 282 657] (GS 1038).

locality. Relict cross-bedding and hummocky cross-stratification is evident. Though unproven, the Turkeyland Member is thought to be of Arundian age and comparable with the lithologically similar Redhill Oolite of the southern Lake District. The Turkeyland Member is up to 25 m in thickness and comprises transgressive marine carbonate which rests, with non-sequence, on the underlying Langness Conglomerate Formation. Locally, reworked material from the conglomerate is contained within the carbonate.

SANDWICK MEMBER The base of the member is defined at the point at which claystone partings become common. The redefined member has a total thickness of around 46 m. It comprises packstone, that is dark, bioclastic and sub-metre in scale with subordinate dark siltstone and claystone (some of which is pyritic). The limestone beds are generally compound and show hummocky cross-stratification. Sharp-based graded beds, produced by waning traction currents, and sharp-based bioclastic claystone beds (some silty) also occur. Some of the claystone beds are laterally persistent, while others are discontinuous and lenticular. Dickson et al. (1987) recognised a succeeding Ronaldsway Member on the basis of increasing bed thickness but this has proved impractical to trace, and we recommend that this part of the succession is merged with the Sandwick Member. The Sandwick Member records continued deepening and the introduction of mid-ramp facies in which the deposition of calcareous claystone was punctuated by frequent high-energy storm events. The interval marks the maximum flooding and highstand part of the contemporary sea level curve. Abundant archaediscid foraminifera, including *Glomodiscus* and *Uralodiscus*, confirm an Arundian age. This member is identical in fauna, age and facies to the Gleaston Formation of the southern Lake District.

SKILLICORE MEMBER Dickson et al. (1987) defined the base of this member at the first bed containing the coral *Michelinia megastoma*. However, on the foreshore at Ronaldsway these coral colonies occur widely scattered at several horizons. Thus, in this report, a gradational base is defined by the appearance and increasing occurrence of fine-grained sandstone, together with an increase in siltstone and a more tabular bedding style. Up sequence, the limestone (packstone) beds become darker, finer grained (in terms of carbonate grains) and more pyritic than those of the underlying Sandwick Member. Some beds display shallow 'tuning fork' wave ripples (e.g. on the foreshore at Ronaldsway). The total thickness of the member is around 21 m.

The increased levels and grade of siliciclastic material, coupled with shallow-water depositional features in the Skillicore Member, record the transition from a late highstand to a lowstand sea level phase. The appearance of sandstone compares with the deposition of the much thicker, late Arundian, Ashfell Sandstone in the southern Lake District.

Knockrushen Formation (Holkerian)

This formation is about 21 m thick and comprises irregularly bedded wackestone and fine-grained packstone. Some of these rocks form large concretions several metres across. Thin beds of black fissile claystone are also present. *Zoophycos* burrows and siltstone are common near the base of the member. The formation contains scattered coralites of the large caninioid coral *Siphonphyllia benburbensis* (Plate 11), as well as valves (some overturned) of the brachiopod *Megachonetes papilionensis*. The presence of overturned brachiopod shells, together with the long wavelength (>1 m) ripples observed in some beds, indicates deposition above storm wave base. The formation lacks primitive archaediscid foraminifera, but contains the first appearance of true *Archaediscus* and paleotextulariid foraminifera, thus suggesting an Holkerian age. The lack of the diagnostic, but facies-controlled, Holkerian (Cf5 Zone) foraminifer *Pojarkovella nibelis* and the brachiopod *Davidsonina carbonaria* is consistent with the deeper water nature of the facies.

Balladoole Formation (Asbian)

The limestone exposed at Balladoole comprises a distinctive suite of pale grainstone and packstone with bioherms of wackestone. These facies record deposition on the southern edge of an extensive

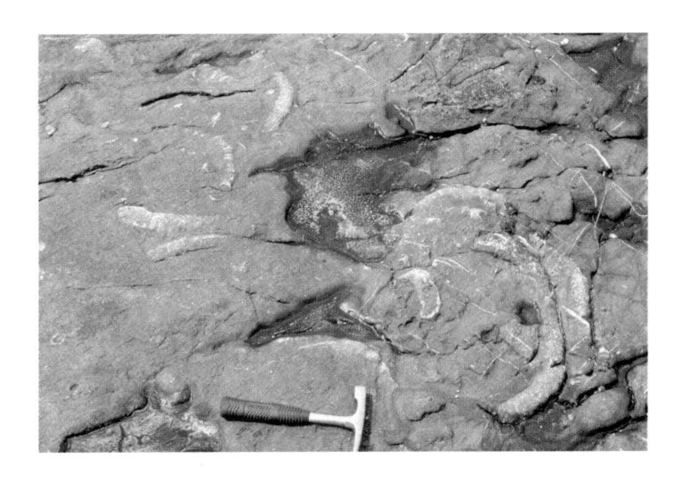

Plate 11 Individuals of the coral *Syphonophyllia benburbensis* on a bedding surface of the Knockrushen Formation. Strandhall foreshore (GS 1039).

carbonate platform, which previously extended to the north of the Isle of Man. This platform may also have had eastward depositional continuity with the Urswick Limestone Formation of south Cumbria/north Lancashire, as the southern platform margin is coincident in trend with that of the Urswick Limestone Formation. The Balladoole Formation was partly coeval with the Bowland Shale Formation (described below) and was subsequently overstepped by it. Crinoids, brachiopods and corals are the dominant macrofossils. Locally, the limestone is altered to dolostone. Owing to faulting at Balladoole the base of the formation is not exposed. Dickson et al. (1987) estimated the thickness of the formation to be about 90 m. Ammonoid faunas from the bioherms recorded by Bisat (1934) include a lower assemblage of *Goniatites hudsoni* and *Bollandites phillipsi*, and a higher level with *Bollandites castletonesis* and *Beyrichoceras vesiculiferum*. These are of late Asbian age (B_{2a} and B_{2b} subzones of Riley, 1990) and confirm that the Manx platform-edge bioherms were the contemporaries of platform-edge bioherms widely developed in Ireland, Wales and northern England. The identification of *G. crenistria* by Lewis (1930) in black limestone at the top of the formation suggests (if correctly identified) a P_{1a} subzonal age, close to the top of the Asbian.

Craven Group

Hodderense Limestone Formation (Holkerian)

Known formerly as the Sea Mount Member (Dickson et al., 1987), this unit comprises a 14 m-thick interval of fine-grained, pale grey to cream-coloured, tabular bedded, porcellaneous wackestone, interbedded with scattered thin, dark, fissile claystone layers. The formation contains blue or grey micrite nodules up to 3 cm in diameter and chert is common. Some beds are multistorey and display lag horizons composed of reworked micrite nodules, inadunate crinoids, bellerophontid gastropods, cephalopods, trilobites and sponges. Cephalopods include the ammonoids *Merocanites henslowi* (type locality Scarlett quarry [SC 258 662]), *Bollandoceras* and *Beyrichoceras*. The similarity of this formation to the type Hodderense Limestone Formation of the Craven Basin is striking. The facies represents a deep-marine hemipelagic carbonate, deposited in a setting that was mainly starved of clastic supply and lay below storm wave base. The presence of the deep-water trace fossil *Helminthoides* lends further support to this interpretation. The unit represents the Holkerian maximum flooding and highstand part of the sea level curve, with water depth accentuated by synrift subsidence and sediment starvation.

Bowland Shale Formation (Asbian–Pendleian)

This division includes and replaces the Poyllvaaish, Close-ny-Chollagh and Scarlett Volcanic formations of Dickson et al. (1987). As in the Craven Basin of the adjacent English mainland, the Bowland Shale Formation marks the first widespread black hemipelagic claystone deposition in the Dinantian. The background sedimentation in both regions was punctuated by localised deposition of carbonate turbidites, debris flows, olistoliths, and uniquely in the Isle of Man, volcaniclastic deposits and submarine lavas.

SCARLETT POINT MEMBER This is the locally occurring basal member of the Bowland Shale Formation on the Isle of Man. Its base is defined at the lowest black claystone overlying the Hodderense Limestone Formation at Scarlett Point [SC 2583 6633]. Here, the member is about 14 m thick (Plate 12). It comprises cherty and pyritious tabular beds of pale wackestone and lime-mudstone, which display gradational (dolomitised in places) boundaries with the interbedded black, fissile, blocky claystone. 'Chondritiform' and *Helminthoides* burrows are common in the limestone. Inadunate crinoid lags and scattered ammonoids (*Beyrichoceras* or *Bollandoceras*) also occur, some preserved in semi-buoyant resting position, with the venter resting on the sea bed. Deposition was in a deep-marine, hemipelagic environment, with periodic gravitational fine clastic and carbonate supply. The member is of (possibly early) Asbian age. The interval probably straddles several glacio-eustatic transgressive–regressive cycles, but defining cycle boundaries is difficult in deeper water strata.

Where the Bowland Shale Formation oversteps the Balladoole Formation (e.g. along the foreshore northwest of Salt Spring Cottage [SC 244 679]), coarse-grained detrital carbonates and debris beds are common. These include erosively based graded packstone beds, conglomerate, megaclasts and olistoliths. The presence of abraded and fragmented macrofossil bioclasts (mainly crinoids, brachiopods and corals), together with carbonate clasts, indicates derivation from a carbonate platform source (i.e. the Balladoole Limestone Formation). Large olistoliths (some up to 10 by 3 m in size) of biohermal wackestone (reef limestone) also occur, associated with peri-reef packstone and grainstone. Geopetal infills within some of these blocks can be used to determine that the blocks have been flipped on their sides or overturned. Dickson et al. (1987) and earlier workers referred to these olistoliths as the Poyllvaaish Formation; however, the blocks sit within the hemipelagic claystone succession of the Bowland Shale Formation and are clearly derived from an adjacent carbonate platform margin. Since olistoliths and megaclasts of reef limestone occur at several levels in the bottom 100 m of the Bowland Shale Formation, the usage of 'Poyllvaaish

Plate 12 The type locality of the Scarlett Point Member of the Bowland Shale Formation, showing deep-water hemipelagic carbonates and black claystones. Scarlett Point (GS 1040).

Formation' as a discrete lithostratigraphical entity is not tenable. Some of these olistoliths have been described in detail by Dickson et al. (1987) and Quirk et al. (1990a). In fact, some of the faults mapped by the latter authors are in fact the boundaries of large olistoliths, rather than structural dislocations. The olistoliths contain spectacularly preserved ammonoid faunas, including *Goniatites crenistria* and *Beyrichoceratoides truncatum*, which together indicate a P_{1a} ammonoid biozone age of latest Asbian.

The middle part of the exposed portion of the formation, well seen at Black Marble Quarry [SC 244 676], comprises black calcareous platy claystone with subordinate beds (up to 2 m thick) of dark wackestone, and dark detrital (skeletal and carbonate lithoclast) packstone debris beds (the so-called 'black marble' worked at the quarry). The claystone contains the ammonoid *Arnsbergites falcatus*, together with the large hemipelagic bivalve *Posidonia becheri*. The discovery of these fossils confirms observations made by Lewis (1930). The assemblage is diagnostic of an earliest Brigantian (P_{1b}) ammonoid subzone age and the assertion by Racey et al. (1999) that the beds at Black Marble Quarry lie in the early Namurian is therefore refuted. These strata broadly comprise the Close-ny-Chollagh Formation of Dickson et al. (1987).

SCARLETT VOLCANIC MEMBER Overlying the claystone south of Black Marble Quarry, close to Close-ny-Chollag Point, are volcaniclastic rocks of the Scarlett Volcanic Member. This unit was designated as a formation by Dickson et al. (1987), but in this report is considered to lie within, and be interbedded with, the Bowland Shale Formation. The member is only exposed along its type section, from Close-ny-Chollag Point to Scarlett Point (Plate 13). It is dominated by submarine volcaniclastic debris flows and gravity slides (illustrated by Lamplugh, 1903). The basal volcaniclastic rocks have a sharp, baked contact with the underlying claystone. The contact steps up and down along bedding planes as a result of plucking or injection of volcaniclastic material into the upper part of the claystone. Claystone rafts and megaclasts are entrained within the volcaniclastic rocks. Between this locality and Scarlett Point there is a 1.5 km-long

Plate 13 The base of the Scarlett Volcanic Member resting with erosive contact on claystone of the Bowland Shale Formation. Close-ny-Chollagh Point [SC 246 671] (GS 1041).

Plate 14 Pillow lavas of the Scarlett Volcanic Member, near Close-ny-Chollagh Point [SC 245 670] (GS 1042).

strike section in the Scarlett Volcanic Member. The top is not seen and although the thickness of the member is difficult to estimate owing to rolling dips, olistoliths, soft-sediment deformation and gravity slides, it is probably no more than 50 m thick. Points of particular interest are the pillow lavas (Plate 14) [SC 245 670], and various olistoliths derived from older Dinantian carbonates, including a rafted block of Skillicore Member.

At Scarlett Point one such rafted block, comprising dolomitised limestone and resembling the Balladoole Formation, contains a palaeokarst pit, containing iron-stained quartz pebbles overlain by tuff. The overlying sequence contains complex imbrication of volcaniclastic units formed by gravity sliding, displaying variable dips and syndepositional (possibly rotational) fault contacts (illustrated by Lamplugh, 1903).

The Scarlett Volcanic Member appears to represent a series of volcaniclastic flows which moved down a submarine fault scarp from a volcanic centre which may have been subaerial or shallow-marine. Isolated vesicular basaltic clasts, representing subaerial or shallow-marine degassing of the extruded magma, occur in some of the volcaniclastic rocks. The interval was interpreted as recording a shallow-marine 'surtseyan-type' setting by Durant and Grant (1985). The association with hemipelagic claystone suggests final deposition of many of the volcaniclastic debris flows in deep water. It is likely that much of the volcanic pile was transported downslope from its original depositional site. Dickson et al. (1987) referred to the occurrence of mid-Brigantian ammonoids in dark limestone megaclasts within the volcanic rocks. It is assumed that offshore the member is overlain by black claystone which extends into the Namurian (Pendleian) part of the Bowland Shale Formation.

DINANTIAN ROCKS IN THE NORTHERN PART OF THE ISLE OF MAN

Dinantian rocks in the northern part of the Island are entirely concealed and are known only from boreholes. The sequence is poorly known, but late Dinantian platform carbonates (Balladoole Formation) are thought to be overlain by a cyclothemic mixed carbonate–clastic sequence, similar to the Gleaston Formation (Yoredale Group) of south Cumbria. This latter division extends at least into the early Namurian and has been proved offshore in BP Well 25/1. Large erratic blocks of the Balladoole Formation also occur within Quaternary deposits (e.g. on the coast north of Peel).

SILESIAN

Onshore, Silesian rocks are known only from the northern part of the Isle of Man. Namurian strata of the Craven Group have been proved only in the Ballavaarkish and Shellag Point boreholes. Namurian strata may also occur in the Ballaghenny Borehole (Lamplugh, 1903, pp.286–288), where cyclothemic 'Yoredale' facies of mixed carbonate–clastic lithologies have been attributed to the Yoredale Group. However, it is also possible that the strata in the Ballaghenny Borehole may be Dinantian in age. Only the Ballavaarkish and Shellag Point boreholes were examined in the recent resurvey. Both of these were described by Quirk and Kimbell (1997) and Racey et al. (1999). Westphalian strata occur only in the Ballavaarkish Borehole and are attributable to the Pennine Lower Coal Measures Formation of the Pennine Coal Measures Group.

BALLAVAARKISH BOREHOLE [NX 4625 0070]
(also known as Shellag North Borehole)

Pennine Coal Measures Group

Lower Pennine Coal Measures Formation (Langsettian)

This unit contains a marine band, between depths of 136.5 and 136.8 m, which yielded the inarticulate brachiopod *Lingula mytilloides* and the ammonoid *Gastrioceras subcrenatum* (Figure 20b). This ammonoid is the definitive marker fossil of the Subcrenatum Marine Band which defines the Namurian (Yeadonian)–Westphalian (Langsettian) boundary. The mid-Marsdenian age interpreted by Racey et al. (1999) using palynology is not supported. The overlying claystone and siltstone (up to the top of the cored section at 120.75 m) are of Langsettian age and lie within the upper part of the Subcrenatum Marine Band cycle.

Millstone Grit Group

Rossendale Formation (Yeadonian)

Fine- to coarse-grained, cross-bedded, feldspathic sandstone underlies the Subcrenatum Marine Band, from 138.4 m to at least 145.55 m; the contact was not seen owing to core loss. This sandstone unit is contemporaneous with the Rough Rock Formation of the Pennine Basin and lower part of the Gwespyr Sandstone Formation of North Wales. However, heavy mineral analysis (by C Hallsworth, BGS Keyworth) indicates that the sandstone is mineralogically distinct from that of the Rough Rock Formation, suggesting a possible westerly rather than northerly (i.e. Rough Rock Formation) provenance. The flooding surface at 152.65 m, which overlies a palaeosol, may correlate with the one overlying the Sandrock Mine Coal in Lancashire and the East Midlands (between the upper and lower 'leaves' of the Rough Rock Formation). No definitive bivalves were found in the small amount of core material available. If this flooding horizon is the same as that observed in the Sandrock Mine, then the fine-grained, trough cross-laminated sandstone between 157.15 and 158.86 m may be equivalent to the lower leaf of the Rough Rock Formation seen in England. From such an interpretation it could be inferred that the listricated claystone lying against the top of the fault zone at 164.55 m might lie in the upper part of the Cancelloceras cumbriense Marine Band. Within the fault zone (164.55 m-172.34 m) the core comprises thin-bedded, listricated and shattered black claystone and siltstone and pale fine-grained sandstone; interpretation is difficult in this interval.

Great Scar Limestone Group (Yoredale Group)

The massive, stylolitised, fractured and sucrosic dolomite which occurs between 172.34 and 179.60 m may be of early Namurian or Dinantian age; diagenesis has completely ruled out any chance of obtaining a biostratigraphical age.

SHELLAG POINT BOREHOLE [NX 4565 9965]
(also known as RTZ 1, Shellag South Borehole)

Craven Group

Bowland Shale Formation (Arnsbergian)

This borehole was cored through 27.55 m of siltstone, claystone and ironstone (Figure 20a). Most of the cored section is of marine origin, apart from a thin siltstone palaeosol between 106.12 and 106.45 m. The presence of the ammonoid *Nuculoceras nuculum* at 102.55 and 107 m demonstrates that two of the three *N. nuculum* (E2c2–4) marine bands, which occur in the latest Arnsbergian (Riley et al., 1987), are present. The late Namurian (Yeadonian) age asigned by Racey et al. (1999) and based on palynology interpretation is unsustainable. Exactly which of the three marine bands are represented in Shellag Point Borehole is impossible to ascertain as the borehole did not core adjacent ammonoid zones (*Isohomoceras subglobosum* or *Nuculoceras stellarum*). The presence of *Nuculoceras nuculum* has important palaeogeographical implications, as strata containing ammonoids of this age are only preserved in basin centres. The major sea level fall at the end of the Arnsbergian led to the widespread erosion and removal of late Arnsbergian strata from sequences in marginal basin settings (corresponding with the Mississippian/Pennsylvanian unconformity). A shelly fauna of calcareous brachiopods (productids, orthotetids and spiriferoids) accompanies the ammonoids in this borehole, together with complete carapaces of the trilobite *Paladin*. The presence of shelly faunas indicates proximity to the late Arnsbergian shoreline. This gave rise to oxygenation of the substrate, which explains the relatively low total organic content (TOC) values obtained by Racey et al. (1999). It is therefore unlikely that their TOC sample is representative of the Namurian claystone in the area.

OFFSHORE CARBONIFEROUS

Carboniferous sedimentary rocks form an important and extensive part of the offshore succession around the Isle of Man and they are preserved in a series of sedimentary basins described in Chapter 4. Seismic data suggest that the Solway, Eubonia and Keys basins probably contain 4000 to 5000 m of Carboniferous sedimentary rocks. However, the present-day distribution of Carboniferous strata is limited by the effects of uplift and erosion as a consequence of the Variscan basin inversion. This resulted in the restriction of the younger Carboniferous succession, particularly the Westphalian, to smaller areas, commonly in the centres of the main basins or along major bounding faults.

During the Carboniferous the Isle of Man region is thought to have lain a few degrees to the south of the equator and gradually drifted northwards (Scotese et al., 1979). Conditions during the Dinantian were seasonally arid (Besly, 1987), becoming wetter and more tropical or seasonally wet during the mid-Carboniferous, and reverting to more arid conditions again during latest Carboniferous times (Guion et al., 2000). These climatic variations, coupled with the effects of glacio-eustatic sea level fluctuations and the change from rifting to thermal relaxation, had a pronounced effect on sedimentation patterns during the Carboniferous.

The Carboniferous of the whole of the Irish Sea area has been described in detail by Jackson et al. (1995) and Jackson and Johnson (1996), whereas this account focuses on the offshore area immediately adjacent to the Isle of Man.

DINANTIAN

During the Dinantian, the Isle of Man area formed part of the south-western extension of the Manx–Lakeland Ridge horst block, bounded to the north by the Maryport Fault and to the south by the Eubonia–Lagman Fault. Extension along these north-east–south-west-trending faults produced the Peel and Solway basins to the north-west of the Isle of Man and the Eubonia and Manx basins to the south-east. Seismic data suggest that the Manx–Lakeland Ridge formed a platform area characterised by a much thinner sediment pile than that of the basinal areas, and regional studies suggest that the Dinantian sequence in the Solway and Peel basins varies between 1000 and 2500 km in thickness. Geophysical evidence suggests that in the Peel Basin the Carboniferous succession has an unconformable base and may rest on a Caledonian granite (Jackson et al., 1995). Our knowledge of offshore Dinantian strata is restricted by the limited number of wells that penetrate the succession.

The term Garwood Group has been introduced for the entire Dinantian succession (Jackson et al., 1995; Jackson and Johnson, 1996), with the top of the group defined at the base of the Cravenoceras leion Marine Band. The following account describes the Dinantian succession chronostratigraphically.

Courceyan–Chadian

Initial rifting along the basin margins was associated with the formation of localised coarse fluvial/alluvial fan facies and volcanism during the Courceyan. On the northern side of the Solway Basin various continental fluvial/alluvial fan and marine facies, including carbonates, have been described (Deegan, 1973; Ord et al., 1988; Maguire et al., 1996). Similar, locally derived conglomerates (Basal Beds Formation; Barclay et al., 1994) are present along the southern margin of the Solway Basin (Mitchell et al., 1978) and from the onshore Isle of Man (Langness Conglomerate Formation).

Within the onshore Solway Basin, sedimentary rocks of Courceyan to Chadian age are represented by the Ballagan Formation of the Inverclyde Group, previously termed the 'cementstones' of the Lower Border Group (Armstrong and Purnell, 1987). This formation comprises cyclical marine sequences of shelly and algal limestone, anhydrite, mudstone and sandstone, indicative of coastal sabkha and fluvio-lacustrine environments (Day, 1970; Leeder, 1974; Leeder et al., 1989). Ward (1997) recognised a significant evaporite component, comprising a cumulative thickness of approximately 100 m of anhydrite, in the Ballagan Formation in the Easton-1 Well, drilled just north of Carlisle. This is thought to indicate deposition in an environment characterised by low-energy conditions and restricted marine circulation.

In west Cumbria, on the Manx–Lakeland Ridge, the conglomerates (Basal Beds Formation) are overlain by the late Chadian Martin Limestone Formation, with a significant non-sequence between the two (Barclay et al., 1994; Akhurst et al., 1997). This formation comprises sandy packstone and sandy lime mudstone deposited in a shallow-marine coastal ramp environment (Barclay et al., 1994; Akhurst et al., 1997). The Martin Limestone Formation is also present in south Cumbria where it comprises facies indicative of tidal flat, beach and lagoonal conditions (Gawthorpe et al., 1989).

There is scant information regarding early Dinantian strata in the offshore area around the Isle of Man. Seismic data suggest that a thick Dinantian succession is present in the basins around the Isle of Man and it is likely that some of this is earliest Carboniferous in age. The extent of the cementstone and carbonate ramp facies recognised from the Solway Basin and west Cumbria, respectively, is unknown. However, the evaporite succession described by Ward (1997) has a distinctive seismic character that can be traced within the Solway Basin over a distance of between 600 and 100 km^2 and may link up with similar facies described from Northern Ireland (Smith, 1986). Hence, it is likely that marine conditions were established in the Solway and Peel basins.

The Dinantian sequence of the Peel Basin is thought to comprise a lower succession of volcanic rocks interbedded with shallow-marine carbonates, overlain by Waulsortian lime mud facies, which are, in turn, overlain by Arundian conglomerates. These coarse clastic rocks may have been deposited in response to a period of renewed rifting or possibly to a period of lowstand conditions. A later deepening phase led to deposition of thick marine shale and calciturbidites during the late Dinantian.

Arundian–Holkerian

Within the onshore Solway Basin, the Arundian to Holkerian stages are represented by sedimentary rocks of the Border Group (formerly the Middle Border Group). These rocks show a change from the south-westerly flowing braided river deposits of the Fell Sandstone Formation in the east to mixed fluviodeltaic and shallow-marine facies, including limestones of the Lyne Formation, in the west (Smith and Holliday, 1991; Chadwick et al., 1995; Maguire et al., 1996). Still farther to the south-west, in Westnewton-1 Well, a minimum thickness of 200 m (base not seen) of Arundian and approximately 260 m of Holkerian strata were proved. These are predominantly fully marine with thick carbonate successions and some Yoredale-like cycles.

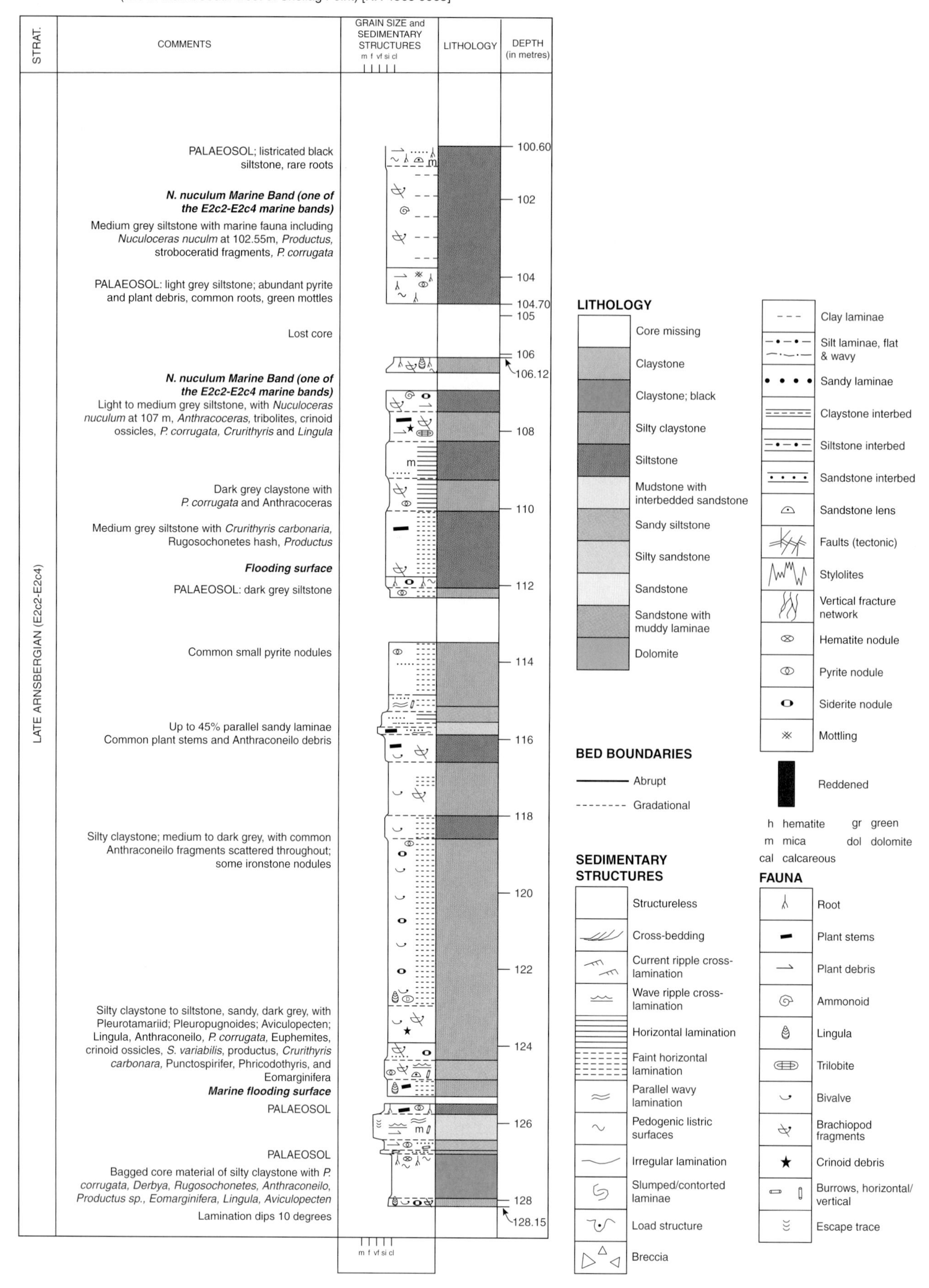

Figure 20a Borehole log for Shellag Point Borehole. (See Figure 2 for location.)

BALLAVAARKISH BOREHOLE

(Isle of Man 2/Shellag North) [NX 4625 0070]

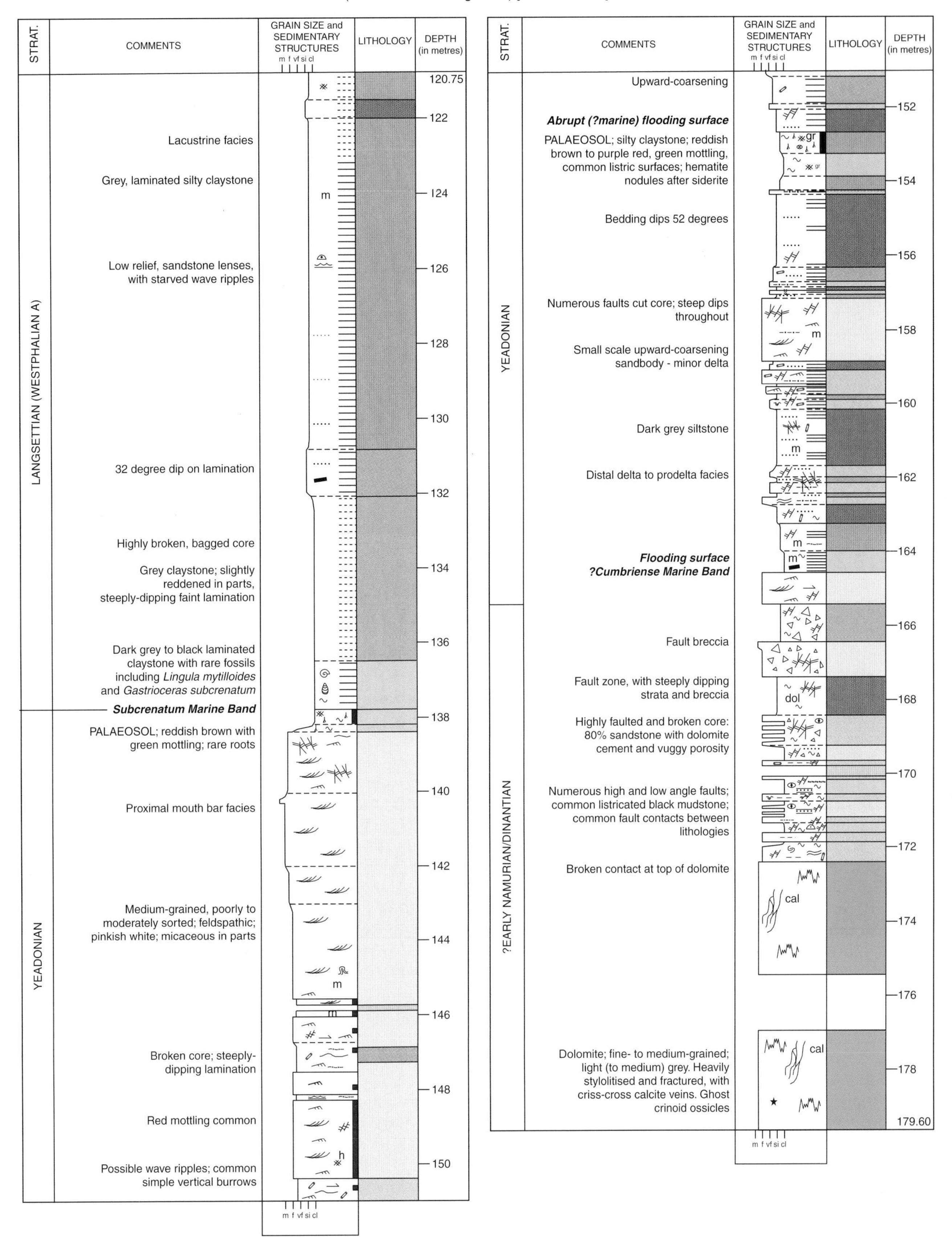

Figure 20b Borehole log for Ballavaarkish Borehole. (See Figure 2 for location.)

Strata of Arundian age are missing from the central Lake District Block area, although Barclay et al. (1994) speculated that they were once present and have been removed by erosion following tectonically driven uplift at the start of the Holkerian. Following this, the influence of active rifting began to diminish into the Holkerian, such that sedimentation was able to spread onto basin footwall blocks (Chadwick et al., 1995). In the Isle of Man, the Arundian is represented by the Derbyhaven Formation, where shallow-marine ramp limestone facies are present.

The Holkerian was marked by transgression across parts of the Lake District leading to deposition of the Frizington Limestone (Barclay et al., 1994). This formation, formerly termed the Seventh Limestone, represents the development of a carbonate ramp in which offshore bioclastic bars separated a periodically hypersaline lagoonal environment from open marine conditions in which bioclastic carbonate sands accumulated (Llewellyn et al., 1968; Barclay et al., 1994). In south Cumbria carbonate platform conditions are represented by the Park Limestone Formation (Gawthorpe et al., 1989). Holkerian strata are represented onshore in the Isle of Man by the Knockrushen Formation and Hodderense Limestone Formation, which represent deposition in carbonate ramp and deeper hemipelagic environments, respectively.

In the offshore area around the Isle of Man, Arundian strata have been proved from Borehole 73/65 on the western edge of the Peel Basin (Jackson et al., 1995). Here, 0.5 m of grey bioclastic limestone contain late Arundian foraminifera (Riley *in* Jackson et al., 1995). In the Peel Basin, Well 111/29-1 proved approximately 366 m of high energy carbonate ramp grainstone and wackestone facies dated as Asbian to Holkerian in age. These facies are low in organic content, with TOC less than 0.04 per cent (Newman, 1999). Well 111/25-1A penetrated approximately 72 m of Dinantian carbonate, thought to be roughly comparable in age with the succession proved in Well 111/29-1 (Newman, 1999).

Hence, it seems likely that, during the Arundian, coastal plain conditions were restricted to parts of the onshore Solway Basin and that Cumbria and the Isle of Man area were marked by shallow-marine carbonate ramp environments. Deeper water conditions may have separated the two areas, although there is no information to substantiate this interpretation. These conditions continued into the early Holkerian, but by late Holkerian times maximum flooding and highstand conditions led to drowning of many of the shallow-water areas and deposition of hemipelagic carbonate deposits in a belt that stretched from the southern Isle of Man across to the Craven Basin. The continuation of carbonate platform conditions in Cumbria at this time suggests that an element of tectonic control was also important.

Asbian–Brigantian

Numerous well penetrations provide much more information about the stratigraphy and sedimentology of the offshore area during latest Dinantian times. It is known that a period of further rifting occurred in this area during the late Holkerian to early Asbian, as indicated by variations in sedimentary thickness across active faults and by the presence of seismically disturbed rocks (Leeder et al., 1989; Barclay et al., 1994; Chadwick et al., 1995). Uplift on the Lake District Block led to a period of prolonged emergence resulting in the formation of a widespread unconformity where the early Asbian strata is absent, and to the presence of a well-developed palaeokarst and palaeosol at the Holkerian–late Asbian boundary (Horbury, 1989; Barclay et al., 1994). This unconformity does not appear to be present in the Isle of Man succession.

Well 111/29-1, which proved approximately 360 m of carbonate facies dated as Holkerian to Asbian in age, provides evidence that a carbonate platform area was present in the Peel Basin at this time. The geophysical log for Well 111/29-1 indicates that the succession is dominated by carbonate, in successions from 40 to 60 m in thickness, that alternate with thinner, more muddy successions up to 15 m thick. A core taken at terminal depth (1450 m–1455.5 m) comprises mainly grainstone and wackestone, although mudstone and packstone are also present, with locally abundant comminuted bioclastic material. Some beds show upward-fining or upward-coarsening and exhibit a poorly defined subhorizontal lamination. These beds contain a varied fauna that includes crinoids, brachiopods, goniatites, foraminifera, bryozoans, bivalves, ostracods and gastropods, which may also occur as basal lags. Rare, interbedded claystone and minor sandstone also occur. The claystone is grey, with some evidence for reddening and reduction. It may be micaceous, carbonaceous and, locally, pyritic and calcareous. The sandstone is light grey, fine grained and calcareous. A likely depositional environment for these facies is a ramp setting with shallow-marine, predominantly oxygenated, bottom waters. The presence of bioclastic lags and subhorizontal lamination could indicate deposition from storm events.

Early Asbian strata have been proved from the west side of the Peel Basin from Borehole 73/67. They comprise 3.6 m of light grey bioclastic limestone containing crinoidal debris and foraminifera (Jackson et al., 1995).

Later Asbian and Brigantian sedimentation on the Lake District Block area was marked by deposition of thick platform carbonates (Second to Sixth Limestones), deposited in warm shallow waters less than 20 m deep (Akhurst et al., 1997). These became emergent during sea level lowstands leading to the formation of numerous palaeokarst surfaces (Akhurst et al., 1997). In south Cumbria, the Urswick Limestone Formation consists of 10 to 20 m thick, grainstone-dominated, upward-shallowing cycles punctuated by emergent surfaces (Horbury, 1989).

Wells in the Lagman and Keys basins (112/25a-1 and 113/27-2) preserve a Brigantian carbonate succession in which packstone, wackestone and grainstone facies have been recognised (Riley, 1992a, b). These carbonates are over 110 m thick in Well 112/25a-1 and approximately 150 m thick in Well 113/27-2. These thicknesses suggest the presence of a fairly extensive and long-lived belt of shallow-water carbonates at this time that may have been in continuity with those deposited around the Lake District.

Well 112/15-1 occurs in the deepest parts of the offshore Solway Basin and consists of approximately 138 m of Brigantian strata. The succession is dominated by mudstone, with rare thin limestone and sandstone beds. No consistent upward-coarsening trends are present on the gamma-ray log, suggesting that upward-shallowing Yoredale-like cycles are absent. A deeper water environment is favoured for deposition of the mudstone, with sandstone and carbonate beds emplaced as turbidity flows.

Well 112/19-1, just off the north-east tip of the Isle of Man, proved 198 m of Brigantian to Pendleian strata above terminal depth at 2023 m. Two main units are recognisable from the gamma-ray log. The lower unit (1925 m to 2023 m) is a predominantly carbonate succession with some interbedded sandstone and mudstone. A core through this comprises grey dolomite with common crinoid fragments, subordinate bivalves, foraminifera and the rugose coral *Diphyphyllum fasciculatum* and possibly *Lithostrotion* sp.. The limestone is highly brecciated in places and there are common near-vertical fractures infilled with anhydrite. Part of the dolomite is reddened and there are nodular horizons. At the base of the core is a grey laminated siltstone. A carbonate ramp environment is likely, although the nodular horizons and reddening could be related to soil formation and may indicate a trend towards platform development. The upper unit within Well 112/19-1 (from 1824.5 to 1925 m) comprises approximately 100 m of predominantly siliciclastic facies. High gamma API mudstone is overlain by an upward-coarsening succession with a few limestones. These are probably Yoredale cycles and represent shallow-water deltaic successions (Newman, 1999). Geochemical analyses from Well 112/19-1 indicate that the succession is organically lean, with TOC up to 0.82 per cent (Newman, 1999).

In Well 112/25a-1, the carbonate ramp succession described previously is overlain by approximately 80 m (from 2590 m to approximately 2670 m) of Yoredale-like facies comprising thin limestones overlain by upward-coarsening mudstone–sandstone cycles. These have been dated as Brigantian to Pendleian (Riley, 1992a) and appear similar to those described from the Solway Basin (see Chadwick et al., 1995). Hence it is envisaged that towards the end of the Brigantian the fluviodeltaic Yoredale complexes that characterise much of the Dinantian of the Solway Firth Basin were able to prograde across the earlier carbonate shelf, reaching at least as far as the Lagman Basin.

The shallow-water conditions inferred for the Peel, Solway, Lagman and Keys basins and onshore Cumbria contrast significantly with the facies described from the southern tip of the Isle of Man. Here, mudstone of the Bowland Shale Formation is a deep-water, hemipelagic facies similar to that described from the Craven Basin and Garstang areas (Brandon et al., 1998). Evidence for the presence of reef facies, slumped beds and synsedimentary faulting from the onshore succession points to a position close to an active fault, with environments to the south marked by deeper water basinal conditions. It is speculated that these deeper water conditions may have been in continuity with those present in the Craven Basin at this time.

NAMURIAN

The Namurian marked a change from the deposition of thick carbonate successions to a setting in which siliciclastic sedimentation was dominant (Guion et al., 2000). The well-developed rift-controlled bathymetric contrasts between block and basin that were characteristic of the Dinantian gave way to less pronounced differences as a result of a change to post-rift thermal subsidence (Guion et al., 2000). Major 'Millstone Grit' delta systems prograded south and westwards across the Pennine Basin, depositing fluvial and deltaic facies on the blocks and feeding sediment as turbidites into the deeper waters. In addition, easterly flowing fluvial systems have been described from Yeadonian strata, indicating the initiation of a western source area during the latest Namurian (McLean and Chisholm, 1996).

In the offshore succession around the Isle of Man, Jackson et al. (1997) and Jackson and Johnson (1996) have grouped all Namurian strata together to form the Bisat Group, with the base of the group defined at the base of the Cravenoceras leion Marine Band and the top placed at the base of the Subcrenatum Marine Band. Three gross associations of sedimentary facies are described for the group: basinal, Yoredale and Millstone Grit (Jackson et al., 1995). The basinal facies comprise dark mudstone and turbidites of deep water origin. They are largely of Pendleian to Kinderscoutian age. The Yoredale facies are similar to those described from the Dinantian succession, with cyclical deposition of limestone and marine mudstone overlain by upward-coarsening and shallowing deltaic and channel sandstone, poorly drained palaeosols and coals. The limestones tend to be thinner than those present in the Dinantian. The Millstone Grit facies lack the limestone of the Yoredale cycles and comprise claystone, siltstone, sandstone, siliciclastic palaeosols and coals. The sandstone tends to be coarser than that of the Dinantian succession, and appears to have been derived from two main sources: an important northerly, feldspathic source and a minor southerly source supplying quartz-rich sand. Fluvial deposits form an important component of the Millstone Grit association.

Namurian sedimentary rocks are present in the offshore area immediately around the Isle of Man and are thickest in the area between the Isle of Man and Anglesey, where they can be up to 2900 m thick (Jackson et al., 1987). They rest conformably on Dinantian rocks and are overlain by either conformable Westphalian or unconformable Permo–Triassic strata.

The offshore BGS Borehole 73/53, on the north side of the Solway Basin, proved 9 m of reddish brown to grey sandstone and mudstone with late Visean to early Namurian palynomorphs (Wilkinson and Halliwell, 1979). Similar lithologies were observed in the nearby Borehole 73/52 (Jackson et al., 1995). On the eastern edge of the Peel Basin, Borehole 71/43 penetrated Namurian strata and proved laminated grey mudstone with thin beds of dolomite and very fine-grained sandstone containing palynomorphs of Kinderscoutian to Marsdenian age (Wilkinson and Halliwell, 1979; Jackson et al., 1995).

Namurian strata are known from Well 112/15-1 in the deepest parts of the offshore Solway Basin. A predominantly mudstone succession of Pendleian age was proved between 2422 and 2570 m RKB (depth in metres relative to kelly bushing). Cuttings indicate that the main lithologies are medium to dark grey claystone, siltstone and sandstone, with minor coals (e.g. at 2484 m RKB) and wackestone to packstone carbonate. The mudstone is likely to be marine and to have accumulated in deeper water environments, although the presence of coals points to periodic emergence and the development of shallow-water, Yoredale-like depositional conditions.

The facies described from Well 112/15-1 are similar to those described from Isle of Man boreholes onshore and also those reported from west Cumbria and Canonbie (e.g. Greig, 1971; Akhurst et al., 1997). Strata of likely Pendleian age occur in boreholes on the northern tip of the Isle of Man and stratigraphical sections show an approximately 70 m-thick interbedded succession of mudstone, thin limestones, coals and sandstone directly overlying the Great Limestone (Taylor et al., 1971). Upper Namurian (possibly Yeadonian) strata from the Ballavaarkish Borehole (also known as Shellag North Borehole) preserve a shallow-water, deltaic succession including upward-coarsening mouth bars, marine bands, palaeosols and channel facies (Figure 20a). Non-sequences are common within the Namurian succession in west Cumbria. The Pendleian to Arnsbergian stages are present, and a substantial non-sequence was developed before the latest Yeadonian Stage (Ramsbottom et al., 1978; Akhurst et al., 1997). Cores through the Pendleian to Arnsbergian Hensingham Group in Cumbria indicate the development of shallow-water, marine-influenced Yoredale-like deltaic facies (Akhurst et al., 1997). The Yeadonian succession comprises similar facies and includes the Cumbriense Marine Band. Coal seams, albeit thin, also become more common and include the Udale seam (Eastwood et al., 1931, 1968; Taylor, 1961).

In the East Irish Sea, Riley (1992a) has reported foraminifera of mid-Brigantian to Pendleian age from limestone within Well 112/25a-1. Well 113/27-2 proved Namurian strata, ranging from possible Arnsbergian to late Namurian or early Westphalian age (McNestry, 1991). Well 112/30-1, on the south side of the Ogham Platform, proved approximately 800 m of Arnsbergian to Yeadonian strata. These ages are supported by palynological studies (Owens, 1988a). The Namurian strata consist of predominantly of dark grey to black carbonaceous mudstone with a few thin sandstone and siltstone beds (Lomas and Neville, 1976). Thin interbeds of dark brown crystalline limestone also occur. The mudstone-dominated nature of this succession indicates deposition in fairly deep-marine conditions. The siltstone, sandstone and limestone are probably turbidite deposits and their relative scarcity suggests that this part of the Irish Sea was located in a distal position relative to the deltaic feeder systems. The combined thickness of Arnsbergian (base not proven) to Alportian strata in this well is 334 m. The top of the Alportian strata is defined above a 10 m-thick sand body, the top of which marks a shift in the gamma-ray log to higher background API values and slightly lower sonic velocities. The overlying 162 m-thick Kinderscoutian succession is as mudstone-dominated as underlying successions, although a sandstone up to 13 m in thickness occurs in the middle of the succession (Jackson et al., 1995). Strata of Marsdenian to Yeadonian age occur from 551 to 891 m RKB and, while still mudstone-dominant, they comprise a greater proportion of sandstone, in upward-coarsening deltaic cycles (Jackson et al., 1995).

The well and onshore data indicate that the palaeogeographical setting during the Namurian was similar to that envisaged by Jackson et al. (1995, fig. 30). Most of the northern area, including the Isle of Man, Solway Basin and the Lake District, is characterised by shallow-water, deltaic (Yoredale-type) cycles throughout the Namurian. Both the Isle of Man and the Lake District probably formed highs on which sedimentation was intermittent. Deeper water marine conditions may have persisted in the Peel Basin where marine shale and turbidite sandstone were deposited. To the south, deep-water basinal conditions appear to have persisted throughout most of the Namurian and led to the accumulation of thick packages of pelagic mudstone which form good source rocks. The lack of good biostratigraphical information for the offshore realm precludes the recognition of the major lowstand that occurred at the end of the Arnsbergian, although it has been identified onshore, where deep-water ammonoid facies are preserved in association with a shallow-water brachiopod fauna. By Marsdenian to Yeadonian times, the sedimentation in the southern basins changed to more deltaic conditions, presumably reflecting decreased subsidence in the basin and the ability of sedimentation to keep pace with subsidence.

WESTPHALIAN

By the start of Westphalian times, the pronounced basinal topography that characterised the earlier Carboniferous had largely disappeared, producing a flat, low-lying, fluviodeltaic environment in which thick peats, later forming coal seams, accumulated. Lithostratigraphically, the entire succession offshore has been termed the Kidston Group (Jackson et al., 1997; Jackson and Johnson, 1996), and onshore it is known as the Pennine Coal Measures Group; the base of the group is defined at the base of the Subcrenatum Marine Band and the top at the base Permo–Triassic unconformity. This unconformity was produced by Late Carboniferous Variscan uplift and erosion and has resulted in only partial preservation of the Kidston Group as erosional remnants. Jackson and Mulholland (1993) suggested, using seismic data, a minimum thickness of up to 4000 m for the Westphalian succession in the East Irish Sea Basin.

Chronostratigraphically, the Westphalian succession is divisible into four stages, with the lower three (Langsettian, Duckmantian and Bolsovian) defined on the basis of marker ammonoids in marine bands. The topmost stage (Westphalian D) is defined by the occurrence of the plant *Neuropteris ovata* (Ramsbottom et al., 1978). The Langsettian and Duckmantian successions comprise largely mudstone-dominated strata with thick coal seams, whereas the Bolsovian and Westphalian D sequences comprise more arenaceous, primary and secondary red beds in which coals are thin or absent.

The coal-bearing part of the Westphalian succession generally produces a clear seismic response, with well-defined, subparallel, high-amplitude, high-frequency seismic reflectors (Jackson et al., 1995). The upper parts, in which coals are generally absent, produce a less distinct seismic response owing to the less well-defined acoustic impedance contrasts. The group can be resolved clearly on seismic sections below the base Permo–Triassic unconformity using these characteristics and it is clear that Westphalian successions are present quite extensively beneath the East Irish Sea in the Lagman and Eubonia basins (see seismic section in Figure 14c), on the Ogham Platform, and in the Quadrant 109 Syncline (see Jackson et al., 1995). A Westphalian succession is also locally present in the central part of the Solway Basin and may also occur in the Peel Basin (Jackson et al., 1995).

The depositional environments that characterised the Westphalian Stage are well established for this area and it is known that sedimentation took place on a broad deltaic plain, where distributary channels of varying sinuosities and dimensions crossed the delta plain. These channels fed and infilled large lakes via crevasse splay and lacustrine delta systems (see Guion and Fielding, 1988; Jones, 1992; Guion et al., 1995). The extensive peat mires that developed on these abandoned and infilled areas have produced, in many cases, economic coal seams. These deltaic sequences formed repetitive cycles in which coals and poorly drained palaeosols (seatearths) formed the top of each cycle (equivalent to the 'cyclothem' of older literature). However, these cycles differ from Yoredale cycles because they lack the predictable vertical facies stacking pattern in which marine sedimentary rocks at the base are overlain by progressively more non-marine and coarser grained siliciclastic deltaic lithologies. The Westphalian cycles tend to have a more random facies stacking pattern that can be explained by autocyclical controls on sedimentation, such as localised, compaction-generated lake formation and delta lobe and channel switching events (Guion and Fielding, 1988).

Periodic glacio-eustatically driven sea level rises drowned the delta plain and established temporary marine conditions. Low-energy conditions led to the deposition of marine mudstones known as marine bands. These were particularly common during early Langsettian times, with up to five marine bands known from the Cumbrian succession (Ramsbottom et al., 1978). It therefore appears that lower delta plain conditions were prevalent at this time, subsequently evolving to form an upper delta plain (Guion and Fielding, 1988). Marine bands are uncommon in the rest of the Westphalian succession, although the base of the Duckmantian and Bolsovian stages are defined on the occurrence of the Vanderbeckei and Aegiranum marine bands, respectively, both of which are known from Cumbria.

Westphalian strata are recorded in boreholes from the northern part of the Isle of Man and northwards into the Solway Basin where they are present in the centre of the basin and across to west Cumbria and Canonbie. On the Ogham Platform, Well 112/30-1 proved up to 425 m of strata of probable Langsettian age, from 126 to 551 m RKB). The Westphalian succession is reddened in parts and comprises fine- to medium-grained sandstone with minor reddish brown and dark greyish red claystone and siltstone (Lomas and Neville, 1976). A number of low-density spikes occur in the succession above 658 m RKB and probably represent coal seams. Thick sandstones are common between 468 and 563 m RKB. Two high API gamma-ray peaks occur at 467 and 551 m RKB, and are interpreted as highly radioactive condensed marine flooding surfaces; the lower one may represent the Subcrenatum Marine Band which marks the base of the Westphalian (Jackson et al., 1995). The upper one is tentatively identified as the Listeri or even the Amaliae Marine Band (Jackson et al., 1995). The resolution of the palynology for this well is not high enough to confirm these interpretations. Alternative interpretations:

- place the base of the Westphalian at 584.9 m RKB
- group the G1 basal Westphalian succession with the top Namurian R2 Zone, and define its base at 891 m RKB.

Farther to the south, Well 113/27-1 proved about 120 m of Langsettian strata (Jackson et al., 1997), and Owens (1988b) has recognised a Langsettian to late Namurian succession below the Permian in Well 113/26-1.

Little is known of the uppermost parts of the Westphalian succession offshore, although Bolsovian to Westphalian D red-bed successions are inferred to be present in the Eubonia Basin (see Figure 14c) and Cantabrian to Stephanian strata may be present in the central parts of Quadrant 109 Syncline (Jackson and Mulholland, 1993). Onshore in west Cumbria, a change in depositional style can be detected in the upper Bolsovian sequence, with thick, reddened, coarse-grained fluvial sand bodies forming the Whitehaven Sandstone Formation (Akhurst et al., 1997). Primary red beds are known from the Crookdale Borehole in Cumbria with a fauna indicative of the Westphalian D Tenuis Zone (Eastwood et al., 1968; Taylor et al., 1971). The uppermost parts of the Westphalian succession in Cumbria are termed the Millyeat Beds Member (Akhurst et al., 1997). At Canonbie, sedimentation seems to have been of a similar style to that of the rest of the basin (Kirk, 1983), with up to 1400 m of Langsettian to Westphalian D sedimentary rocks present. Upper Coal Measures sedimentary rocks are reddened, and the presence of calcrete palaeosols and *Spirorbis*-bearing lacustrine limestones indicates that a change towards a more seasonally arid climate may have occurred, with primary reddening of sediments.

6 Permian

INTRODUCTION TO PERMIAN AND MESOZOIC DEPOSITION

Permian to Jurassic rocks of the offshore Isle of Man region have been a neglected topic in studies of the United Kingdom continental shelf because of the scarcity of well information, and in spite of shared links to Permian–Jurassic basins in four directions (Figures 1, 12b). Permian to Lower Jurassic successions proved in petroleum wells (Figures 2, 13), drilled recently in the Isle of Man area† infill a gap in the offshore database and form the basis of chapters 6 and 7.

The Permo–Triassic succession of the Isle of Man area comprises two megasequences of terrestrial, marginal marine and evaporitic strata, overlain by the lowest beds of a marine megasequence of uppermost Triassic to Lower Jurassic strata (Figure 13). During Permian to Early Jurassic times, a unified Isle of Man depositional area was contiguous with the East Irish Sea Basin, but the strata laid down during this interval are now preserved only in large erosional outliers in discrete basins (North Channel, Peel, Solway Firth, and East Irish Sea basins, Figure 12b). The entire succession shows continuous overlap, except probably for a brief contraction in the depositional area during the period when the Ormskirk Sandstone Formation was laid down; however, post-Permian overlap is only seen outside the Isle of Man area at the present-day. Although the well database is relatively small, a definite pattern can usually be observed amongst the various basins, in the comparative thicknesses of individual formations and members. The greatest thicknesses generally occur in either the East Irish Sea Basin (especially Well 113/26-1 in the Keys Basin) or the North Channel Basin (Well 111/15-1), followed by the Solway Firth Basin. Thicknesses decrease towards the Isle of Man massif (Well 112/19-1) and are lowest in the Peel Basin (especially in Well 111/29-1). Thicknesses of the evaporitic Upper Permian and Middle to Upper Triassic successions north of the Ramsey–Whitehaven Ridge (BGS, 1994) are comparable with those of the mudstone-dominated lateral equivalents in the southern part of the East Irish Sea Basin, rather than with the much thicker evaporite successions in the adjacent northern part of the East Irish Sea Basin.

The Permian, Triassic and Jurassic rocks are entirely concealed beneath thick Quaternary deposits, both offshore and on the Isle of Man. Onshore, Permo–Triassic deposits are confined to the drift-covered northern plain of the Isle of Man, where their presence was first reported by Boyd Dawkins (1894). Much of our knowledge of the onshore Isle of Man succession stems from Lamplugh (1903), who, following Boyd Dawkins' work, discussed the geology of six boreholes that prove various parts of the sequence, and compiled a map of the Permo–Triassic subcrop beneath the Quaternary deposits. Additional onshore information is provided by a borehole drilled between 1904 and 1907 at the Point of Ayre (Gregory, 1920), and also at Cranstal in 1987 (location on Figure 2; Quirk and Kimbell, 1997, fig. 9). Offshore, the presence of Permo–Triassic strata was first predicted by Dickinson (*in* Boyd Dawkins, 1894).

The Isle of Man region is now seen to have played a pivotal role as a gateway in providing interbasinal links in the Permian to Early Jurassic geological evolution of the British Isles. The Bakevellia transgressions of the Late Permian (Smith and Taylor, 1992) and the Röt transgression of the Triassic encroached on the area from the north-west, passing through the North Channel, and veering eastwards towards north-west England and southwards to the Cheshire Basin. In the Early Triassic, the north-flowing Budleighensis River adopted a similar course, but in the reverse direction, following an abrupt and major lowering of base level. A regional reversal in palaeoslope occurred probably during the latest Anisian (mid-Triassic). Subsequently the Rhaetian and Early Jurassic transgressions encroaching from the south are considered here to have advanced via a proto-St George's Channel through the Isle of Man area, along a low-lying gap through the North Channel, finally reaching the Hebrides Basin (Warrington and Ivimey-Cook, 1992; Bradshaw et al., 1992; Morton, 1992).

This account comprises a stratigraphical summary based on detailed wireline log correlations of eight offshore wells (six of which have been drilled since 1993; Figure 13). Tectonic and structural aspects of the Permian to Jurassic basins, and stratigraphical information derived from seismic interpretation, are described in Chapter 4. Regional background information has been kept to a minimum; palaeogeographical reconstructions were produced by Smith and Taylor (1992), Warrington and Ivimey-Cook (1992) and Bradshaw et al. (1992). The Permian to Lower Jurassic geology of the area has been outlined by Fyfe et al. (1993), Jackson et al. (1995) and Newman (1999), while specific topics were covered by Meadows et al. (1997). Wireline log profiles of type sections of the stratigraphical units were illustrated by Jackson and Johnson, (1996); figured wells adjacent to the Manx area also include 110/6b-1 and 113/27-3. Other important sources of information include publications by Lamplugh (1903), Holliday and Rees (1994), Akhurst et al. (1997) and Wilson (1999).

The wireline log motifs and stratigraphical thicknesses of the offshore wells (Figures 21, 23, 24) show that the revised stratigraphical nomenclature originally intended for the East Irish Sea Basin (Jackson and Johnson, 1996) is applicable throughout the Manx area. However, for the North Channel Basin (Portpatrick Sub-basin), the corresponding stratigraphical term from Northern Ireland has been used in this account, unless the unit has not been previously

† Isle of Man area refers to that shown in Figure 1.

recognised in Northern Ireland, in which case the appropriate term from the East Irish Sea Basin has been used as a temporary measure (e.g. Fylde Halite Member equivalent). Warrington et al. (1980, p.28) assigned formation status to the Ballyboley and Carnduff halites of the Mercia Mudstone Group, but they are treated here as members within the Craiganee Formation, as in their formal introduction (Manning and Wilson, 1975). As with many frontier petroleum exploration areas, extensive revision of geological boundaries identified on composite well logs has been necessary to ensure consistent usage of nomenclature and stratigraphy with adjacent basins. Nevertheless, uncertainties remain, and some of the boundaries chosen in chapters 6 and 7 will require modification as further drilling takes place.

PERMIAN

Permian rocks in the area comprise a lower sequence of scattered terrestrial deposits and an upper marine to terrestrial sequence that is more widespread; these were formerly placed in the Lower Permian and the Upper Permian, respectively (see below). The lower sequence consists largely of aeolian sandstone with locally developed alluvial fan breccia (Appleby and Enler groups,). The sequence is overlapped everywhere by an upper sequence of evaporitic and marginal marine to locally aeolian strata (Cumbrian Coast and Belfast groups). The isolated basins of the Appleby and Enler groups were linked by the Bakevellia Sea transgressions into a single area of deposition covering much of the present-day offshore area.

Traditionally, Permian strata of central Britain have been divided into bipartite Lower and Upper Permian series, with the junction placed at the incoming of marine strata (Smith et al., 1974, p.7; Smith and Taylor, 1992, p.87). The International Subcommision on Permian Stratigraphy has recently divided the Permian system into three formal series: Cisuralian (Lower Permian), Guadalupian (Middle Permian) and Lopingian (Upper Permian) (Jin Yu-gan et al., 1997). Following this decision, the use in Britain of the terms Lower Permian (*as applied to* a lower division of clastic rocks, such as the Appleby Group or Rotliegend) and Upper Permian (*as applied to* an upper division of evaporitic rocks, such as the Cumbrian Coast Group or Zechstein) is no longer acceptable (written communication, G Warrington, BGS, February 2001).

A further complication arises, because the former tacit assumption (Smith et al., 1974; Colter, 1978; Arthurton et al., 1978; Jackson and Johnson, 1996; Akhurst et al., 1997) that the barren 'Lower Permian' strata in the Irish Sea area and north-west England were deposited during the early Permian can no longer be sustained. The recently revised dates of Rotliegend successions in the southern North Sea (Glennie, 1998) indicate that the age of the equivalent Appleby and Enler groups must also be refined. Recognition of the Illawarra Magnetic Reversal event (at approximately 262–263 Ma) near the base of the Upper Rotliegend 2 unit in Germany and the southern North Sea, coupled with palynological dating, demonstrates that the traditional 'Lower Permian' aeolian sandstone units (including the Leman Sandstone Formation; Cameron et al., 1992) of the southern North Sea are actually of early Tatarian age (Late Guadalupian) (i.e. latest Mid-Permian rather than Early Permian; Glennie, 1998, pp.139, 157; Jin Yu-gan et al., 1997, p.13, figs 2, 3). The Enler and Appleby groups, including the Collyhurst Sandstone Formation (a correlative of the Leman Sandstone Formation), must similarly be regarded as early Tatarian (Late Guadalupian) in age, though they probably extend up into the earliest Lopingian (Jin Yu-gan et al., 1997, fig. 3).

APPLEBY AND ENLER GROUPS

These are the oldest Permian rocks in the Isle of Man area (assigned to the Lower Permian *in* Smith et al., 1974; Arthurton et al., 1978; Smith and Taylor, 1992, Jackson and Johnson, 1996), and are now believed to be of early Tatarian age (Glennie, 1998). In this report, these mixed aeolian, alluvial fan and fluvial sedimentary rocks in the North Channel Basin (Portpatrick Sub-basin) are referred to the Enler Group and the aeolian-dominated sequence over the remainder of the Isle of Man area is referred to the Appleby Group.

Over most of the area, thin aeolian sands accumulated in small hollows and depressions on a low-lying and gently undulating topography (possibly below sea level, Smith and Taylor, 1992). These areas were floored largely by Dinantian bedrock (Chapter 5), possibly with sedimentation restricted to dolines (sinkholes) and uvalas (coalesced dolines) in a karstic terrain. The depressions were separated by broad hammada (bare rocky desert surfaces), probably covered by a litter of *remanié* stones coated in desert varnish. Thicker aeolian sands were banked against the Ramsey– Whitehaven Ridge, to be deposited as draas (large complex aeolian dunes) in the ergs (sand seas) of the Lagman and Eubonia basins (Jackson and Johnson, 1996). Overlooking these low-lying areas were steep-sided hills of Lower Palaeozoic rocks in the Southern Uplands, Longford–Down Massif and the Isle of Man. In these areas, water-laid deposits (now preserved as fluvial sandstone overlying breccia) were deposited in canyons and on proximal alluvial fans and screes which coalesced to form bajadas (confluent alluvial fans at the base of a mountain range), probably controlled by syndepositional fault movements (e.g. Loch Ryan Fault of the Stranraer Basin; Chapter 4; Brookfield, 1978; Smith and Taylor, 1992). Thicker deposits were laid down by the longer and larger streams flowing south from the Southern Uplands into the basinal area, in contrast with the thinner deposits of the north-flowing streams which originated from the Isle of Man.

Appleby Group

The Appleby Group comprises the aeolian Collyhurst Sandstone Formation over most of the Isle of Man area, together with the poorly known alluvial fan breccias of the Loch Ryan Formation in the Stranraer Basin, and the Brockram equivalent on the Isle of Man.

The group is characterised by very abrupt but local changes in thickness (Chapter 4; Figure 21; Jackson and Johnson, 1996). It is absent or less than 10 m

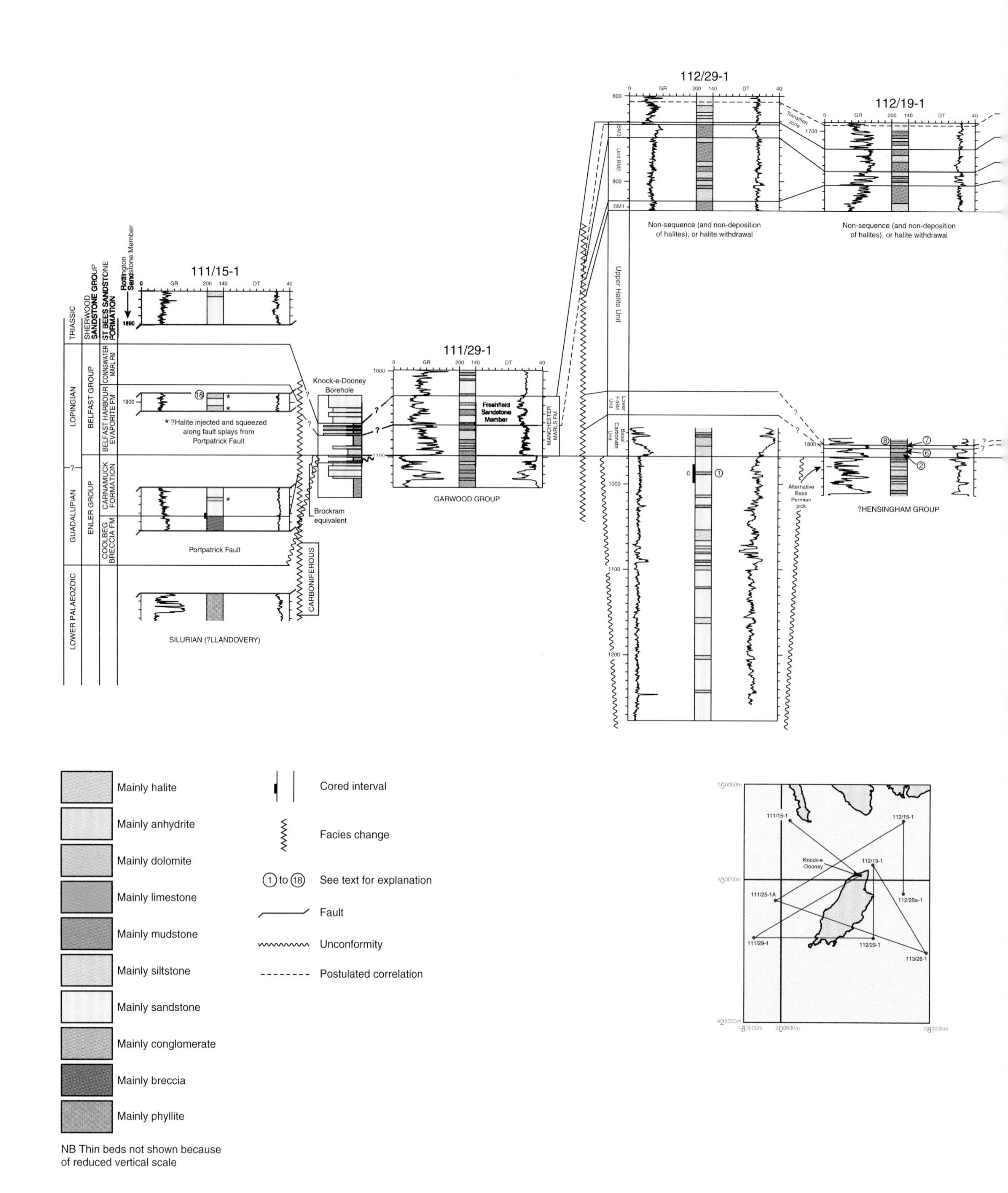

Figure 21 Correlation of wells proving Permian rocks in the Isle of Man area. The figure is tied primarily to the Top Appleby Group (= top Enler Group in Well 111/15-1), but also incorporates a subsidiary tie line on the base Barrowmouth Mudstone Formation. The wells are arranged with the thickest preservation of the St Bees Evaporites Formation on the right, with sequences becoming less evaporitic and more marginal towards the left. The figure is shown in 'exploded view', firstly, to demonstrate the extent of stratigraphical omission in the St Bees Evaporites Formation and its likely cause, and secondly, to facilitate comparison of the internal subdivisions of Barrowmouth Mudstone Formation. See text for further explanation.

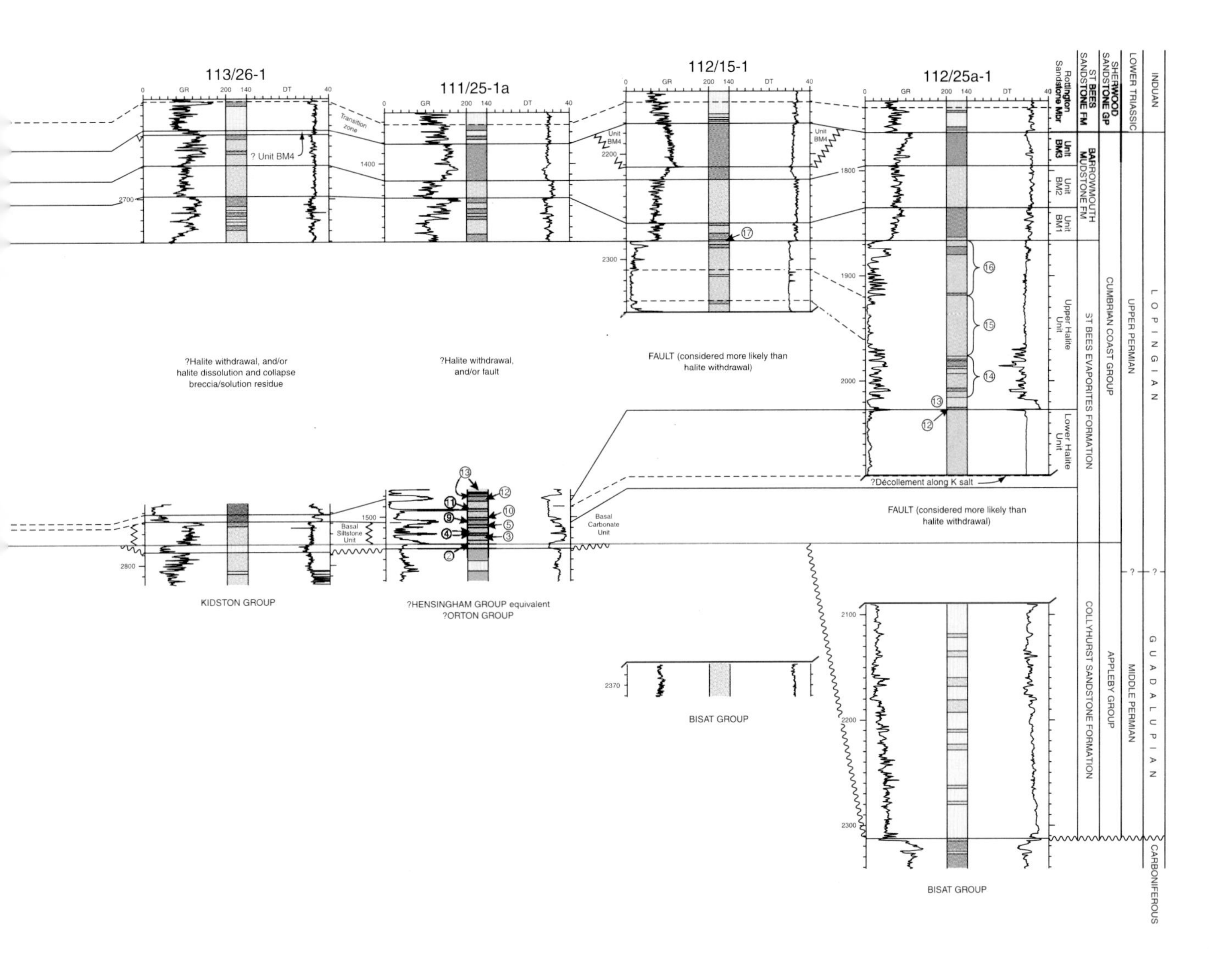

thick over much of the area, though offshore wells to date have been drilled only on structural highs. In basinal areas of low palaeorelief, the widespread absence of the group may be partly related to reduced surface run-off, arising from the development of a karstic topography and underground drainage systems beneath secondarily reddened Dinantian limestone bedrock (Newman 1999, fig. 6; Jackson et al., 1995, fig. 24). It is thought that the Appleby Group was not deposited around wells 112/19-1 and 111/29-1, and is either faulted out or was not deposited around Well 112/15-1 (Figure 21). Lopingian and Triassic sedimentary rocks are commonly well developed in all these basinal areas which suggests that active rifting did not occur at these sites during the Guadalupian, and that new and long-lasting sedimentation patterns were ushered in by the Bakevellia Sea transgressions. The group is also believed to be absent from Well 112/30-1 (Jackson and Johnson, 1996, p.161), though this was disputed by Quirk and Kimbell (1997, figs 13, 17).

In the Isle of Man area, as in the East Irish Sea Basin, drilled successions of the largely aeolian **Collyhurst Sandstone Formation** currently fall into two categories: thin successions, less than 10 m, and much thicker successions, 50 to over 310.3 m (Figure 21). The full succession in the Eubonia Basin is estimated at 700 m from seismic interpretation (Chapter 4). A thick sequence of the formation has not yet been completely penetrated in the area, but partial sections were proved in Well 112/25a-1 (over 222 m, faulted top) and Well 112/29-1 (upper 310.3 m proved). Both wells lie to the north of the Quadrant 109 Arch–High Haume Anticline in a Caledonian-trending depositional belt of the Appleby Group (Jackson and Johnson, 1996, p.127) and in the hanging wall of the Lagman–Eubonia Fault.

In Well 112/25a-1 (Figure 21; Jackson and Johnson, 1996, pp.127, 133) a lower sequence of water-laid sandstone is overlain at 2182 m relative to kelly bushing (RKB) by aeolian sandstone. The lower sandstone is very fine grained with sporadic mudstone and siltstone partings, and was probably deposited in a damp interdune or damp sabkha environment (compare with Herries and Cowan, 1997). The aeolian upper sandstone is mainly fine to medium grained, and shows lower gamma-ray values and lower sonic velocity than the lower sandstone. However, this two-fold division cannot be differentiated along the depositional strike in Well 112/29-1, where the section may lie stratigraphically above the fault postulated in Well 112/25a-1. In Well 112/29-1, red-brown friable sandstone with some quartz grains of high sphericity appears to be interbedded with sporadic but well-developed and well-cemented siltstone. The sublinear log signature is more akin to that of an aeolian (probably interdune), rather than a fluvial, regime, but scattered pebbles (including granite) suggest some water-laid deposits. A matrix-supported conglomerate, 3 m thick, was identified in core between 985.4 and 988.4 m depth, near the top of the succession, and to judge from the nondiagnostic log response (Figure 21, item 1), the proportion of conglomerate may have been underestimated. Thin sequences of low-velocity, aeolian Collyhurst Sandstone Formation are identified in Well 111/25-1A (6 m thick; contrast Newman, 1999) and Well 113/26-1 (7.31 m thick; see Jackson, in press, for further discussion and interpretation).

ONSHORE ISLE OF MAN Unfossiliferous rocks belonging to the Appleby Group occur on the Isle of Man (Figures 1, 21, 22) and were classified by Lamplugh (1903) as the Brockram Series (here termed the **Brockram equivalent**). No suitable stratigraphical name exists at present for these rocks, though they resemble the Basal Breccia of large parts of south and west Cumbria (Arthurton and Hemingway, 1972; Rose and Dunham, 1977). Lamplugh's use of the term Brockram (Akhurst et al., 1997) is retained, together with the suffix 'equivalent'. Following correlation with the offshore wells, the thickness of these rocks in the Knock-e-Dooney Borehole (mostly sandstone overlying conglomerate) has been revised from Lamplugh's account to 8.61 m (193.95–202.56 m), and tentatively revised to 5.94 m (311.38–317.32 m) in the Ballagenney Borehole where the rocks consist mostly of breccia. The two sections show considerable lateral variation, especially in the thickness of individual beds of breccia ('brockram') and in their stratigraphical position (Lamplugh, 1903). A 6 m-thick 'conglomerate' *(sic)* was proved in the recent Cranstal Borehole (location on Figure 2). These records demonstrate that, adjacent to the Isle of Man, a lateral passage takes place from limestone bedrock with no Appleby Group rocks (wells 111/29-1 and 112/19-1), or only a thin aeolian sandstone (Well 111/25-1A), into equally thin, breccia-dominated successions (Figure 21), deposited in areas of greater palaeorelief on the flanks of the Isle of Man massif. The broad distribution of upland areas during deposition of the Appleby Group was thus not dissimilar to that of the present day (Smith and Taylor, 1992).

STRANRAER BASIN The sparse outcrop and borehole information available from the simple half-graben of the Stranraer Basin is currently restricted to deposits of the Appleby Group (Brookfield, 1978; Stone, 1988, 1995). The basin deepens to the south-east (Mansfield and Kennett, 1963; Bott, 1964) and the bounding Loch Ryan Fault has a maximum throw of 1525 m (Bott, 1964; Kelling and Welsh, 1970).

The most continuous record is from the Stranraer isthmus where the West Freugh Borehole penetrated the **Loch Ryan Formation**, which is composed of coarse, alluvial fan breccia (over 134 m thick, top is not seen), overlying an unbottomed 24 m-thick sandstone (Stone, 1988, 1995). This exceeds the thickness of breccia in the Appleby Group proved elsewhere in the area. The breccia, which was deposited largely from southward-flowing debris flows and sheetfloods, contains predominantly locally derived Ordovician greywacke clasts. Heavy mineral analyses indicate an additional Carboniferous component which is confirmed by scarce Carboniferous clasts (Brookfield, 1978). The borehole location, together with the isopachs of Mansfield and Kennett (1963), suggests that these rudaceous deposits are at least 300 m thick and extend offshore into the Luce Bay sub-basin. This expanded thickness reflects a position in the hanging walls of both the Loch Ryan and Cairnholy faults (Figures 12b, 16a; Stone, 1995; Kelling and Welsh, 1970).

The formation is regarded here as an approximate lateral equivalent of the Penrith Brockram of the Vale of Eden and of the Coolbeg Breccia Formation (see below). The facies is more akin to the successions of southern Scotland (Brookfield, 1978), Ballantrae (Stone, 1988), the Newtownards Trough (Smith et al., 1991), Larne (Penn et al., 1983) and probably the North Channel Basin (especially adjacent to the Portpatrick Fault), than to the predominantly aeolian successions seen elsewhere in the Appleby Group, and reflects proximity to contemporaneous uplands of Lower Palaeozoic strata. The likely presence in the Stranraer Basin of Permo–Triassic rocks younger than the Appleby Group is discussed by Jackson (in press).

WIGTOWN BAY Strata of the Appleby Group, probably rudaceous and similar to but thinner than those of the Stranraer Basin, are likely to be present in Wigtown Bay (BGS, 1994).

Enler Group

In Northern Ireland, the Enler Group (Smith et al., 1991) is the equivalent of the Appleby Group, and generally comprises a breccia (Coolbeg Breccia Formation) overlain by a sandstone (the water-laid Carnamuck Formation of the Isle of Man area; Table 4). The Enler Group occurs in the North Channel Basin of the report area.

The alluvial fan breccia of the **Coolbeg Breccia Formation** (Smith, 1986; Smith et al., 1991) is thought to have been proved in Well 111/15-1 where it displays moderately high gamma-ray values which are probably caused by the feldspathic sand matrix (as in the thick Enler Group breccias of the Larne No. 2 Borehole, Penn et al., 1983, p.341). The breccia is 18.9 m thick (1943.12–1962.0 m RKB) in the well where it is faulted against Lower Palaeozoic phyllite by the Portpatrick Fault or an associated splay (Figures 16a, 21). Crystal-lithic tuff that numerically dominates the breccia clasts is probably related genetically to the thick, presumed Guadalupian volcanic sequence proved in the Larne No. 2 Borehole, and to similar lavas in southern Scotland (Brookfield, 1978). The dominant clast lithology thus differs from that of the Loch Ryan Formation, but in each case reflects the local bedrock upslope; a similar environment of deposition to the Brockram of west Cumbria is envisaged (Akhurst et al., 1997, fig. 30a).

In a modified interpretation of the above, British Gas (composite log) positioned the breccia at the base of a thick undifferentiated 'Lower Permian' (i.e. Enler Group) sandstone sequence (1579.19–1962.0 m RKB; but see p.85). A third, more radical interpretation is that the alluvial fan breccia is a component part of the Rottington Sandstone Member in which clasts

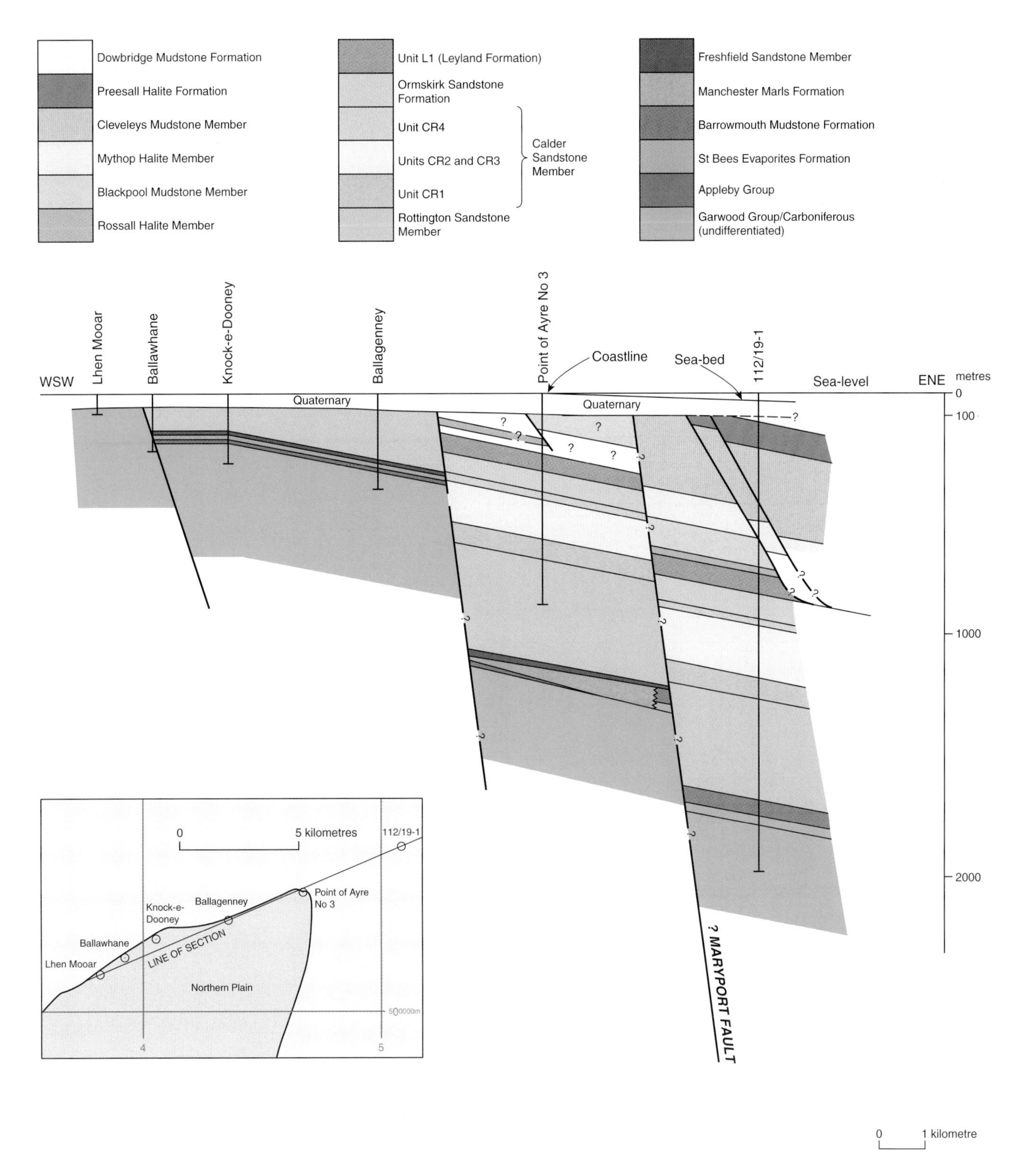

Figure 22 Cross-section through the boreholes at the northern end of the Isle of Man and across to Well 112/19-1 (extensively modified from Lamplugh, 1903 and Gregory, 1920). The figure is based on the following assumptions:

(i) in contrast to the Peel Basin, the Ormskirk Sandstone Formation is present on the Isle of Man
(ii) the Sherwood Sandstone Group succession in both Point of Ayre No. 3 and Well 112/19-1 is unfaulted
(iii) the depth differences of the top Rottington Sandstone Member in Point of Ayre No. 3 and Well 112/19-1 are accounted for by the extension of the Maryport Fault passing between Point of Ayre No. 3 and Well 112/19-1, rather than by an abrupt steepening of the dip
(iv) there is some thinning of all stratigraphical horizons towards the Isle of Man massif

The cross-section has not been checked against seismic profiles; if the fault between Ballagenney and Point of Ayre does not exist, then the regional dip corresponds to 14°, and if there is no fault between Point of Ayre and Well 112/19-1, then the regional dip is 7°.

System	Stage	Group	Formation	Member	Formation	Member	Formation	Member	Formation	Group	Formation	Member	Group	Formation	Member
Jurassic	Hettangian	Lias Group	Lower Lias	*undivided*	Not preserved		Lower Lias	*undivided*	Lower Lias *undivided*	Lias Group	Lower Lias	*undivided*	Lias Group	Penda Formation	*Unit P2*
				'Pre-Planorbis' Beds				*'Pre-Planorbis' Beds*	*'Pre-Planorbis' Beds*			*'Pre-Planorbis' Beds*			*Unit P1*
Triassic	Rhaetian	Penarth Group	Lilstock Formation				Lilstock Formation		Lilstock Formation	Penarth Group	Lilstock Formation		Penarth Group	*Upper Division*	
			Westbury Formation				Westbury Formation		Westbury Formation		Westbury Formation			*Lower Division*	
		Mercia Mudstone Group	Blue Anchor Formation				Blue Anchor Formation		Blue Anchor Formation	Mercia Mudstone Group	Collin Glen Formation		Haisborough Group	Triton Formation	
	Norian		Elswick Mudstone Formation						Brooks Mill Mudstone Formation		Port More Formation, Knocksoghey Formation				
	Carnian		Warton Halite Formation		Breckells Mudstone Formation	*mudstone collapse breccia*	Stanwix Shales		Wilkesley Halite Formation		Glenstaghey Formation	*?Larne Halite Member*		Dudgeon Formation	*Keuper Halite Member*
	Ladinian		Dowbridge Mudstone Formation						Wych Mdst Fm on Byley Mdst Fm						
			Preesall Halite Formation		Kirkham Mudstone Formation	*Preesall Salt Member*		*Preesall Salt*	Northwich Halite Formation			*Larne Halite Member*		Dowsing Formation	*Muschelkalk Halite Member*
	Anisian		Leyland Formation (*Units L1, L2*)	*Cleveleys Mudstone Member (Units CM1, 2, 3)*					Bollin Mudstone Formation		Craiganee Formation				
				Mythop Halite Member (Units MH1, 2, 3)	Singleton Mudstone Formation	*Mythop Salt Member*						*Carnduff Halite Member*			
				Blackpool Mudstone Member											
				Rossall Halite Member		*Rossall Salt Member*						*Ballyboley Halite Member*			
				Ansdell Mudstone Member					Tarporley Siltstone Formation		Lagavarra Formation				*Röt Halite Member*
				Fylde Halite Member	Hambleton Mudstone Formation										
				Stanah Member											
	Olenekian	Sherwood Sandstone Group	Ormskirk Sandstone Formation (*Units OS1, 2*)		Ormskirk Sandstone Formation		Kirklinton Sandstone Formation		Helsby Sandstone Formation	Sherwood Sandstone Group	Absent		Bacton Group	Absent	
	–?—?–		St Bees Sandstone Formation	*Calder Sandstone Member (Units CR1, 2, 3, 4)*	Calder Sandstone Formation		St Bees Sandstone Formation		Wilmslow Sandstone Formation		Sherwood Sandstone Group (*undivided*)			Bunter Sandstone Formation	
	Induan			*Rottington Sandstone Member*	St Bees Sandstone Formation				Chester Pebble Beds Formation					Bunter Shale Formation	
Lopingian (Upper Permian)	Tatarian	Cumbrian Coast Group	Barrowmouth Mdst Fmn (*Units BM1, 2, 3*)		St Bees Shale Formation		Eden Shales			Belfast Group	Connswater Marl Formation				*Bröckelschiefer Member*
			St Bees Evaporites Formation	Freshfield Sandstone Member	St Bees Evaporite Formation (basinal areas) / Manchester Marls Formation (marginal areas)	Absent (?not preserved)			Kinnerton Sandstone Formation		Belfast Harbour Evaporite Formation	Absent (?not preserved)	Zechstein Group	Grenzanhydrit Formation	
														Aller Halite Formation	
														Pegmatitanhydrit Formation	
														Roter Salzton Formation	
			Upper Halite Unit											Leine Halite Formation	
				Manchester Marls Formation		*Fleswick Anhydrite*		*D-Bed*	Manchester Marls Formation			*'B' Anhydrite Member*		Hauptanhydrit Formation	
						Fleswick Dolomite		*Belah Dolomite*				*Avoniel Limestone*		Plattendolomit Formation	
														Grauer Salzton Formation	
						Absent (?not preserved)						*Thick halite in Larne 2*		Stassfurt Halite Formation	
			Lower Halite Unit									*Thin anhydrite in Larne 2*		Basalanhydrit Formation	
														Hauptdolomit Formation	
						Sandwith Anhydrite		*B-Bed*				*'A' Anhydrite Member*		Werraanhydrit Formation	
			Basal Carbonate Unit			*Sandwith Dolomite*								Zechsteinkalk Formation	
	Guadalupian (Middle Permian)		*Basal Siltstone Unit*			*Saltom Siltstone*		*A-Bed*				*'Magnesian Limestone'*		Kupferschiefer Formation	
–?—?–		Appleby Group	Collyhurst Sandstone Formation		Collyhurst Sandstone Formation / Basal Breccia, Brockram		Penrith Sandstone Formation / Penrith Brockram		Collyhurst Sandstone Formation	Enler Group	Carnamuck Formation/Kennel Sandstone Formation / Coolbeg Breccia Formation		Rotliegende Group	Leman Sandstone Formation	

Table 4 Stratigraphical table for the Permian, Triassic and Jurassic rocks of the Isle of Man and adjacent areas. Compiled from Jackson and Johnson, (1996), Johnson et al. (1994), Lott and Knox (1994), Smith (1986) and Smith et al. (1991), and references in the text. Note that in the southern North Sea, the Bröckelschiefer Member is included in the Bacton Group and regarded as Scythian (Induan) in age, whereas west of the Pennines, the equivalent Barrowmouth Mudstone Formation and St Bees Shale Formation are placed in the Cumbrian Coast Group and regarded as Lopingian (Late Permian) in age.

were also derived from the footwall of the Portpatrick Fault (in a similar manner to the supposed Triassic breccia in the Cranstal Borehole, Chapter 7).

Undifferentiated Enler Group sandstone (incorporating 'beds' of halite near the base) was recognised by British Gas between 1579.19 and 1943.12 m RKB in Well 111/15-1, overlying the breccia. Although there are both stratigraphical and structural ambiguities in the bottom part of this well, which are not conclusively resolved by seismic data, much of this interval is referred here to the Rottington Sandstone Member (Figure 23; Chapter 7). However, assuming that the contact between the breccia and the overlying sandstone is unfaulted, and that the 'beds' of halite originate from the Belfast Group evaporite (see below) and comprise steeply dipping veins lining minor splay faults, then the interpretation preferred here is that the interval from approximately 1896.49 to 1943.12 m RKB consists of fault-bounded screens of Enler Group sandstone (**Carnamuck Formation**, Smith et al., 1991). This dark red-brown silty fluvial sandstone with mudstone partings, possesses a hematite-rich matrix and a pervasive calcite or, more rarely, silica, cement. The explanation is, however, inconclusive because the lithology and log response of the sandstone are largely indistinguishable from those of the fluvial sandstone of the Rottington Sandstone Member (above 1896.49 m RKB in this interpretation). An alternative view is that the sandstone from approximately 1896.49 to 1943.12 m RKB belongs to the Rottington Sandstone Member, and is juxtaposed against a fault sliver of Coolbeg Breccia Formation.

CUMBRIAN COAST AND BELFAST GROUPS

The youngest Permian rocks were formerly labelled 'Upper Permian' in the Isle of Man region. They are of late Tatarian age (Glennie, 1998), and are assigned to the Cumbrian Coast Group over most of the area, or to the equivalent Belfast Group in the North Channel Basin (Portpatrick Sub-basin). The Appleby and Enler groups were overlapped everywhere by the deposits of the Cumbrian Coast and Belfast groups during the first Bakevellia Sea transgression. It has long been argued (Smith and Taylor, 1992 and references therein) that the entry point for the multiple Bakevellia Sea transgressions of the Lopingian, from the Boreal Ocean into the East Irish Sea and Cheshire basins, was via a sinuous 'north-west passage' along the present-day North Channel and through the Solway Firth. The distribution and facies of Lopingian evaporites proved in the recent offshore wells of the area strengthen these arguments.

The postulated identification of an equivalent of the Grenzanhydrit Formation of the southern North Sea (Table 4; Cameron et al., 1992) at the top of the St Bees Evaporites Formation further supports the idea that the Barrowmouth Mudstone Formation and equivalent strata in the Bakevellia Sea Basin are younger than the entire Zechstein succession of the southern North Sea and are equivalent to the basal Triassic Bröckelschiefer Member (Holliday, 1993a; see discussion in Jackson and Johnson, 1996, pp.99, 102). However in this account, for convenience of description and in the absence of biostratigraphical evidence, the Permian–Triassic boundary is taken at the top of the Barrowmouth Mudstone Formation and at the top of the Manchester Marls Formation, rather than, as in the southern North Sea, at the base of the correlative Bröckelschiefer Member (Table 4; Johnson et al., 1994).

Cumbrian Coast Group

The Cumbrian Coast Group is separated from the Appleby Group by a non-sequence (Arthurton and Hemingway, 1972; Jackson and Johnson, 1996) in wells 111/25-1A, 112/29-1 and 113/26-1. In Well 112/19-1 the lower contact is probably unconformable on, rather than faulted against, Carboniferous strata. The remaining offshore wells have faulted contacts with the Appleby and Enler groups or Carboniferous rocks (Figure 21).

Two broad facies belts have been identified in the Cumbrian Coast Group in the Isle of Man region. In the more rapidly subsiding basinal areas and in hanging wall sites, the evaporites of the St Bees Evaporites Formation (150–250 m thick) are overlain by the silty mudstone of the Barrowmouth Mudstone Formation (70–100 m thick) interpreted as coastal plain deposits. The evaporite zone (Jackson and Johnson, 1996, p.109) is thought to have occupied the axis of a narrow waterway (Bakevellia Sea Basin) that stretched from the East Irish Sea Basin, through the Solway Firth Basin and the straits of the North Channel Basin, past Northern Ireland and beyond to the Boreal Ocean (Smith and Taylor, 1992). This inner facies belt was bordered by an outer zone of more slowly subsiding mud-flats, in which an upward succession of marginal marine, estuarine and distal floodplain mudstones of the Manchester Marls Formation (approximately 70 m thick; Jackson and Johnson, 1996, p.115) were deposited, commonly with an aeolian or water-laid sandstone at the top (Freshfield Sandstone Member). The mud-flat facies has been recognised in Well 111/29-1 in the Peel Basin (Newman, 1999), and in Well 110/6b-1 just outside the Isle of Man area (Jackson and Johnson, 1996, p.115), and was more extensive on the south side of the waterway than on the north.

Regional considerations suggest that two proximal facies belts also occur in the area, though they have not yet been proved in offshore wells. An arenaceous aeolian facies, which is laterally equivalent to the upper part of the Kinnerton Sandstone Formation (Evans et al., 1993; Jackson et al., 1995), probably accumulated in topographically favourable areas with a low water table, proximal to the Manchester Marls Formation. The Freshfield Sandstone Member thickens progressively towards such areas (Jackson and Johnson, 1996, p.118). A rudaceous facies, comparable with the Newforte Breccia Formation of the Newtownards Trough (Smith et al., 1991) and the Brockram of west Cumbria (Akhurst et al., 1997; Rose and Dunham, 1977), occurred as breccio-conglomeratic screes and alluvial fans in the more hilly areas of Lower Palaeozoic bedrock and possibly also in the Stranraer Basin and Wigtown Bay.

The **St Bees Evaporites Formation** is a basinal evaporite facies that is dominantly halitic in distal and hanging wall settings, but passes to anhydritic and dolomitic preservation in more proximal and footwall settings. The formation was deposited during successive transgressive–regressive cycles of the Bakevellia Sea, and is overlain by the Barrowmouth Mudstone Formation. As in the East Irish Sea Basin (Jackson and Johnson, 1996), the formation can be subdivided in the Isle of Man area into a thin Basal Siltstone or Carbonate Unit, overlain by a thicker Lower Halite Unit of clean halite, which in turn is overlain by an Upper Halite Unit containing numerous thin mudstone beds and partings (Figure 21). The formation was identified by Newman (1999) in wells 111/25-1A and 112/19-1. Depositional settings appropriate for the Basal Carbonate Unit, and for anhydrite in the halite units were illustrated by Akhurst et al. (1997, figs 30b, c).

The evaporites have been subjected to extensive halokinetic disruption (including possible salt withdrawal), faulting along detachments and mild pillowing (Chapter 4, Figures 14a, c, 17). Most preserved sequences now represent a fragmented succession, but one which retains the correct stratigraphical order (Figure 21). The maximum original thickness for the formation is likely to have been about 150 m in the Solway Firth and Peel basins (compared with 180–350 m in the East Irish Sea Basin). No well in the Isle of Man area has proved the full sequence, but the thickest and most complete section is preserved in Well 112/25a-1 (where it is 225.0 m thick, with a faulted base). The successions proved in the six wells appear vastly different at first sight (Figure 21), but by acknowledging the extreme lateral persistence of individual beds in the halite units and by comparing with the complete succession preserved locally in the East Irish Sea Basin (Jackson and Johnson, 1996), the approximate thickness and evaporitic profile of certain wells in the area can be reconstructed. Detailed correlations demonstrate that the halite sequences drilled in wells 112/15-1 and 111/25-1A, although superficially similar, actually belong to different halite units within the formation (Figure 21). Several of the preserved sections (e.g. in wells 112/19-1, 112/29-1 and 111/25-1A) resemble the onshore type section of the formation near St Bees Head, Cumbria (Arthurton and Hemingway, 1972), in that halite is absent because of dissolution, nondeposition, or salt withdrawal; the preserved sequence consists merely of the basal transgressive anhydrite and dolomite beds from one or more cycles.

The full succession also bears close similarities with the Zechstein evaporite sequence of the southern North Sea (Johnson et al., 1994; Jackson and Johnson, 1996, p.108). Although the Bakevellia succession is much thinner, equivalents of many of the dolomite, anhydrite and halite formations in cycles Z1–Z5 can be recognised (Table 4; see Jackson, in press, for discussion and detailed correlations with the southern North Sea and St Bees Head sequences). Sidewall cores from 1503 to 1509 m RKB in Well 111/25-1A (uppermost Basal Carbonate Unit and basal Lower Halite Unit) yielded a rich, but poorly preserved palynomorph assemblage. The assemblage is similar to those occurring in Z1 sequences of the southern North Sea (Newman, 1999) and is of earliest Lopingian age. It contains bisaccate pollen, with abundant to common specimens of *Lueckisporites virkkiae*, *L. parvus*, *Jugasporites* spp., *Limitisporites* spp. and *Lunatisporites* sp., together with scarce *Vittatina* spp. A similar, rich, assemblage, including *L. virkkiae,* was also recovered from sidewall cores between 1802 and 1812 m RKB in Well 112/19-1.

The **Basal Siltstone Unit** is thought to have been deposited preferentially in distal locations. In Well 113/26-1, the unit (21.64 m, true vertical thickness in this deviated well) consists of a grey and green-grey, locally dolomitic, siltstone, fining upwards to mudstone at the top (Figure 21). The **Basal Carbonate Unit** is thickened preferentially in basin margin locations (Arthurton and Hemingway, 1972; Akhurst et al., 1997, fig. 31) but was also well developed over offshore shoal areas and footwall blocks (Jackson and Johnson, 1996); it is believed to pass laterally into the Basal Siltstone Unit. The individual carbonate and anhydrite beds in the Basal Carbonate Unit are correlated by Jackson (in press) with the various elements of the Saltom, Sandwith and Fleswick cycles at St Bees Head (Table 4).

In Well 111/25-1A, the basal bed of the Basal Carbonate Unit comprises a 3.75 m-thick grey anhydritic siltstone (item 2, Figure 21). This passes gradually upwards into a 5 m-thick, grey to black anhydritic and argillaceous dolomite that becomes more carbonate-rich upwards and displays a distinctive gamma-ray log profile (item 3). This dolomite is overlain by a thin sequence of alternating mudstone and anhydritic dolomite (item 4). The succession is capped by a 4.5 m-thick anhydrite, split into two leaves (item 5; see Jackson, in press, for a bed-by-bed correlation with the sequence at St Bees Head). A similar sequence, albeit twice as thick as that of Well 111/25-1A, occurs in Well 112/29-1 and individual gamma-ray log spikes can be matched (Figure 21), though the record is partly equivocal and the composite log is at variance with the cuttings description.

In Well 112/19-1, the base of the formation is here revised upwards from that shown on the composite log (and in Newman, 1999, fig. 8), and in this chapter is placed at 1814.25 m RKB (rather than 1824.5 m RKB), at the base of a 4.5 m-thick grey, pyritic, anhydritic and dolomitic mudstone (item 2, Figure 21 and with a similar log profile to that in Well 112/29-1). The underlying red and orange-brown dolomite (with chert) and dolomitic mudstone are regarded here as secondarily reddened 'Yoredale facies' of the Carboniferous succession. Correlations are inconclusive in the remainder of the succession, but the 4.5 m-thick mudstone is overlain successively by 3 m of greyish brown dolomite, 6.5 m of dolomitic mudstone and a 7 m-thick bipartite anhydrite (items 6, 7, 8 respectively). The upper two items are thought to equate to the Fleswick Cycle of Cumbria. The basal dolomite is also thought to have been proved in Well 112/30-1 (Jackson and Johnson, 1996, p.161).

The Basal Siltstone Unit was proved in the BGS shallow offshore boreholes 73/54 and 72/74, and the Saltom Dolomite was proved in Borehole 72/74. The Sandwith Anhydrite and the Sandwith Dolomite were cored in BGS Borehole 72/74 (Table 4; Figure 2; BGS, 1994; Wilkinson and Halliwell, 1979; Jackson et al., 1995, p.52, fig. 41).

In the Isle of Man area, the basal beds of the **Lower Halite Unit** are considered here to have been proved only in Well 111/25-1A, where they comprise a 4 m-thick, high gamma-ray value greyish black mudstone (item 9, Figure 21; equivalent to the Hauptdolomit Formation, Z2, of the southern North Sea, Johnson et al., 1994), overlain by a 1 m-thick anhydrite bed (item 10). Three anhydrite beds occur in the lower part of the St Bees Evaporites Formation in Well 111/25-1A, and, by analogy with the southern North Sea, this 1 m-thick highest anhydrite is interpreted as an equivalent of the Basalanhydrit (Z2; Table 4). The Basalanhydrit equivalent is overlain by a clean halite (14.75 m thick) bisected by a median mudstone parting that displays a very high gamma-ray value and possibly includes impure potassium salts (item 11). In character and stratigraphical position, the latter closely resembles the similar median parting in the much thicker Lower Halite Unit of Well 113/27-3 (Jackson and Johnson, 1996, p.109). The upper half of the Lower Halite Unit has also been drilled in the much thicker succession of Well 112/25a-1 (63.5 m thick, with a faulted base); the lower half is thought to be faulted out by a detachment that soles out on the median mudstone (Figure 21; Jackson and Johnson, 1996, p.133). The pre-fault thickness of the St Bees Evaporites Formation is estimated as approximately 85 m in Well 111/25-1A (including the Upper Halite Unit, which is largely faulted out), approximately 270 m in Well 112/25a-1, and approximately 180 m in Well 112/15-1.

The **Upper Halite Unit** was postulated to equate with the combined Leine (Z3) and Aller (Z4; Table 4) cycles of the southern North Sea by Jackson and Johnson (1996, p.108). The unit is believed to be complete in Well 112/25a-1 (103.3 m thick; Jackson and Johnson, 1996, Panel 4), whereas in the closely similar but thinner succession of Well 112/15-1 (67.36 m thick, with a faulted base), the lower part is missing beneath a detachment developed at a mudstone parting. In Well 112/25a-1, the succession begins with a basal, very high gamma-ray value mudstone parting (2.25 m thick, item 12, Figure 21), correlated with the Grauer Salzton Formation (Z3) of the southern North Sea by Jackson and Johnson (1996, p.108; Johnson et al., 1994). It is overlain by a 9 m-thick anhydrite (item 13) with a distinctive 'wedge-shaped' sonic log profile of upward decreasing velocity (compare with wells 113/27-3 and 110/3b-4, in Jackson and Johnson, 1996, pp.109, 133). In Well 111/25-1A, the Grauer Salzton equivalent is thicker (5.5 m) than in 112/25a-1, and is overlain, successively, by thin beds of mudstone, dolomite, and anhydrite that jointly exhibit a similar wedge-shaped sonic log profile to the equivalents in Well 112/25a-1.

The remainder of the Upper Halite Unit in Well 112/25a-1 can be divided into three sub-equal sections (items 14, 15, 16, Figure 21) comprising lower and upper sections of alternating halite and mudstone separated by a clean halite. The middle and upper sections have counterparts in Well 112/15-1 (see tie lines on Figure 21). In Well 112/15-1, the topmost bed comprises an anhydrite cap approximately 1 m-thick (item 17; also present in Well 113/27-3, Jackson and Johnson, 1996, p.109) interpreted here as an equivalent of the Grenzanhydrit Formation, Z5 (Johnson et al., 1994). As in Well 112/25a-1, this anhydrite is overlain abruptly by the Barrowmouth Mudstone Formation. Well 113/26-1 preserves an anomalous sequence spanning the interval between the Basal Siltstone Unit and the Barrowmouth Mudstone Formation, and is interpreted as a solution or collapse 'breccia' and halite residue (20.73 m thick; Jackson and Johnson, 1996, pp.106, 109) that is otherwise unknown in the wider Irish Sea area.

The preceding account suggests that all successions of the St Bees Evaporites Formation in the area are either faulted or halokinetically disrupted. Sequences can be divided into those with thick halites and no carbonates ('bottom absent' successions, where the halites are thought to be riding on a *décollement*), and the more common 'top absent' successions, which contain one or more preserved carbonates but no, or only thin, overlying halite (Figure 21). The absence of halite in the latter type of sequence is probably the result of a variety of causes, such as: a condensed succession with non-sequences, non-deposition of halite and restricted depositional area during evaporative drawdown (Warren, 1999), and halite withdrawal at basinal locations. A more detailed discussion of this subject is provided by Jackson (in press), together with the implied halite distribution in the Isle of Man area in relation to the gravity-sliding model of Penge et al. (1999).

The **Barrowmouth Mudstone Formation** (formerly the St Bees Shales of the offshore East Irish Sea Basin, Jackson and Johnson, 1996, p.101) has been identified by Newman (1999) in wells 111/25-1A and 112/19-1. Remarkably, given the halokinetic complexities of, and stratigraphical omission in, the underlying St Bees Evaporites Formation and the implications of rift–raft tectonics and the gravity sliding model of Penge et al. (1999), the Barrowmouth Mudstone Formation appears to be unfaulted in all six wells from three basins in the Isle of Man area (Figure 21). Thus it can be regarded as the basal layer of the 'Sherwood Sandstone Group raft' of Penge et al. (1999). There is a low variation in thickness in recorded offshore penetrations (from 72 m in Well 112/19-1 to 109.7 m in Well 112/15-1), and the four highest values range from only 100.58 m (in Well 112/29-1) to 109.7 m. The beds were deposited as a relatively uniform blanket, thinning slightly north-westwards and also towards the Isle of Man massif. However, a dramatic thinning takes place from Well 112/19-1 to the Isle of Man boreholes (Figure 22; see below).

There are two types of succession. First, the three wells in the East Irish Sea Basin (113/26-1, 112/25a-1 and 112/29-1) and Well 112/15-1, show the typical tripartite succession of argillaceous and upward-fining Units BM1 and BM3 separated by the aggradational Unit BM2 siltstone (Figure 21; Jackson and Johnson, 1996, p.102). These slightly more proximal, and axial, sequences in the east and south-east are all overlain sharply by the Rottington Sandstone Member and all contain a well-developed Unit BM2. Significantly, a new element 40 m thick, and here designated Unit BM4, is identified in Well 112/15-1, the northernmost well in the area, and is responsible for the thickness maximum. The unit comprises an upward-coarsening sequence beneath the Rottington Sandstone Member, and equivalents of the basal few metres of Unit BM4 may also occur in the other three wells (Figure 21). Unit BM4 is interpreted here as the deposit of a flood-plain lake that was rapidly and progressively infilled from the north by a small delta.

Second, in the more distal locations to the north-west, the thinner successions (largely deriving from a very thin Unit BM2) of wells 111/25-1A (92.5 m) and 112/19-1 (72 m) reveal a transitional contact with the

Rottington Sandstone Member. A similar contact is also reported from onshore Cumbria (Akhurst et al., 1997; Arthurton et al., 1978) and indicates a pulsed introduction of fluvial deposits of the Budleighensis River (Wills, 1970; Audley-Charles, 1970) to these distal locations. These distal wells display higher average gamma-ray values, especially in the mudstone units; this is also seen in the mudstone units of the Mercia Mudstone Group (Figure 24) and may also reflect greater proximity to a subsidiary micaceous (?granitic) source. Floodplain lacustrine laminites and loessic silt deposits are widespread in the Barrowmouth Mudstone Formation (Akhurst et al., 1997; Holliday, 1993a; Arthurton et al., 1978) and the formation has been interpreted as a coastal plain to distal floodplain deposit (Akhurst et al., 1997, fig. 30d; Johnson et al., 1994).

The **Manchester Marls Formation**, including the **Freshfield Sandstone Member** in the upper part, were described by Newman (1999) in Well 111/29-1 (70 m thick, Figure 21). The basal high gamma-ray value mudstone of the formation rests unconformably on the Garwood Group. In Well 111/29-1, the formation comprises two subequal parts. The lower part, which is 30 m thick, comprises a prograding sequence of five thin upward-coarsening cycles. The upper part is 40 m thick and constitutes the Freshfield Sandstone Member (Newman, 1999); it comprises pale red to greyish red, very fine- to fine-grained, poorly cemented aeolian sandstone (with gamma-ray values some 20 API units lower than those of the argillaceous sandstone of the Rottington Sandstone Member). Biostratigraphical examination of sidewall cores yielded only a single specimen of the long-ranging and non-diagnostic bisaccate pollen, *Taeniaesporites* sp., at 1041 m RKB, together with rare non-striate bisaccate pollen and *Cyathidites* sp. near the base of the formation.

The ratio of the thickness of the Freshfield Sandstone Member to that of the Manchester Marls Formation increases towards the basin margin (Jackson and Johnson, 1996, p.118 and Panel 4), and suggests a proximal site for Well 111/29-1. Conversely, the feather-edge of the Freshfield Sandstone Member may occur in Well 112/29-1 (Figure 21); similar occurrences were noted in wells 110/3b-4 and 110/6b-1 (Jackson and Johnson, 1996, pp.115, 133).

Onshore Isle of Man Attenuated sections of the Cumbrian Coast Group have been proved in boreholes on the Isle of Man and were assigned by Lamplugh (1903) to the 'Lower Red Marls' (Permian). The sandy mudstone with thin interbeds of sandstone is treated here as a basin margin development of the Manchester Marls Formation in the footwall of the Maryport Fault (Chapter 4). In common with other thin marginal sequences of the group, it is possible that they comprise only the highest beds of an overlapping succession. Re-evaluation of the records and detailed correlations with Well 111/29-1 suggest that the formation is 23.72 m thick (with a faulted base) in the Ballawhane Borehole (151.64–175.36 m), 38.92 m thick in the Knock-e-Dooney Borehole (155.04–193.96 m), and 32.23 m thick in the Ballagenney Borehole (279.15–311.38 m). Corresponding thicknesses for the Freshfield Sandstone Member are 13.56 m in the Ballawhane Borehole (151.64–165.20 m), 15.32 m in the Knock-e-Dooney Borehole (155.04–170.36 m), and ?27.02 m in the Ballagenney Borehole (279.15–?306.17 m) (Figures 21, 22). A reduction in formation thickness of 56 per cent towards the Isle of Man massif takes place between Well 111/29-1 and Knock-e-Dooney.

Using these revised correlations, the cross-sections constructed by Lamplugh (1903, plate V) and Gregory (1920, fig. 2) have been updated as Figure 22, and also tied to Well 112/19-1. The correlations highlight the thinning towards the Isle of Man massif in all units. The fault postulated by Gregory (1920, fig. 2), between the Ballagenney Borehole and Point of Ayre, has a throw at the top Cumbrian Coast Group level which is tentatively estimated at 725 m. Figure 22 also shows another fault that is likely to intervene between Well 112/19-1 and Point of Ayre (throw estimated at 400 m at top Cumbrian Coast Group level). One of these faults is probably the Maryport Fault or an *en échelon* continuation (Chapter 4). The cross-section also emphasises the role of growth faults in accentuating the facies change from a mudstone on evaporite succession in the hanging wall to a sandstone on mudstone succession in the footwall.

In contrast, on the east side of the island in the Cranstal Borehole (Figure 2) at a hanging wall location believed to be close to an active fault (Chapter 7), the Cumbrian Coast Group comprises an attenuated evaporite–mudstone succession otherwise similar to that of Well 112/19-1. The St Bees Evaporites Formation consists of 5 m of dolomite overlain by 6 m of interbedded anhydrite and red mudstone, and is succeeded by 32 m of red calcareous siltstone and mudstone (the condensed Barrowmouth Mudstone Formation).

Stranraer Basin Rocks belonging to the Cumbrian Coast Group have not been identified to date in the Stranraer Basin (Stone, 1995). They are almost certainly concealed by blown sand deposits covering the Stranraer isthmus and extending offshore into Luce Bay, and are more likely to comprise a facies comparable with the Manchester Marls Formation, the upper part of the Kinnerton Sandstone Formation or the Newforte Breccia Formation, than to an evaporite-bearing sequence (Jackson, in press).

Belfast Group

North Channel Basin (Portpatrick Sub-Basin) In the more rapidly subsiding parts of the Ulster and North Channel basins, the Belfast Group (Smith et al., 1991) comprises the Belfast Harbour Evaporite Formation (equivalent to the St Bees Evaporites Formation) overlain by the Connswater Marl Formation (Smith, 1986; equivalent to the Barrowmouth Mudstone Formation, Table 4). Although bedded rocks of the Belfast Group were not conclusively proved in Well 111/15-1, their occurrence as marine limestones and thick evaporites at Larne (Penn et al., 1983), and the role of the North Channel Basin as the entry point for the Bakevellia Sea transgression into north-west England (Smith and Taylor, 1992), implies that marine rocks of the Belfast Group should occur throughout the North Channel Basin.

On the southern margin of the East Irish Sea Basin and over the interbasinal divide with the Cheshire Basin, the entire Manchester Marls Formation passes into an aeolian sandstone succession (the upper part of the Kinnerton Sandstone Formation, Evans et al., 1993; Jackson et al., 1995). In Well 111/15-1, British Gas (composite log) presents a strong case for a similar lateral passage within the Belfast Group from an evaporite–mudstone succession into an undifferentiated arenaceous facies (1477.99–1579.19 m RKB), directly underlying the Sherwood Sandstone Group (Chapter 7). However, in this account, following the identification of the sonic shoulder 'marker' of Unit CR2 in Well 111/15-1, the arenaceous facies of British Gas is assigned here to Unit CR1 of the Calder Sandstone Member (Figure 23).

Evidence for the presence of the Belfast Group in, and adjacent to, Well 111/15-1 is limited to six 'beds' of coarse crystalline halite, commonly with cone-in-cone structure, penetrated between 1889.78 and 1926.97 m RKB (maximum individual 'bed' thickness is 6.4 m, item 18, Figure 21). These 'beds' are treated here as steeply dipping veins of halite, derived from the **Belfast Harbour Evaporite Formation** by diapiric injection from below and smearing along the Portpatrick Fault or associated splinter faults (Figures 12b, 16a). Gravity and seismic data also suggest the presence of salt (Maddox et al., 1997, p.103).

7 Triassic and Jurassic

During the Triassic and Early Jurassic, the rate of subsidence and sediment accumulation was higher in the Keys Basin in the eastern part of the Isle of Man area† than anywhere else in the British Isles (Figures 16a, b; Jackson et al., 1995). The tectonic regime for the Triassic and Jurassic rocks is described in Chapter 4. Triassic rocks in the region comprise the arenaceous Sherwood Sandstone Group, (600–1400 m) overlain by the exceptionally thick, argillaceous and evaporitic sequences of the Mercia Mudstone Group (1200–3100 m), with the much thinner, argillaceous and calcareous Penarth Group (35 m) at the top (Table 4). Over most of the area, the boundary between the Sherwood Sandstone Group and Mercia Mudstone Group is believed to be a minor non-sequence (Jackson and Johnson, 1996). In wells 111/25-1A and 111/29-1 in the Peel Basin, a more substantial disconformity is postulated in this account because of the apparent absence of the Ormskirk Sandstone Formation (Figure 23).

The Permian evaporite distribution (Chapter 6) indicates that the Bakevellia Sea transgressions from the Boreal Ocean repeatedly entered the area from the north, via the North Channel, en route to the East Irish Sea and Cheshire basins (Smith and Taylor, 1992, fig. 1). Beyond the Cheshire Basin, the ground rose steadily southwards to the Wales–Brabant Massif. It is suggested here that the same route to the ocean through the Isle of Man area was utilised during the Induan stage by the Budleighensis River (Wills, 1970), which flowed northwards from mountains in Armorica and deposited the Rottington Sandstone Member (St Bees Sandstone Formation, Table 4). Later in early Olenekian times, this river was probably diverted from the English Midlands into the southern North Sea, where the fluvial Bunter Sandstone Formation accumulated (Warrington and Ivimey-Cook, 1992; Audley-Charles, 1970; Johnson et al., 1994). The abandoned floodplain through the Isle of Man area silted up, and became the site of aeolian and siliciclastic sabkha deposition (the Calder Sandstone Member of the St Bees Sandstone Formation). Fluvial processes resumed at the end of Olenekian times (uppermost Calder Sandstone Member) and during the earliest Anisian (Ormskirk Sandstone Formation; Figure 23), on a westward-tilted palaeoslope (Cowan, 1993, fig. 6; Cowan et al., 1993, fig. 15; Jones and Ambrose, 1994, fig. 5; Akhurst et al., 1997). It would appear that the drainage system received a contribution, possibly major, via streams of more local provenance from the Lake District. It is postulated here that the apparent absence of the Ormskirk Sandstone Formation from the two Peel Basin wells (Figure 23) was caused by uplift in the earliest Anisian of a ridge, trending north-north-east–south-south-west from the Rhins of Galloway through the Peel Basin. This feature temporarily severed the depositional link between the eastern part of the area and the North Channel Basin.

Slightly later in the Anisian, well-developed halites in the lower part of the Mercia Mudstone Group indicate re-occupation of the Bakevellia waterway, during the Röt transgression. However, thickness variations of the highest halites in the Mercia Mudstone Group suggest that the waterway may have again declined in influence during latest Anisian to end Carnian times. Until this time, most of Britain and the Isle of Man area had lain on a northward- and later westward-inclined palaeoslope, directed towards the Boreal Ocean. A reversal to a southward-directed palaeoslope throughout Britain is proposed in the latest Anisian, indicated by a switch of the dominant marine route into the Isle of Man area, from the Boreal 'north-west passage' (p.79) via the North Channel, to a 'south-west passage' along the present-day St George's Channel. This 'south-west passage' became wider and more influential over time, with successive marine transgressions from the south during the Rhaetian (Penarth Group; Warrington and Ivimey-Cook, 1992) and Early Jurassic (Lias Group; Bradshaw et al., 1992; Morton, 1992), and eventually usurped the dominant role of the 'north-west passage'. The 'south-west passage' (and an overall south-facing palaeoslope throughout onshore and offshore Britain) has been retained to the present day, as the more prominent of the two links that the Isle of Man area shares with the Atlantic Ocean.

TRIASSIC

SHERWOOD SANDSTONE GROUP

The Sherwood Sandstone Group, of Induan to early Anisian age, comprises the thick St Bees Sandstone Formation (585–1180 m), overlain by the thinner Ormskirk Sandstone Formation (100–250 m) (Table 4). Within the Isle of Man area, recorded group thicknesses range from 585 m in Well 111/29-1 to 1376.8 m in Well 113/26-1. There is generally a doubling in thickness across major growth faults (Figures 14a, c). Eight shallow BGS offshore boreholes have also penetrated the Sherwood Sandstone Group in the Isle of Man area (Figures 1, 2; Wright et al., 1971; BGS, 1994; Jackson et al., 1995, p.59).

Mechanically, the Sherwood Sandstone Group behaves as a thick, unfaulted, competent slab or raft, bounded above and below by incompetent mudstone and evaporite (Figures 14, 17; Penge et al., 1999). In contrast to the faulting and halokinetic disruption seen in the evaporitic Cumbrian Coast and Mercia Mudstone groups, all subdivisions of the Sherwood Sandstone Group occur throughout the Isle of Man region, with the probable exception of the Ormskirk Sandstone Formation in the Peel Basin. Although partly a reflection of the paucity of stratigraphical

† Isle of Man area refers to that shown in Figure 1.

markers in the group, faulting has been detected only in Well 111/15-1 (Figure 23). The Calder Sandstone Member of the St Bees Sandstone Formation, and the Ormskirk Sandstone Formation display greater lateral facies variation across the area than any other lithostratigraphical units in the Permian to Lower Jurassic succession.

No palaeontological information is available for the area, but a magnetostratigraphic Chron date of slightly younger than 239.5 Ma (intra-Anisian on palaeontological grounds, Warrington in Jackson and Johnson, 1996, and references therein) has recently been obtained in the East Irish Sea Basin for the topmost beds of the Ormskirk Sandstone Formation. A Chron of 242.7 Ma (Anisian–Olenekian boundary from palaeontology) has also been obtained for the base of the Ormskirk Sandstone Formation (Mange et al., 1999).

St Bees Sandstone Formation

The St Bees Sandstone Formation is divided into two members of approximately equal thickness: the lower, fluvial, Rottington Sandstone Member, which is equivalent to the St Bees Sandstone Formation of Barnes et al. (1994) and Akhurst et al. (1997) in onshore Cumbria, and the upper, aeolian, Calder Sandstone Member, which is equivalent to the Calder Sandstone Formation of Barnes et al. (1994) and Akhurst et al. (1997). The boundary between the two members is the Top Silicified Zone event (Colter, 1978; Jackson et al., 1995), which marks the abrupt cessation of continuous fluvial deposition. The event is marked by a prominent 'shoulder' on the sonic log, and is generally coincident with an abrupt upward decrease in background gamma-ray values and an upward decrease in the abundance of mudstone and siltstone partings (Figure 23). The formation has been fully drilled only in six wells, and ranges in thickness from 585 m in Well 111/29-1 to 1182.72 m (true vertical thickness) in Well 113/26-1.

The **Rottington Sandstone Member** comprises a thick, vertically monotonous and laterally uniform, very fine-grained, micaceous fluvial sandstone that is well cemented by pervasive silica and dolomite. It contains numerous red-brown silty mudstone and siltstone partings throughout. The salient wireline log features, namely a highly linear and distinctive sonic log with very high velocities, and a sublinear to finely serrate gamma-ray log of moderately high API background values with numerous high gamma-ray value mudstone spikes, are exhibited by all wells (Figure 23; Jackson and Johnson, 1996, including the nearby Well 110/6b-1, Panel 3; Barnes et al., 1994; Akhurst et al., 1997). The sandstone was laid down as a multistorey channel system by a large braided river (Budleighensis River of Wills, 1970) on a northerly directed palaeoslope (Warrington and Ivimey-Cook, 1992; Jones and Ambrose, 1994; see Akhurst et al., 1997, fig. 30f, for environmental setting).

Thickness variations conform to the usual pattern in the region (p.72), and range from 300.5 m in Well 111/29-1 to 610.7 m in Well 112/25a-1. The lower part of the member is faulted out in Well 111/15-1 (Figure 23), where seismic evidence (Chapter 4) suggests an exceptional thickness (700 m, and possibly over 1000 m in the centre of the Portpatrick Subbasin of the North Channel Basin). However, the preserved section in Well 111/15-1, (1620.6 to 1889.8 m relative to kelly bushing in this interpretation) was assigned on the British Gas composite log to an undifferentiated 'Lower Permian' (now Guadalupian) succession (equivalent to the fluvial Carnamuck Formation of this account, Chapter 6).

Vertical variation in log response is slight, and there are few area-wide correlatable features. Thin and sporadic poorly cemented layers occur as low velocity troughs with abrupt symmetrical shifts in successions that record rapid subsidence (Figure 23, items 1, 2, 3, 4 in wells 113/26-1, 111/15-1 and 112/25a-1). Their stratigraphical clustering (see also Well 110/2b-9, Jackson and Johnson, 1996, Panel 3) suggests brief interludes of slightly reduced fluvial activity, and the accumulation of wind-derived fluvial (and possibly aeolian) sand on abandoned marginal bars and sandflats; in such monotonous sequences they have the potential to act as marker horizons.

Throughout most of the offshore East Irish Sea Basin and especially in basinal settings (wells 112/25a-1 and 113/26-1), the basal contact is sharp on the Barrowmouth Mudstone Formation (Jackson and Johnson, 1996). Nevertheless, a transition zone (15–30 m thick) of thinly interbedded sandstone and mudstone is developed at the base of the member and is displayed as an overall upward-fining sequence on the gamma-ray log (seen more clearly on Figure 21). Where this is well developed, on the basin margins (Akhurst et al., 1997) and in the distal (i.e. northwest) parts of the area in wells 111/25-1A and 112/19-1, the transition zone contains several low value gamma-ray spikes interpreted as thin, sharp-based, sheetflood sandstones deposited from abrupt fluvial discharges entering a coastal plain (Akhurst et al., 1997, pp.79, 81). In Well 112/15-1, north of the axis of the Solway Firth Basin, the base of the Rottington Sandstone Member is also sharp, and rests

Figure 23 Correlation of wells proving the Sherwood Sandstone Group in the Isle of Man area. The figure is tied to the top of the Rottington Sandstone Member Top Silicified Zone event, though in wells 112/15-1 and 111/15-1 a prominent gamma-ray log shift has been selected as the tie point (see text). The figure has been arranged to show the thickest successions on the right with thinning taking place towards the left, and to demonstrate the apparent absence of the Ormskirk Sandstone Formation from the Peel Basin. The figure incorporates environmental interpretation from Meadows and Beach (1993), Jackson and Johnson (1996), Herries and Cowan (1997) and Newman (1999). Zones 1–6 and the Cemented Unit of Newman are also shown alongside the Ormskirk Sandstone Formation of Well 112/19-1. The calibrated velocity log rather than the sonic log is depicted between 570 and 1450 m in Well 112/25a-1. The Scythian series is now divided into the Induan stage (approximately corresponding with deposition of the Rottington Sandstone Member) and the Olenekian stage (approximately corresponding with deposition of the Calder Sandstone Member; see Johnson et al. 1994, p.32, and references therein). See text for further explanation.

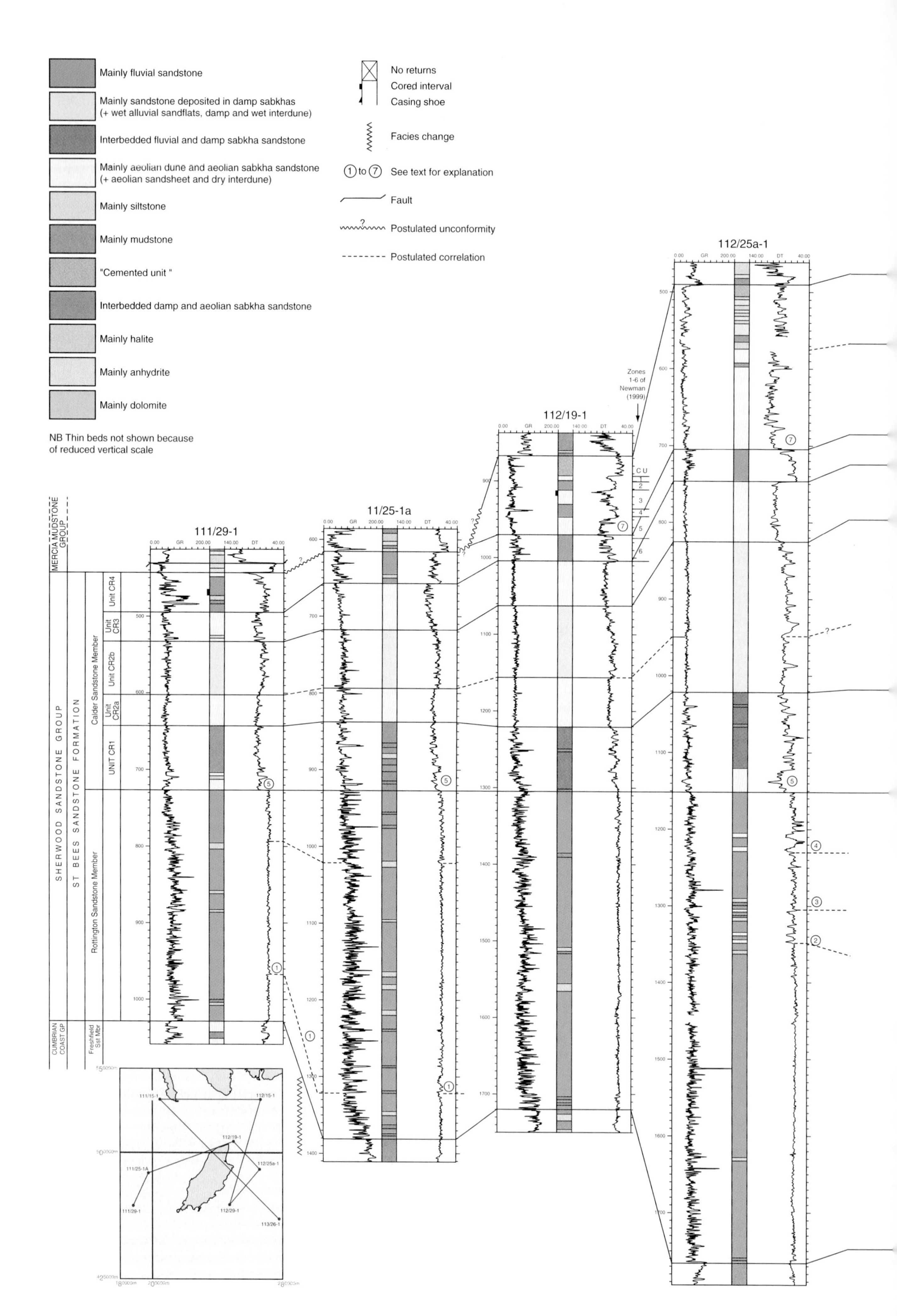
Mainly fluvial sandstone
Mainly sandstone deposited in damp sabkhas (+ wet alluvial sandflats, damp and wet interdune)
Interbedded fluvial and damp sabkha sandstone
Mainly aeolian dune and aeolian sabkha sandstone (+ aeolian sandsheet and dry interdune)
Mainly siltstone
Mainly mudstone
"Cemented unit "
Interbedded damp and aeolian sabkha sandstone
Mainly halite
Mainly anhydrite
Mainly dolomite
NB Thin beds not shown because of reduced vertical scale
No returns
Cored interval
Casing shoe
Facies change
① to ⑦ See text for explanation
Fault
Postulated unconformity
Postulated correlation
111/29-1
11/25-1a
112/19-1
112/25a-1
GR
DT
Zones 1-6 of Newman (1999)
MERCIA MUDSTONE GROUP
SHERWOOD SANDSTONE GROUP
ST BEES SANDSTONE FORMATION
Calder Sandstone Member
Rottington Sandstone Member
Unit CR4
Unit CR3
Unit CR2b
Unit CR2a
UNIT CR1
CUMBRIAN COAST GP
Freshfield Sst Mbr
111/15-1
112/15-1
112/19-1
111/25-1A
112/25a-1
111/29-1
112/29-1
113/26-1

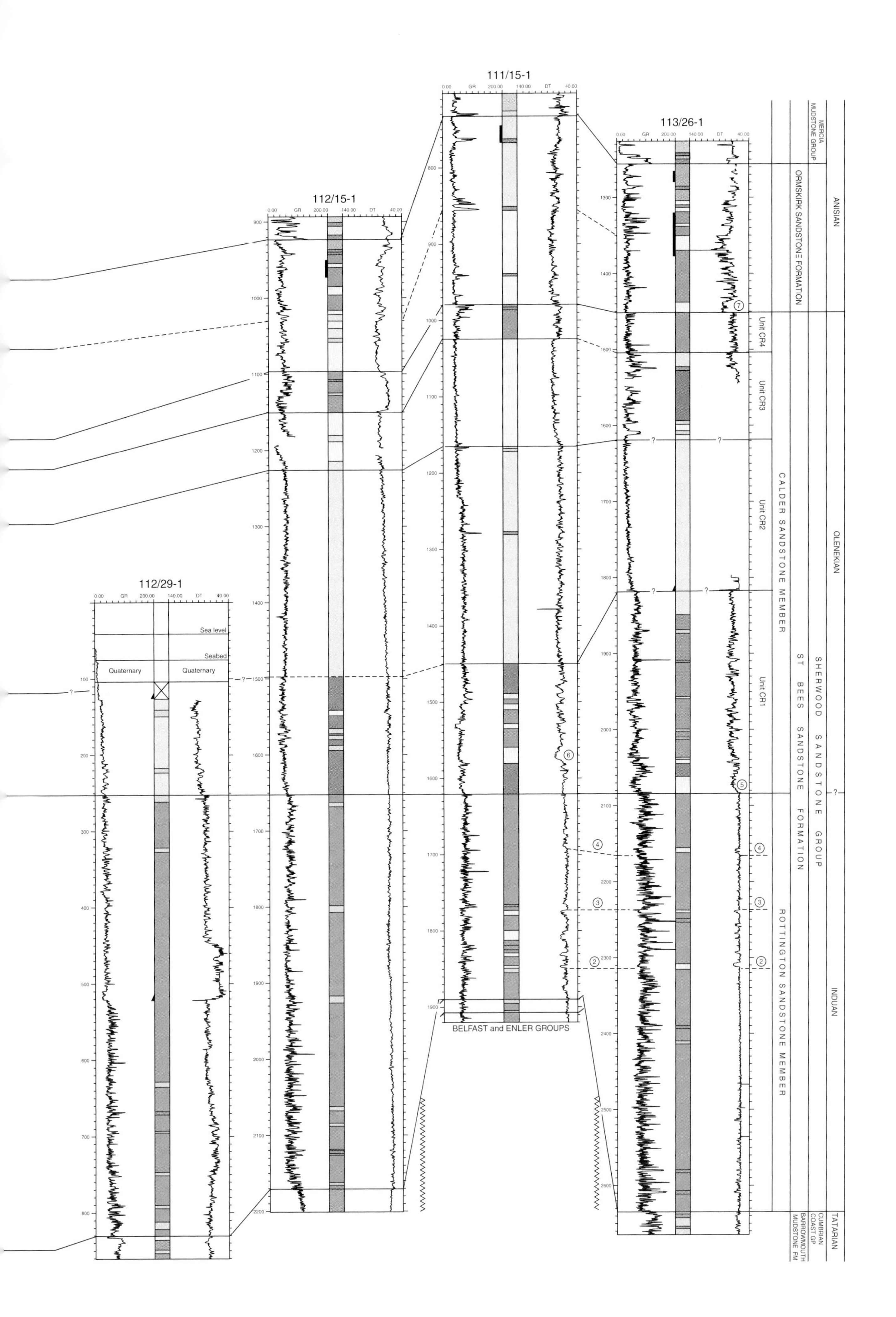

111/15-1
113/26-1
112/15-1
112/29-1
GR
DT
Sea level
Seabed
Quaternary
BELFAST and ENLER GROUPS
MERCIA MUDSTONE GROUP
ORMSKIRK SANDSTONE FORMATION
Unit CR4
Unit CR3
Unit CR2
Unit CR1
CALDER SANDSTONE MEMBER
ROTTINGTON SANDSTONE MEMBER
ST BEES SANDSTONE FORMATION
SHERWOOD SANDSTONE GROUP
CUMBRIAN COAST GP
BARROWMOUTH MUDSTONE FM
ANISIAN
OLENEKIAN
INDUAN
TATARIAN

on the upward-coarsening Unit BM4 (Barrowmouth Mudstone Formation, Figure 21) rather than on Unit BM3 as elsewhere. It is suggested that the prograding deposits of the north-west-flowing Budleighensis River arrived in the Solway Firth and Peel basins slightly later than in the East Irish Sea Basin. In west Cumbria, a much thicker transitional unit, 80 to 100 m thick, is known as the North Head Member (of the redefined onshore St Bees Sandstone Formation Akhurst et al., 1997, fig. 33; Rose and Dunham, 1977). It has not been possible to pinpoint the upper boundary of the North Head Member in the Isle of Man area.

The 'sonic shoulder' of the Top Silicified Zone is blurred in some of the thicker or more deeply buried successions at basin centres where the palaeo-water table was high, or where the basal Calder Sandstone Member comprises interdune deposits rather than aeolian dune sandstone. In wells 112/15-1 and 111/15-1, the Top Silicified Zone sonic event is not coincident with a shift in the gamma-ray log (Figure 23); in these wells a prominent gamma-ray change and an abrupt upward decline in the number of argillaceous partings was chosen as the top of the Rottington Sandstone Member (Jackson and Johnson, 1996, pp.84, 93).

The **Calder Sandstone Member** has been proved in seven wells in the Isle of Man area, and ranges in thickness from 284.5 m in Well 111/29-1 to 641.31 m in Well 111/15-1. It is largely aeolian in origin, consisting of interbedded aeolian sabkha and damp sabkha deposits, except for an uppermost fluvial sandstone showing palaeocurrent indicators directed towards the west-south-west (Figure 23; Barnes et al., 1994; Jones and Ambrose, 1994; Jackson and Johnson, 1996; Akhurst et al., 1997, fig. 30g). Following a channel avulsion of regional scale in the English Midlands, the Budleighensis River adopted a north-easterly course and began to discharge into the southern North Sea basin and to deposit the Bunter Sandstone Formation (Table 4; Audley Charles, 1970, plates 7, 8; Warrington and Ivimey-Cook, 1992; Johnston et al., 1994). As a consequence, in the Isle of Man area, the laterally equivalent Calder Sandstone Member was deposited as aeolian conditions were established over abandoned floodplain and river channels. The Rottington–Calder sandstone boundary also provides a striking example of a change from fluvial to aeolian conditions that arises, not for climatic reasons but because of a change in sediment supply and transfer of the fluvial facies to another location.

The Calder Sandstone Member was subdivided by Jackson and Johnson (1996, p.79) into four units, CR1 to CR4 (see below). The predominant lithology in Units CR1 to CR3 is a very fine- to fine- and medium-grained, friable to moderately cemented, colourless to pale red sandstone and unconsolidated sand. Good porosity has been preserved between the subangular and subrounded, poorly to moderately sorted quartz grains. Typical aeolian characteristics of medium and coarse grade, frosted quartz grains of high sphericity appear to be scarce, and much scarcer than in the cored Sellafield boreholes. The palaeowind direction was from the north-east (Barnes et al., 1994; Jones and Ambrose, 1994; Akhurst et al., 1997). Environmental interpretation of the Calder Sandstone Member has been greatly clarified following a detailed study by Herries and Cowan (1997) of similar lithologies in the Ormskirk Sandstone Formation in relation to modern siliciclastic sabkhas; the preliminary environmental interpretation of the Calder Sandstone Member (Jackson and Johnston, 1996) has been modified in view of both the Herries and Cowan investigation, and the detailed core examination of the equivalent Calder Sandstone Formation of Cumbria (Jones and Ambrose, 1994; Akhurst et al., 1997). It appears that the level of the water table was the prime control on sediment type and rate of accumulation. (Herries and Cowan, 1977; Newman, 1999). A more detailed wireline log interpretation and facies analysis of individual sequences for all four units is documented in Jackson (in press).

Unit CR1 ranges in thickness from 82 m in Well 112/19-1 to 266.5 m in Well 113/26-1. It comprises interdigitating fluvial, damp sabkha and aeolian deposits, and in some wells (e.g. Well 112/15-1) is transitional between the fluvial Rottington Sandstone Member and the dominantly damp sabkha environments of Unit CR2. In others (e.g. Well 111/29-1) it marks an abrupt and sustained change from fluvial to aeolian deposition (Figure 23). The average API values of the slightly serrate gamma-ray log are commonly lower than in both the Rottington Sandstone Member and Unit CR2, whereas the average sonic velocity is intermediate between the average velocities of the Rottington Sandstone Member and Unit CR2. The unit exhibits the most erratic and ragged log response within the member, especially where sonic log spikes result from anhydritic mudstone and siltstone and patchily silica- and dolomite-cemented sandstone (e.g. in wells 111/25-1A, 112/19-1 and 113/26-1). Collectively, these features suggest a greater preponderance of cleaner, poorly cemented low porosity aeolian sandstone and also well-cemented fluvial sandstone, compared to the uniform, more silty, damp sabkha sandstone of Unit CR2.

There are few area-wide internal markers. In several wells (e.g. 113/26-1, 112/25a-1, the 110/6b-1 type section, Jackson and Johnson, 1996, p.31) the base of the Calder Sandstone Member is marked by a clean, low gamma-ray count, low velocity motif interpreted as aeolian dune sandstone (20–30 m thick, item 5, Figure 23); the same feature is weakly developed in wells 111/29-1 and 111/25-1A. A comparable feature (item 6) in Well 111/15-1 may be the same horizon, but here the member base has been chosen some 40 m lower at the prominent gamma-ray shift. Successions of Unit CR1 are thought to range from sites with thick, high water table sequences (Well 113/26-1) or sustained fluvial influences (Well 111/15-1) to thinner successions with interbedded aeolian sabkha and damp sabkha deposits (wells 111/25-1A and 111/29-1; Jackson, in press).

Unit CR2 is the thickest unit of the Calder Sandstone Member except in Well 113/26-1. It ranges in thickness from 110 m in Well 111/29-1 to 286.21 m in Well 111/15-1. The unit thins consistently towards the Isle of Man massif with a minimum in the Peel Basin (Figure 23). The top of the unit is marked by a 'sonic shoulder', similar to the Top Silicified Zone event, though the feature is more accentuated in the deeply buried sections (e.g. in Well 111/15-1). In the East Irish Sea

Basin, the unit was differentiated by linear to sub-linear gamma-ray and sonic log profiles, and by moderately elevated gamma-ray values, albeit with very scarce argillaceous partings (Jackson and Johnson, 1996, p.79). In the Isle of Man area, although argillaceous partings are locally more common (e.g. in Well 111/25-1A) than in the East Irish Sea, the gamma-ray log generally shares the same characteristics and allows the unit to be distinguished from the Rottington Sandstone Member (e.g. Well 111/15-1). In most wells the average gamma-ray values are slightly higher than in both Units CR1 and CR3 and, together with the sonic log profile, indicate a very fine-grained, slightly argillaceous, siliciclastic sabkha sandstone (Figure 23). Two sonic log motifs are recognised, reflecting differences in facies and unit thickness within the Isle of Man area. Well 112/25a-1 provides a crucial intermediate profile between the two end-member types.

i In thick and deeply buried successions, greater than 1100 m at the present-day (wells 112/15-1; 111/15-1; 110/6b-1, Jackson and Johnson, 1996, p.81, and probably 113/26-1), the sonic log has a similar appearance to profiles from many wells in the East Irish Sea Basin, with a linear motif at near-matrix velocity that is reminiscent of the Rottington Sandstone Member. These thicker successions denote a depositional setting characterised by stable conditions and a relatively high water table, which was conducive to trapping and retaining wind-blown silt and very fine sand. A damp sabkha to wet interdune environment is suggested (compare with Herries and Cowan, 1997; Newman, 1999; Jones and Ambrose, 1994), where well-cemented, slightly silty, sandstone sequences would have built up quickly. The linear sonic logs of these deeply buried, thick sequences (e.g. Well 112/15-1) have potential for depth of burial and uplift studies (Chadwick et al., 1994).

ii The thinner successions, which also coincide with areas of shallower burial (less than 1100 m at the present-day, namely wells 111/29-1, 111/25-1A, 112/19-1 and 112/25a-1), show a clear-cut, two-fold subdivision of the sonic log profile that has not been recognised previously in the unit. The lower and thinner subdivision (Unit CR2a) exhibits a linear, vertical trace; the better cemented Unit CR2b displays a blocky or spiky, commonly bow-shaped, sonic log and slightly higher average gamma-ray (API) values than both units CR2a and CR3 (Figure 23). These areas of slower accumulation reflect lower water table levels with less efficient sediment trapping, where deposition of an initial drier, aeolian sabkha and dry interdune phase (Unit CR2a) was followed by a rise in the water table to a fluctuating damp sabkha and damp interdune regime with more efficient sediment trapping (Unit CR2b).

Unit CR3 (38.5 m thick in Well 111/29-1 to 137.17 m thick in Well 111/15-1). With the exception of Well 113/26-1, Unit CR3 is a relatively thin aeolian dune and aeolian sabkha unit with a vertical and area-wide uniformity that is distinguished by the lowest sonic velocities and best porosities in the Calder Sandstone Member (Figure 23). As with Unit CR2, the unit isopachs show a steady and progressive westerly thinning towards the Peel Basin and towards the Isle of Man. Except at basin centre sites with a dominant fluvial regime (e.g. Well 113/26-1), the top of the unit marks the cessation of widespread aeolian deposition, and is abruptly overlain everywhere by the high velocity, fluvial Unit CR4. The base of the unit is chosen at a 'sonic shoulder' and at the significant upward decrease in average sonic velocity (especially in thicker successions, e.g. Well 111/15-1) or, where the shoulder is absent, at a gamma-ray shift marking the top of the linear Unit CR2 motif (wells 112/15-1 and 113/26-1).

The succession in Well 113/26-1 (about 115 m drilled thickness in this deviated well) contrasts with that of the other wells (Figure 23) in recording a perennial fluvial, or fluvially influenced site at a rapidly subsiding location. The log profile resembles that in 110/61-1 nearby (Jackson and Johnston, 1996, p.81) and the facies is a forerunner of the fluvial Unit CR4 sandstone. All other successions are characterised by a linear to low variability sonic log with low velocities. Except in Well 112/15-1, the linear to sub-linear gamma-ray log indicates uniform conditions with a low and stable water table and aggradational deposition of a clean sandstone with few argillaceous partings. The three thinnest successions (wells 111/29-1, 111/25-1A and 112/19-1, Figure 23) show greater small-scale variation on the sonic log with dominantly friable aeolian (possibly dune) sandstone interbedded with minor dolomite-cemented silty sandstone (possibly aeolian sabkha).

Unit CR4 (35–53 m thick) is a ubiquitous, higher velocity, sharp-based fluvial sandstone marker with low thickness variation (Figure 23). Paradoxically, the thickest development (53 m in Well 111/29-1) occurs as part of the thinnest overall succession of the Calder Sandstone Member. The unit is internally and laterally variable in detail, and thin-bedded silty sandstone, siltstone and mudstone are sporadic to common throughout. No consistent area-wide gamma-ray log trends have emerged, which may indicate that the rivers and small distributaries were confined to a particular basin or sub-basin. The sonic log profiles can be arranged in order of increasing aeolian influence and concomitant increase in porosity (Jackson, in press). Sequences range from those with a blocky to coarsely serrate vertical sonic profile (Well 111/15-1; Well 113/26-1, Meadows and Beach, 1993, fig.4), through those with a distinctive arcuate sonic trace (wells 111/29-1, 112/15-1 and 112/25a-1), to wells with a more responsive sonic motif (112/19-1, approximately Zone 6 of Newman, 1999, fig.10; 111/25-1A).

Ormskirk Sandstone Formation

The main hydrocarbon reservoir of the Ormskirk Sandstone Formation ranges in thickness, over five wells, from 103.5 to 246.89 m in the Isle of Man area. One unexpected finding is that the formation appears to be absent from both wells in the Peel Basin (Figure 23), though further drilling will be required to substantiate this conclusion. In the East Irish Sea Basin, the formation is divided into Units OS1, OS2a and 2b, although it was not possible to identify the precise divisional boundaries in every well (Jackson and Johnson, 1996, p.69). The formation has not been subdivided in this account because correlation has been hampered by the small database of widely scattered points. Nevertheless, a crude two-fold subdivision into a lower part with lower sonic velocities, dominated by aeolian and aeolian sabkha deposits, and an upper, higher velocity part dominated by fluvial and damp sabkha deposits can be recognised in all the wells (Figure 23). The detailed reservoir zonation of Newman (1999) in Well 112/19-1 has been added to Figure 23, including the anhydrite-cemented, high velocity 'Cemented Unit' at the top of the formation.

Palaeoenvironmental interpretation has been carried out using the same wireline log criteria, especially the sonic log response, as for the Calder Sandstone Member (Herries and Cowan, 1997; Newman, 1999; Meadows and Beach, 1993). The aeolian-dominated lower part of the formation comprises repeated upward-drying sandstone rhythms (2–10 m thick) deposited in damp sabkha, aeolian sabkha and aeolian dune environments (Herries and Cowan, 1997). Palaeowinds in the East Irish Sea Basin and west Cumbria were from the north-east (Cowan et al., 1993; Cowan, 1993; Jones and Ambrose, 1994; Akhurst et al., 1997). The fluvial-dominated upper part of the formation represents the deposits of a major braided river system with thick units (up to 80 m) of stacked perennial channel sandstone, alternating with units of thin sandstone deposited in ephemeral fluvial channels and on siliciclastic sabkhas and wet sandflats (Herries and Cowan, 1997; Newman, 1999). Palaeocurrents in the East Irish Sea Basin were directed to the west and west-south-west (Herries and Cowan, 1997; Cowan et al., 1993). Intercalations of argillaceous and arenaceous, lacustrine and playa deposits occur in the uppermost 50 m of the formation. In this part of the sequence the sandstone is locally well cemented by anhydrite and/or dolomite (the 'Cemented Unit' of Newman, 1999; wells 112/19-1 and 113/26-1); these features indicate a regional rise in the water table.

Lateral and vertical variation in log signature is observed, but few area-wide markers and trends have been detected. In the Solway Firth and North Channel basins, there are fewer argillaceous partings and flooding events than in the East Irish Sea Basin (Jackson and Johnson, 1996, p.71, Panel 3), and in general a lower water table with stronger aeolian influences, also typical of basin margin locations, appears to have prevailed (compare with Jones and Ambrose, 1994, fig. 6). A basal, low velocity aeolian dune sandstone (20–30 m thick, and approximately equal to Zone 5 of Newman, 1999, in Well 112/19-1) is prominent in wells 113/26-1 and 112/25a-1 (item 7, Figure 23), but weakly developed in wells 111/15-1 and 112/15-1. A low velocity 'aeolian waist' commonly occurs near the mid-point of the formation (e.g. wells 113/26-1 and 112/19-1).

Overall, successions range from those deposited under prevailing fluvial influences (or under a high water table) in Well 113/26-1 (Meadows and Beach, 1993; Herries and Cowan, 1997) and Well 112/19-1 (Newman, 1999), through mixed, intermediate settings (wells 112/15-1 and 112/25a-1) to those with stronger aeolian influences (or deposited at sites with a lower water table, Well 111/15-1; Figure 23; Jackson, in press). The variation in gamma-ray log motif of the uppermost sandstone suggests some degree of truncation beneath the Röt transgression at the base of the Mercia Mudstone Group.

Well 111/15-1 may constitute the most north-westerly recorded occurrence of the formation (or lateral equivalent) in the United Kingdom. Traditionally, an equivalent of the Ormskirk Sandstone Formation has not been recognised in Northern Ireland, where the Mercia Mudstone Group is believed to overlie the Sherwood Sandstone Group at a disconformity (Penn et al., 1983). An alternative view was expressed recently by Maddox et al. (1997, fig. 7, p.104) who proposed that the uppermost 286 m of the Sherwood Sandstone Group in Larne No. 2 Borehole equates with the Ormskirk Sandstone Formation; however, their view is not substantiated by the correlations proposed on Figure 23. At the southern end of the East Irish Sea Basin, Jackson and Johnson, (1996, p.58) detected minor internal overlap and a non-sequence at the base of the Mercia Mudstone Group, though others (Warrington and Ivimey-Cook, 1992 and references therein; Herries and Cowan, 1997; Thompson and Meadows, 1997) have ascribed these and similar relationships to diachroneity between the Mercia Mudstone Group and Sherwood Sandstone Group.

Contrary to the findings of Newman (1999, fig. 9), the Ormskirk Sandstone Formation has not been recognised in wells 111/25-1A or 111/29-1; certainly in Well 111/25-1A, the Stanah Member appears to rest at an unfaulted contact on Unit CR4 (Figure 23). The typical high-amplitude triplet of the Ormskirk Sandstone Formation at the top of the Sherwood Sandstone Group seismic package appears to be replaced in the Peel Basin by a superficially similar, but thinner, high-amplitude doublet, created by the acoustic impedance effects of the high velocity Stanah Member and Unit CR4. The identification of the Unit CR4 sandstone blanket on all well logs in the Isle of Man region is considered, in this account, as the most convincing evidence for the apparent absence of the Ormskirk Sandstone Formation from wells 111/29-1 and 111/25-1A, and by implication from across the entire Peel Basin.

Although the effects of the Hardegsen Disconformity in the East Irish Sea Basin are non-existent (Cowan et al., 1993; Cowan, 1993; Meadows and Beach, 1993; Jackson et al., 1995), this observation does not apply to Northern Ireland (Penn et al., 1983) nor to parts of the Cheshire Basin (Evans et al., 1993) and thus it may not apply to the Peel Basin. It is postulated here that, as a result of the combined Hardegsen earth movements and the later non-sequence between the Mercia Mudstone Group and Sherwood Sandstone Group, the Ormskirk Sandstone Formation was not deposited over an emergent inter-basinal high that extended north-north-east–south-south-west from the Peel Basin area to the Rhins of Galloway. This high separated depositional areas in the Solway Firth Basin (and the adjacent onshore Isle of Man, see below) from the North Channel Basin (Figure 7; Newman, 1999, fig. 3; Jackson et al., 1995, fig. 16). A similar, but less severe, relationship between the Mercia Mudstone Group and Sherwood Sandstone Group appears to be developed on the northern fringe of the Lake District Massif (Eastwood et al., 1968, pp.217–218; Arthurton et al., 1978, p.202).

Sherwood Sandstone Group of the Isle of Man

The proximity of Well 112/19-1 (with a Rottington Sandstone Member thickness of 415.75 m) to the Isle of Man onshore boreholes allows the accounts of Lamplugh (1903) and Gregory (1920) to be placed in a modern stratigraphical context. The lower part of the **Rottington Sandstone Member** was proved in the Ballawhane (99.52 m thick), Knock-e-Dooney (102.31 m thick) and Ballagenney (214.37 m thick) boreholes; in each case the member rests on beds interpreted in this account as the Freshfield Sandstone Member (Figures 21, 22). The highest beds of the Rottington Sandstone Member (estimated thickness of 172.67 m, see discussion below) were penetrated in Point of Ayre No. 3 Borehole.

The lower 316 m of the Rottington Sandstone Member were supposedly also proved in the Cranstal Borehole (location on Figure 2) though the record, which consists of units (mostly 20–40 m thick) of fine-grained red sandstone (Quirk and Kimbell, 1997, fig. 9b) alternating with 'fossiliferous red coarse breccia' or brockram (presumably angular Dinantian limestone clasts), is highly anomalous, in comparison with all records in the Irish Sea area and Cumbria. The occurrence of thick beds of brockram, up to at least 285 m above the interpreted base of the Rottington Sandstone Member, is without parallel, exceeding that found near Egremont (Smith, 1924, p.19), where thin beds of brockram were found up to 80 m above the base. Most occurrences of brockram in west Cumbria, formerly thought to interdigitate with the basal Rottington Sandstone Member (Arthurton et al., 1978, fig. 66), are now assigned to the Cumbrian Coast Group (Akhurst et al., 1997, fig. 31). If reliable, the Cranstal log suggests a hanging wall location with scree and proximal alluvial fan deposits spilling over and banked against a syndepositional fault scarp, and interdigitating with fluvial deposits of the Budleighensis River near the basin margin. It implies that the Isle of Man was a local source area, with widespread Dinantian outcrops in the footwall block, until late into Induan times.

In the Point of Ayre No. 3 Borehole, Gregory (1920) estimated that the 'Keuper Sandstone', which he equated with the Kirklinton Sandstone of the Solway Firth Basin, was 286.29 m thick. This correlation was accepted by Colter (1978, fig. 4) and by Jackson et al. (1995, p.67), since the thickness was only slightly greater than that of the supposedly equivalent **Ormskirk Sandstone Formation** of the East Irish Sea Basin. The top of the 'Bunter Sandstone' (equivalent to the top of the **Calder Sandstone Member** of this account) was positioned by Gregory at 615.70 m, at the first downhole occurrence of 'brown shale', in a thinly interbedded sequence of sandstone with mudstone that persisted to the borehole termination depth (865.18 m). Gregory's correlation has been questioned recently by Barnes et al. (1994, p.59). Correlations between Well 112/19-1 and Point of Ayre No. 3 Borehole (Figure 22) now confirm that Gregory's thickness estimate of 'Keuper Sandstone' can no longer be sustained, since the Ormskirk Sandstone Formation is only 103.5 m thick in Well 112/19-1, and its maximum thickness in the area is only 246.89 m in Well 111/15-1. Gregory's interpretation has been revised, by detailed matching of the wireline logs of Well 112/19-1 with the Point of Ayre No. 3 record, and the following approximate correlations are now suggested to be more appropriate.

Units CR2 and CR3 of the Calder Sandstone Member are dominantly aeolian (with a patchy cement) in Well 112/19-1 (Figure 23) and their occurrence in Point of Ayre No. 3 Borehole has been equated with the two thick intervals of 'soft red sandstone' (together with the intervening strata) from 442.19 to 615.70 m. The first downhole occurrence of brown shale (at 615.70 m) has been placed at the top of Unit CR1 (see Well 112/19-1, Figure 23) rather than at the top of the 'Bunter Sandstone' (Gregory, 1920). The top of the Rottington Sandstone Member has been positioned at the downhole colour change to reddish brown sandstone at 692.51 m (Figure 22); above this the sandstone is generally described as 'red (with minor grey bands)' in colour. Further retrospective matching suggests that the fluvial Unit CR4 can be tentatively identified between 408.66 and 442.19 m; thus in Point of Ayre No. 3 Borehole, the respective thicknesses of Ormskirk Sandstone Formation (103.5 m thick in Well 112/19-1) and Calder Sandstone Member (334.25 m in Well 112/19-1) are approximately 79.25 and 283.85 m. This order of thinning from Well 112/19-1 towards the Isle of Man massif seems reasonable (Figure 22). However, it does make the absence of the Ormskirk Sandstone Formation from the Peel Basin even more puzzling and unexpected.

These findings also suggest that former accounts (Gregory, 1920; Colter, 1978; Warrington et al., 1980; Jackson et al., 1995, p.67), which equate the largely aeolian Kirklinton Sandstone with the Keuper Sandstone (and hence with the Helsby and Ormskirk Sandstone formations), should be treated with caution. It seems more likely that the Kirklinton Sandstone Formation (largely confined to the Carlisle plain, Arthurton et al., 1978, p.202) is equivalent to the combined Ormskirk Sandstone Formation and Calder Sandstone Member (Barnes et al., 1994; Jones and Ambrose, 1994).

Sherwood Sandstone Group (undivided)

Drilling information from the Luce Bay sub-basin of the Stranraer Basin is restricted to BGS Borehole 70/02 which proved 11.5 m of red-brown sandstone beneath 31 m of Quaternary deposits (Wright et al., 1971; Wilkinson and Halliwell, 1979). Based on seismic reflector characteristics and evidence from adjacent shallow BGS boreholes in Wigtown Bay and farther south, the 11.5 m-thick sandstone was assumed to be Triassic in age by Jackson et al. (1995) and BGS (1994), and probably belonging to the St Bees Sandstone Formation.

MERCIA MUDSTONE GROUP

The maximum thickness (3025 m) of the Mercia Mudstone Group (Anisian to early Rhaetian in age). occurs in the Keys Basin, (Figure 16b). The group comprises a two component lithological system of halite (both haselgebirge and clean halite) and mudstone. Below the Blue Anchor Formation, it is subdivided into five thick silty mudstone units, dominantly red-brown in colour but with subordinate grey-green beds (Wilson and Evans, 1990), separated by five thick halites (Table 4). Definitions of the stratigraphical units are given in Jackson and Johnson (1996). Results from the Isle of Man area indicate that variation in thickness of individual formations and members in the various basins, generally follows the standard pattern (see p.72). Although each major subdivision has been penetrated at least once amongst the seven available offshore wells (Figure 24), the succession is extensively affected by faulting and halokinetic disruption (Chapter 4). Faulting appears to have focused particularly on the interbedded halite/mudstone successions of the incompetent Mythop Halite and Cleveleys Mudstone members.

The group was originally deposited across virtually the entire area (Jackson et al., 1995, fig. 51), but post-Early Jurassic erosion has left only large erosional remnants (Figure 1), which are probably coincident with the areas of most rapid Triassic subsidence. The group has also been penetrated in three old boreholes on the Isle of Man (Lamplugh, 1903; Gregory, 1920), and in eight shallow BGS offshore boreholes (Wright et al., 1971; Wilkinson and Halliwell, 1979; Jackson et al., 1995, p.59; BGS, 1994).

All the basins in the Isle of Man area contain substantial salt deposits. Although the reduced group thickness in the Solway Firth and Peel basins (Figure 24) is comparable with that in the southern part of the East Irish Sea Basin where halites in the Leyland Formation are less well developed (Jackson and Johnson, 1996), in terms of facies, the well developed halites of the Leyland Formation in the Solway Firth and Peel basins more closely resemble those of the more rapidly subsiding northern part of the East Irish Sea Basin. In the Solway Firth and Peel basins, the mudstone intercalations and partings (especially those in the Rossall and Mythop Halite members and Preesall Halite Formation) display higher gamma-ray (API) values than in the East Irish Sea Basin, possibly reflecting greater proximity to a northerly (?granitic) source of fine-grained micaceous clastic material in the Southern Uplands.

In the East Irish Sea, the Leyland Formation thickens northwards into the Keys Basin, and, to the north-west of the Ramsey–Whitehaven Ridge, is still relatively thick with well-developed halites across the whole of the Isle of Man area. The halites fail southwards towards the Cheshire Basin (Jackson and Johnson, 1996). The halites are also well developed in Northern Ireland bordering the North Channel (Manning and Wilson, 1975; Penn et al., 1983; Warrington and Ivimey-Cook, 1992). This cumulative evidence is taken here to indicate that during the Röt transgression (or possibly a Solling precursor) at the base of the Mercia Mudstone Group, the sea entered the area from the north-west through the North Channel Basin along the same route as the Bakevellia Sea transgressions. In contrast, the younger formations (Preesall Halite Formation and above) appear to be considerably thinner to the north of the Ramsey–Whitehaven Ridge than to the south. There is also slender evidence for a southward-developing unconformity (p.97) beneath the Preesall Halite Formation, which would account for the regional southerly thinning of the highest division of the Cleveleys Mudstone Member (Figure 24; Jackson and Johnson, 1996, p.34, and Panel 2B). This event may be a break-up unconformity linked to the regional palaeoslope reversal and the rise to prominence of the 'south-west passage' (p.84) on a southward-directed palaeoslope. The Cleveleys Mudstone Member and Preesall Halite Formation also show the greatest differences in thickness across faults and between basin-centre and basin-margin successions; this might be linked to a brief period of locally accelerated rifting and extension.

The biostratigraphy of the Mercia Mudstone Group in East Irish Sea Basin was outlined in Jackson and Johnson (1996, Appendix 1 and p.12); see also Warrington et al. (1980), Wilson and Evans (1990) and Warrington and Ivimey-Cook (1992) and references therein.

The **Leyland Formation** is estimated at 600 to 950 m in thickness, but all successions are faulted or eroded. Above a thin basal transgressive sabkha evaporite (Stanah Member), the formation can be divided, in the more rapidly subsiding areas of the Isle of Man region, into a series of alternating mudstone and halite members (Table 4; Jackson and Johnson, 1996). In the more slowly subsiding successions adjacent to the Ramsey–Whitehaven Ridge, the lower halites pass laterally into a thinner mudstone succession (Unit L1 mudstones, Figure 24) proved in wells 112/25a-1 and 112/19-1.

The very thin **Stanah Member** (6–13 m thick) comprises a thinly interbedded, heterolithic coastal sabkha evaporite with marked lateral facies variations, deposited during the Röt transgression (Jackson and Johnson, 1996, p.58). The member is characterised by very high sonic velocities that generate the top reflector of the 'Ormskirk Sandstone Formation seismic package' (Figures 14, 18, 19a), and by high gamma-ray value spikes from the dark grey to black mudstone partings. Remarkably, given the extensive faulting in the Mercia Mudstone Group, the member is present in all seven wells in the area, testifying to *its* role, rather than the top of the Sherwood Sandstone Group, as the *décollement* surface at the mudstone/sandstone competence contrast.

Successions in the area are dominantly anhydritic (Figure 24), and pass south-eastwards into a wide dolomite-rich fringe (e.g. Well 113/26-1) along the depositional feather-edge in the northern and central parts of the East Irish Sea Basin. Farther south, the member is overlapped by the Fylde Halite Member (Jackson and Johnson, 1996, p.58). These facies belts corroborate the idea that the sea entered the area from the north-west via the North Channel during the Röt transgression. Gamma-ray values of successive individual mudstones generally decrease up section, indicating increasingly aerobic conditions with time. The anhydrite successions range from a single mudstone–evaporite subcycle in wells 112/19-1 and 112/25a-1, through sequences comprising two subcycles (Well 111/29-1) and three subcycles (wells 111/15-1, 111/25-1A and 112/15-1) before passing outwards to Well 113/26-1 (Jackson and Johnson, 1996, p.58) in the dolomite fringe (see also Jackson, in press). Following Newman (1999, fig. 9), a 13 m-thick thick ferruginous sandstone of exceptionally high sonic velocity (including two thin anhydrites) in Well 111/29-1 is viewed here as a sandy basin margin facies of the Stanah Member (resting disconformably on the Calder Sandstone Member), rather than a condensed Ormskirk Sandstone Formation deposit. A thin representative of the Stanah Member probably occurs in the Point of Ayre No. 3 Borehole at the base of a 30.48 m-thick unit, described as 'brown and grey marl with gypsum beds' (Gregory, 1920).

As in the East Irish Sea Basin, the **Fylde Halite Member** is largely a topography-filling, syndepositional fault deposit, precipitated during evaporative drawdown following the Röt transgression, and with a more limited distribution than all other halites. The mudstone intercalations increase progressively upwards in abundance and thickness, the reverse pattern to that observed in the Rossall Halite Member. Orange potassium salts were noted in Well 111/15-1 (composite log) and possibly in Well 111/25-1A. In the type section in Well 113/26-1 (183.5 m, the thickest succession recorded to date, Figure 24; Jackson and Johnson, 1996), the upper three of the customary six halite leaves are much thinner than the rest. In the complete but much thinner succession of the member equivalent in Well 111/15-1 (72.24 m thick), the halite to mudstone ratio of the member is higher than elsewhere, and the upper three halites can be differentiated only with difficulty. This halite has been incorrectly identified as the Ballyboley Halite Member on the composite log.

In the Peel Basin (Well 111/25-1A) and the Solway Firth Basin (Well 112/15-1) the gamma-ray values of the predominantly grey mudstone intercalations are much higher than in the East Irish Sea Basin, and the upper three halite spikes ensure a low halite to mudstone ratio at the top of the member. The section in Well 111/25-1A (88.5 m thick) includes a dolerite sill (12.5 m thick) that appears to have indurated the adjacent mudstone (Figure 24). The exact boundaries of the second and third halites cannot be firmly identified. In Well 112/15-1 (32.77 m), an attenuated basal Unit L1 mudstone replaces the two lowest, and much of the third, leaves of halite (see below).

The **Ansdell Mudstone Member** represents a brief mud-rich interlude (probably lacustrine mud-flats) during halite deposition, and is generally characterised by a near-median halite stringer (Figure 24; Jackson and Johnson, 1996, p.50). In Well 113/26-1, the member comprises an atypical expanded succession (61.26 m thick) close to the Keys Basin depocentre, with some six to seven thinner impure halite and dolomitic siltstone beds in both the upper and lower packages recognised by Jackson and Johnson (1996). Similarly, in Well 111/15-1, a slightly expanded succession (41.15 m thick) near the Portpatrick Fault (Chapter 4) contains four thin halite stringers separating mudstones that show a progressive upward increase in gamma-ray values. In slightly condensed successions, the mudstone interdigitates with halite at both lower and upper contacts. Provisional thicknesses are 16.91 m in Well 112/15-1 and 18.5 m in the similar succession of Well 111/25-1A, both of which are dominated by the thin but ubiquitous, single near-median halite (Figure 24).

The **Rossall Halite Member** is generally the thinnest halite in the report area, and its upper boundary is sharply delineated. In Well 113/26-1 (109.5 m thick, Figure 24), the member displays the internal features characteristic of basinal locations of the East Irish Sea Basin: four main halite leaves that become progressively cleaner and thicker upwards, separated by three red-brown mudstone intercalations with progressive upward decreasing gamma-ray values (Jackson and Johnson, 1996). A similar, complete, but thinner succession, in which each lithological component can still be clearly identified, occurs in both Well 111/25-1A (73 m) and Well 112/15-1 (68.58 m) (Figure 24). Possible potassium salts were noted in Well 111/25-1A (composite log). In contrast, attenuation occurs over and adjacent to the Ramsey–Whitehaven Ridge, and the lower halite leaves of the basinal settings pass laterally and progressively from the base upwards into the thinner topmost Unit L1 mudstones. In Well 112/25a-1 (37.25 m) only the upper two halites were precipitated, and in Well 112/19-1 (26 m) only the uppermost and cleanest halite leaf is present (Figure 24; see below). These abbreviated halite sequences compare directly with those in the southern part of the East Irish Sea Basin (Jackson and Johnson, 1996, e.g. Well 110/11-1, p.47 and Well 110/12a-1, p.43) and onshore in west Lancashire (Wilson, 1990; Wilson and Evans, 1990).

This lateral variation in internal development demonstrates that early in the depositional history of the member, the individual fault-controlled brine pans of the East Irish Sea and North Channel basins and a possibly united Solway Firth–Peel Basin were separated by Unit L1 evaporitic mud-flats developed over interbasinal ridges such as the Ramsey–Whitehaven Ridge (see below). Halite precipitation occurred during evaporative drawdown in a series of progressively expanding shallow salterns (Warren, 1999, p.95), and only during precipitation of the topmost halite leaf did a brine pan extend uninterruptedly from the North Channel Basin to the East Irish Sea Basin (contrast Jackson et al., 1995, fig. 55).

The same halite is thought to have been proved in all three boreholes at the Point of Ayre on the Isle of Man (Lamplugh, 1903; Gregory, 1920). In this account, the top of the member is tentatively placed at 192.18 m (Gregory, 1920) in Point of Ayre No. 3 Borehole (Figure 22). Previously, it was thought that the individual beds of halite in the boreholes belonged to the Rossall Halite Member, because they increased progressively upwards in thickness (Jackson et al., 1995, p.76). However, revised correlations with Well 112/19-1 suggest that either faulting juxtaposes the Mythop and Rossall Halite members in Point of Ayre No. 3 Borehole, or complications occur owing to 'wet' rockhead deposits and associated disturbed beds (Earp and Taylor, 1986; Rose and Dunham, 1977) above a brine run (identified in Point of Ayre No. 1 Borehole, Lamplugh, 1903).

In the North Channel Basin (Portpatrick Sub-basin), the **Ballyboley Halite Member** (Manning and Wilson, 1975; Warrington et al., 1980) of the Craiganee Formation is the direct correlative of the Rossall Halite Member (Jackson et al., 1995, p.72), and similarly contains four halite leaves where fully developed (e.g. Larne No. 2 Borehole, Penn et al., 1983). However, in Well 111/15-1 (where it is 31.09 m thick), only the lowest two halites and adjacent mudstone are present below a thick dolerite sill (Figure 24) (compare wells 110/2-5 and 113/27-3, Jackson and Johnson, 1996, Panel 1B). The remainder of the member has been assimilated by the sill and/or faulted out. The Ballyboley Halite Member has been both misnamed and misidentified on the composite log of Well 111/15-1.

Figure 24

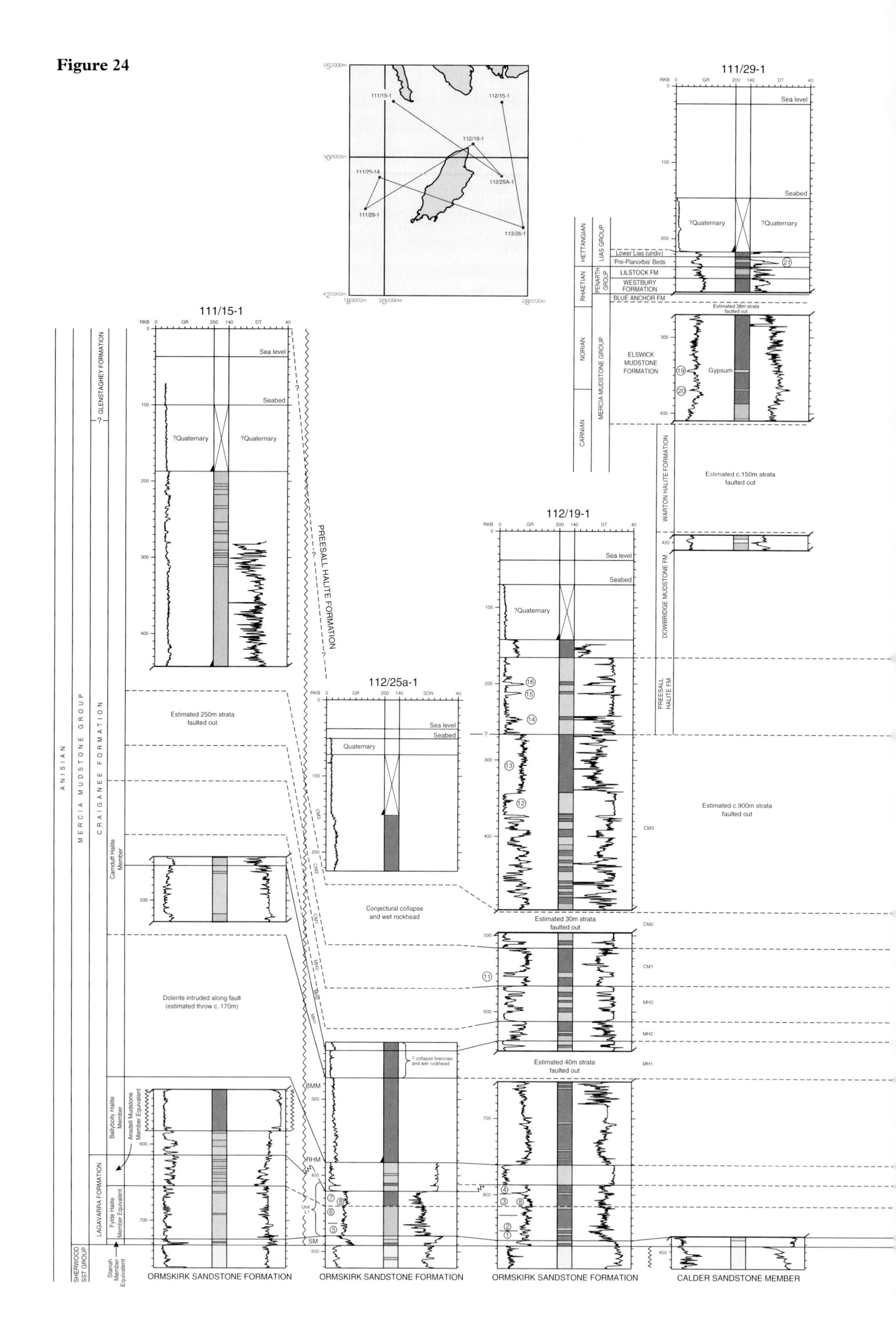

111/15-1
112/25a-1
112/19-1
111/29-1
111/25-1A
112/15-1
112/25A-1
113/26-1
Sea level
Seabed
?Quaternary
Quaternary
Estimated 250m strata faulted out
Dolerite intruded along fault (estimated throw c. 170m)
Conjectural collapse and wet rockhead
Estimated 30m strata faulted out
Estimated 40m strata faulted out
Estimated c.150m strata faulted out
Estimated c.900m strata faulted out
Estimated 38m strata faulted out
? collapse breccias and wet rockhead
PREESALL HALITE FORMATION
ANISIAN
MERCIA MUDSTONE GROUP
CRAIGANEE FORMATION
GLENSTAGHEY FORMATION
LAGAVARRA FORMATION
Carnduff Halite Member
Ballyboley Halite Member
Ansdell Mudstone Member Equivalent
Fylde Halite Member Equivalent
Stanah Member Equivalent
SHERWOOD SST GROUP
HETTANGIAN
RHAETIAN
NORIAN
CARNIAN
LIAS GROUP
PENARTH GROUP
Lower Lias (undiv)
'Pre-Planorbis' Beds
LILSTOCK FM
WESTBURY FORMATION
BLUE ANCHOR FM
ELSWICK MUDSTONE FORMATION
Gypsum
WARTON HALITE FORMATION
DOWBRIDGE MUDSTONE FM
PREESALL HALITE FM
ORMSKIRK SANDSTONE FORMATION
CALDER SANDSTONE MEMBER
BMM
RHM
SM
Unit L1
CM1
CM2
CM3
MH1
MH2
MH3

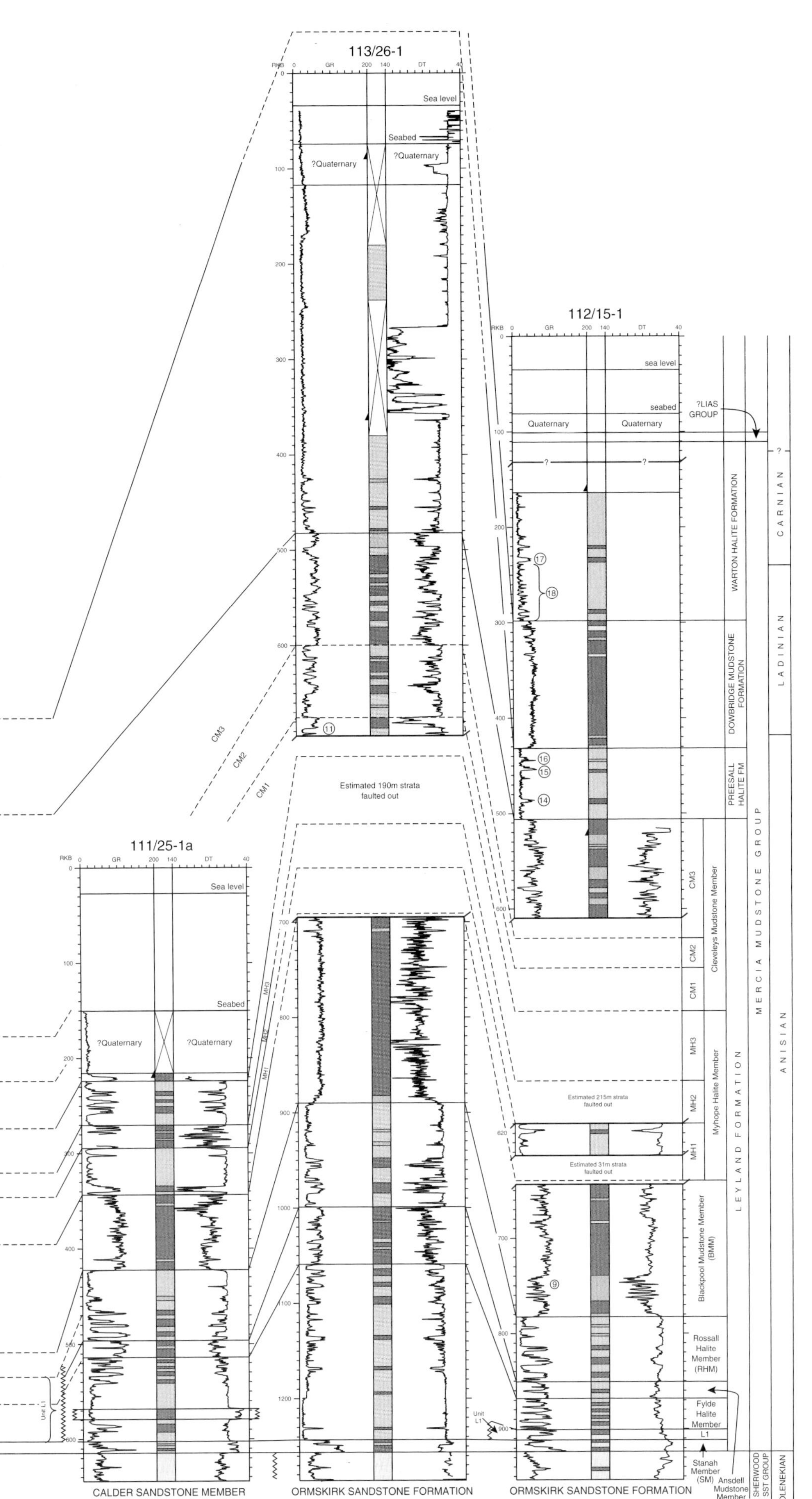

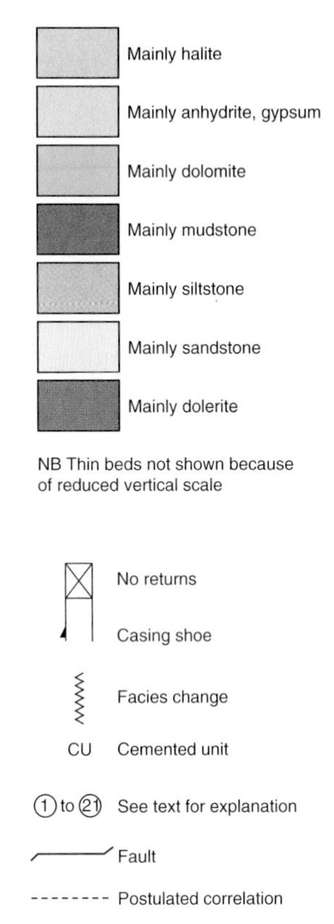

Figure 24
Correlation of wells proving the Mercia Mudstone Group, Penarth Group and Lias Group in the Isle of Man area. The figure is tied to the base of the Mercia Mudstone Group and has been arranged to show the thickest successions on the right with thinning taking place towards the left. The stratigraphical nomenclature of Northern Ireland, applicable to Well 111/15-1, is also shown on the left. The figure is shown in 'exploded view', to highlight the extent of faulting in all Mercia Mudstone Group successions; in some cases, a numerical estimate of fault throw has been included in an appropriately scaled 'gap'.

Depending on location, part or all of the 100 to 200 m-thick succession comprising the Fylde and Rossall Halite members (and the intervening Ansdell Mudstone Member) in basinal and hanging wall settings passes laterally into thinner (around 60 m thick) **Unit L1 mudstones** of the Leyland Formation on structural swells, on footwalls and towards the basin margins (Jackson and Johnson, 1996). These mudstones have been penetrated in two wells (112/19-1 and 112/25a-1) adjacent to the Ramsey–Whitehaven Ridge; their equivalent in Northern Ireland, and parts of the North Channel Basin, is the Lagavarra Formation (Manning and Wilson, 1975; Jackson et al., 1995, p.72).

In Well 112/19-1 (where the Unit L1 mudstones are 74 m thick) four informal lithological subdivisions of variously saliferous and anhydritic mudstone can be recognised (items 1, 2, 3, 4, Figure 24). In Well 112/25a-1 (58.75 m), a tripartite subdivision of successively, grey mudstone and very fine-grained sandstone (462.5–479 m RKB), grey siltstone (439–462.5 m RKB), and red-brown anhydritic mudstone (420.25–439 m RKB) is apparent (items 5, 6, 7, respectively). The boundary at 816.5 m in Well 112/19-1 and at 439 m in Well 112/25a-1 (item 8) is thought to equate (Jackson and Johnson, 1996, p.30) with that between the grey Hambleton and the red Singleton mudstone formations of west Lancashire (Wilson and Evans, 1990; Wilson, 1990). On the wireline logs of both wells, Unit L1 displays a ragged and coarsely serrate motif, and can be divided unequally (at item 8) into a thicker silty lower portion and a thinner upper portion. There is a marked upward increase in gamma-ray values and a slight upward decrease in sonic velocity at the boundary between the two portions (especially in Well 112/19-1); these shifts correspond with the top of the Fylde Halite Member (compare wells 110/8a-5 and 110/13-8 in the southern part of the East Irish Sea Basin, Jackson and Johnson, 1996, Panel 2B).

The Unit L1 mudstones probably represent a complex combination of water-laid and lacustrine sediment and loess, deposited on ridges and low water table sites on near-coastal sabkhas, and on the mudflats separating, and the strandlines surrounding, shallow salterns. The water table was progressively lowered during deposition of the formation. During depositional episodes, salt may have been precipitated initially, but it was blown from the ridge as it dried out, repeatedly exposing the underlying mudstone (Warren, 1999; Wilson, 1990).

Along strike from Well 112/19-1, a very similar thickness of Unit L1 mudstones has been proved in the Point of Ayre No. 3 Borehole on the Isle of Man (Gregory, 1920; identified in this account as 70.48 m thick, from 258.93 to 329.42 m, Figure 22). Sporadic sandstone 'ribs' (Gregory, 1920) denote a more sandy facies than in Well 112/19-1, transitional to the marginal, arenaceous development of the equivalent Lagavarra Formation seen in Larne No. 1 Borehole (48.31 m; Manning and Wilson, 1975). A featheredge arenaceous development of the basal Unit L1, of similar facies to the Lagavarra Formation, is probably present in Well 112/15-1, where a 9.45 m-thick interbedded mudstone and sandstone unit occurs between the high velocity arenaceous Stanah Member and the Fylde Halite Member (Figure 24). The whole of the lowest two halite leaves and most of the third halite leaf of the Fylde Halite Member are thought to pass laterally into the 9.45 m unit.

The **Blackpool Mudstone Marker** forms a wireline log marker in the East Irish Sea Basin (Jackson and Johnson, 1996), and the succession in Well 113/26-1 (194.46 m thick, faulted top, Figure 24) in the northern part of the basin typifies several of the wireline log characteristics. These include a relatively linear gamma-ray log motif and an erratic and spiky sonic log trace (with very low velocities at possible dissolved gypsum veins and small solution cavities in the loessic mudstone, Wilson 1990). In addition, though this is less well developed in Well 113/26-1, the informal division into a lower package without halite and anhydrite stringers, and an upper package with four to five thin halites is observed (Jackson and Johnson, 1996, p.89, Panel 1B).

North of the Ramsey–Whitehaven Ridge, the member loses its marker status and distinctive gamma-ray log profile as the silt content and halite to mudstone ratio increase. In Well 112/19-1, a thickness (109 m was drilled, faulted upper contact) although the upper package (with four to five thin impure halite and dolomitic siltstone beds) and the lower package are still discernible (boundary at 710 m, Figure 24), a thin basal unit of upward-increasing gamma-ray values (compare with Well 113/26-1) dictates a more logical tripartite subdivision (also apparent on the sonic log). In Well 112/15-1 (139.29 m), the same three-fold subdivision on the sonic log and the lower and upper packages on the gamma-ray log are still apparent, but a low velocity siltstone unit (item 9, Figure 24) introduces a striking new feature (also weakly developed in Well 113/26-1). In Well 111/25-1A (79.5 m), a logical tripartite sonic log subdivision closely resembles that of Well 112/15-1, whereas the upward-coarsening trend on the gamma-ray log is more reminiscent of Well 112/19-1. On the Isle of Man (Lamplugh, 1903; Gregory, 1920), the Blackpool Mudstone Member is present in the Point of Ayre boreholes beneath Quaternary deposits, but the records are ambiguous, and firm boundaries cannot be fixed at present.

As in the East Irish Sea Basin, the **Mythop Halite Member** of the Peel and Solway Firth basins also contains the highest proportion of mudstone of any halite in the Mercia Mudstone Group. This incompetent succession is extremely susceptible to faulting (Figure 24), but nevertheless, the internal stratigraphical features are uniform throughout the report area. Well 111/25-1A (120.5 m) probably proves a complete and unfaulted succession that closely resembles the slightly thicker sequence in the offshore type section of Well 113/27-3 (165.5 m thick; Jackson and Johnson, 1996, p.39). The basic features of the informal tripartite subdivision of the member are well illustrated:

Unit MH1 is dominantly halitic with two halite leaves, the lower generally being the thickest in the entire member

Unit MH2 is mudstone-dominant and forms a prominent central 'waist' on wireline log profiles

Unit MH3 is halitic, with five main halites; the lowest and highest halite are slightly thicker than the rest).

Several mudstone intercalations are dolomitic at the top and bottom, producing thin high velocity projections on the sonic log (see Well 113/27-3, Jackson and Johnson, 1996, p.39). The lowermost mudstone intercalation of Unit MH1 is particularly well developed in Well 111/25-1A (item 10, Figure 24; compare with Well 113/27-3).

The individual halites and mudstone intercalations in Units MH2 and MH3 of Well 112/19-1 (85.5 m, faulted base; Figure 24) can be closely matched with those in Well 111/25-1A, though the dolomitic mudstone fringes appear to occur in different intercalations. As in the East Irish Sea Basin, individual halites are represented by a round-shouldered appearance on the wireline logs. This arises from a haselgebirge facies enclosing a central clean halite (Jackson and Johnson, 1996, p.38). Detailed correlations with the similar, albeit fragmented, succession in Well 112/15-1 (34 m, faulted top and bottom) demonstrate that, in addition to the major fault detachment on the top of Unit MH1, a small fault probably cuts out the basal 31 m of Unit MH1 (Figure 24).

In Well 112/25a-1 (47.75 m, faulted top), the low gamma-ray interval from 224.75 to 272.5 m (recorded behind thick casing) is considered here to represent the basal part of Unit MH2 overlying a complete Unit MH1, although the cuttings description throughout records very soft red-brown anhydritic mudstone with swelling properties. The mudstone may constitute a halite residue and collapse breccia of Unit MH1 at a shallow 'wet' rockhead contact (Wilson and Evans, 1990; Rose and Dunham, 1977; Earp and Taylor, 1986), faulted against the Cleveleys Mudstone Member (Figure 24).

In Well 111/15-1, above a dolerite sill, the log profile of a clean halite with red-brown mudstone and siltstone partings (84.12 m, faulted top and bottom) resembles the lower section of the **Carnduff Halite Member** (Craiganee Formation) in Larne No. 2 Borehole (Penn et al., 1983; Jackson et al., 1995, fig. 59, p.72), and can be correlated in turn with the thick lower halite in Unit MH1 of the Mythop Halite Member (Figure 24). Traces of potassium salt were noted throughout the halite (composite log). Detailed correlations indicate that the siltstone/dolerite contact at 528.53 m RKB lies only about 2.5 m above the true base of the member. The equivalents of Units MH3 and MH2 (with the exception of the basal 9.1 m siltstone of Unit MH2) are thought to be faulted out at 444.71 m RKB.

The **Cleveleys Mudstone Member** comprises a thick and complex heterolithic succession. Three subdivisions are recognised: Units CM1 to CM3. Units CM1 and CM3 are dominantly interlaminated and interbanded red and green 'striped' lacustrine laminites (silty mudstone and siltstone) with sporadic thin dolomites, and are separated by a halite sequence, Unit CM2, which is well developed in areas that experienced rapid subsidence (Jackson and Johnson, 1996, p.34). The syndepositional member displays abrupt vertical and lateral facies changes and is largely waterlaid in origin. Depositional environments ranged from shallow lakes with sporadic lacustrine and fluviodeltaic sands to brine pools and thin dolomitic sabkha deposits (Wilson, 1990; Wilson and Evans, 1990).

An unfaulted succession of the member has not been drilled in the Isle of Man area, probably because of the internal contrasts in lithological competence. The most complete succession, albeit atypical in the upper part in relation to those from the East Irish Sea Basin, is the very thick sequence in Well 112/19-1 (299.25 m thick, Figure 24). Unit CM1 (49 m thick) presents a similar development to that in the East Irish Sea Basin, with erratic but broadly vertical gamma-ray and sonic log traces, abruptly interrupted by a thin but clean, persistent paired halite (item 11, Figure 24, Jackson and Johnson, 1996, Panel 1B, item A). The top of Unit CM2 cannot be fixed with certainty, but only the basal halites (21.25 m) are thought to be present below a fault that has an estimated throw of 30 m. On the sonic log, small but characteristic projecting peaks (probably dolomite) distinguish the top and bottom of some halites, as in the East Irish Sea Basin. The remainder of the succession, displaying a highly erratic gamma-ray log response, has been tentatively identified as Unit CM3 (229 m). However, the clean halite (343.5–372 m, item 12, Figure 24) and the overlying saliferous mudstone with sublinear gamma-ray trace (267.25–373.5 m, item 13) are anomalous and do not appear to have been recorded elsewhere in the Isle of Man area or East Irish Sea Basin.

One explanation for these anomalies is that a hitherto unrecognised regional unconformity may develop southwards from Northern Ireland beneath the Preesall Halite Formation and equivalents. In support of this suggestion, the isopachs of Unit CM3 appear to show a steady southward thinning from the Isle of Man area towards and throughout the East Irish Sea Basin (Jackson and Johnson, 1996, Panel 1B, p.34). The unconformity may represent an intra-Mercia Mudstone Group break-up unconformity bordering the North Atlantic, as recently postulated for the British Isles by Ruffell and Shelton (2000). It may date the decline in the influence of the 'northwest passage', and may be the tectonic event responsible for the reversal of the regional palaeoslope (p.84) from north to south.

In Well 113/26-1 (213.36 m, faulted base), only the highest 19.81 m of Unit CM1 have been proved, and the thin but clean paired halite seen in Well 112/19-1 (item 11, Figure 24) rests at a *décollement* on the top of the Blackpool Mudstone Member. Unit CM2 (74.98 m thick) contains six individual halites (compare with the type section of Well 110/3-2), some with small projecting spurs on the sonic log profile indicating anhydrite and/or dolomite. Unit CM3 (118.57 m) includes several symmetrical cycles of interbedded grey-green and red silty mudstone and siltstone that typify the northern part of the East Irish Sea Basin.

Unit CM3 in Well 112/15-1 (103.18 m, faulted base) consists of pale grey dolomitic siltstone, interlaminated grey-green and red-brown slightly dolomitic and saliferous silty mudstone, and sporadic thin dolomite and halite beds. The highly erratic gamma-ray log motif is more akin to that of Well 112/19-1 than Well 113/26-1, and reflects the higher proportion of mudstone. Cuttings descriptions for the postulated Cleveleys Mudstone Member in Well 112/25a-1 (?>151.75 m) record mostly soft red-brown (with minor interbedded grey) mudstone, possibly comprising a 'wet' rockhead deposit.

The upper part of the **Craiganee Formation** in Well 111/15-1 (255.73 m) above the Carnduff Halite

Member (Wilson and Manning, 1978; Jackson et al., 1995, p.72) approximately equates to the Cleveleys Mudstone Member, though the threefold subdivision of that member cannot be recognised in Well 111/15-1. It is possible that either the succession is faulted and highly expanded, or the equivalent Unit CM2 halites have been partly dissolved at a 'wet' rockhead (Figure 24). The linear gamma-ray log motif, although compromised behind thick casing, resembles that of equivalent strata in Larne No. 2 Borehole (Penn et al., 1983). A thick, monotonous, lower division of red-brown saliferous and dolomitic siltstone with thin, pale grey dolomite beds and argillaceous sandstone is overlain by a complex upper division of interbedded red-brown dolomitic and saliferous siltstone and associated mudstone and sandstone, together with halites (up to 4.57 m thick), traces of potassium salts, and thick pale blue-grey dolomite (up to 12.19 m thick). The last are probably contemporaneous with dolomite in the Dowsing Formation of the southern North Sea (Table 4; Johnson et al., 1994). The halites were mistakenly termed the Larne Halite Member of the Glenstaghey Formation on the composite log (from 232.87 to 279.50 m RKB).

Well 113/26-1 proves a thick sequence of clean massive halites (>313.03 m, top not seen, Figure 24) with sporadic red-brown mudstone partings, that is typical of hanging wall successions of the **Preesall Halite Formation** in the East Irish Sea Basin. The formation was probably precipitated as the aggradational infill of a halite saltern (Warren, 1999) or a coastal salina (Wilson and Evans, 1990). It possesses the highest halite to mudstone ratio of all the halites and consequently, although mudstone partings are the least common of any halite in the Mercia Mudstone Group, they are extraordinarily persistent (Jackson and Johnson, 1996, p.26). In the East Irish Sea Basin, the formation also shows marked attenuation over penecontemporaneous swells (e.g. Morecambe Field), towards the basin margins and in footwall successions. Thus although implausible at first sight, detailed correlations demonstrate that the much thinner successions of Well 112/19-1 (100.25 m) and Well 112/15-1 (74.83 m) to the north of the Ramsey–Whitehaven Ridge are also complete. In both wells, the three most prominent mudstone partings (items 14, 15, 16, Figure 24), dominantly red-brown to purple-red in colour, correlate directly with those in wells 110/2a-8, 110/3b-4 and 110/13-8 (Jackson and Johnson, 1996, pp.88, 90), and also with those separating the A-Bed, B-Bed, and various C-Bed halites in the 100 to 130 m-thick Preesall Salt Member of the eponymous saltfield in west Lancashire (Wilson and Evans, 1990; Wilson, 1990). This correlation now allows an informal four-fold subdivision of the formation to be made throughout the combined Isle of Man and East Irish Sea Basin area.

The lower two-thirds of the **Dowbridge Mudstone Formation** in Well 112/15-1 (133.35 m, Figure 24) comprises brown-red loessic mudstone and minor interbedded siltstone, with thin pale grey argillaceous dolomite beds near the base; the basal beds are seen also in Well 112/19-1 (>23 m). The upper third of the formation in Well 112/15-1 consists of a heterolithic assemblage of dolomitic mudstone, mostly red-brown, but with thin and sporadic, well-cemented beds of pale grey dolomitic silty sandstone, dolomitic siltstone, and dolomite. An origin on a distal floodplain and sabkha is envisaged. The relatively linear gamma-ray log profile of Well 112/15-1 bears very close comparison with that of 110/2a-8 (Jackson and Johnson, 1996, p.23), but the low gamma-ray spikes in the upper third of the formation are probably generated by beds of dolomite, rather than halite and anhydrite. The formation thickness is about 55 per cent of that in Well 110/2a-8 (242.5 m) which implies that:

- the condensation seen in the Preesall Halite Formation to the north of the Ramsey–Whitehaven Ridge was repeated during deposition of the Dowbridge Mudstone Formation
- there is a regional southward thickening of the latter into the equivalent Wych and Byley mudstone formations of the Cheshire Basin (Earp and Taylor, 1986; Wilson, 1993; Jackson and Johnson, 1996, panels 1B, 2B)

The lower 70 per cent of the clean, massive **Warton Halite Formation** (Jackson and Johnson, 1996) in Well 112/15-1 (>134.87 m thick, Figure 24) is recorded as a 'box-car' gamma-ray log motif that reveals numerous brown-red mudstone partings. The vertical spacing of these persistent mudstone partings, and the identification of shoaling-up clastic cycles (Warren, 1999, p.68) allow for very precise internal correlation of the formation. The 'marker' parting (item 17, Figure 24) in Well 112/15-1 equates with correlation line B on panels 1A and 2A of Jackson and Johnson (1996), and indicates that the thickness of item 18 in Well 112/15-1 is 57.3 per cent of the same interval in Well 110/2a-8. Two complete (and the lower part of a third) shoaling-up clastic cycles can be identified in Well 112/15-1 using the gamma-ray values of mudstone partings. The same cycles can be identified in the East Irish Sea Basin (wells 110/2a-8, 110/8a-5 and 110/13-8) and Cheshire Basin (Prees No. 1 Borehole, Wilkesley Borehole; Jackson and Johnson, 1996, panels 1A, 1B), from which it is concluded that:

- a single brine pan with a common evolution stretched uninterruptedly from the Solway Firth Basin to the Cheshire Basin
- southward thickening occurred from the Solway Firth to the East Irish Sea Basin
- a full succession of the Warton Halite Formation has not yet been drilled in the Isle of Man area or the East Irish Sea Basin (the maximum recorded succession is around 70 per cent in both the 110/13-8 and 112/15-1 wells).

Precipitation occurred in a successor saltern to that of the Preesall Halite Formation.

The **Elswick Mudstone Formation** has been recognised above a major halite detachment in Well 111/29-1 by the distinctive, sinuous and sympathetic tracking of both gamma-ray and sonic logs (Figure 24). Confirmation is provided by the recovery of a very impoverished Norian miospore assemblage of *Classopollis* spp. and *Ricciisporites tuberculatus* at 297.5 m RKB (sidewall core). Approximately 133 m of the formation were drilled in the well, but both the upper and lower contacts were faulted, and the full succession is estimated at 156 m; this constitutes the thickest development of the formation proved to date in the entire Irish Sea and Isle of Man area. It is also the only reliable wireline log profile that has not been muted by thick casing (Jackson and Johnson, 1996, p.16). The proportion of anhydrite in the formation is higher than elsewhere in the Mercia Mudstone Group. The wireline log response and reddish brown and brick-red mudstone and silty mudstone lithology compare very closely with the laterally equivalent Brooks Mill Mudstone Formation in the Prees No. 1 and Wilkesley boreholes (Penn, 1987; Jackson and Johnson, 1996, Panel 2A; Poole and Whiteman, 1966; Wilson, 1993), with the combined Port More and Knocksoghey formations of the Port More Borehole (Wilson, 1993; Wilson and Manning, 1978), and with the Triton Formation of the southern North Sea (Johnson et al., 1994) (Table 4).

The 3 m-thick anhydrite (item 19, Figure 24), of supratidal sabkha origin (Warrington and Ivimey-Cook, 1992), is an equivalent of the Tutbury Sulphate (Taylor, 1983). The anhydrite is also a correlative of the 6.4 m-thick anhydrite beds in the Wilkesley Borehole (portion 'b' in the Brooks Mill Mudstone Formation of Wilson, 1993; Poole and Whiteman, 1966) and in Prees No. 1 Borehole (Penn, 1987, Jackson and Johnson, 1996, Panel 2A). An important chronostratigraphical peg is afforded by the dolomitic silty sandstone or skerry (item 20, Figure 24) that correlates with the Coolmaghra Skerry of the Port More Borehole of Northern Ireland (Wilson, 1993, fig. 16; Wilson and Manning, 1978), with the Arden Sandstone equivalent in the Wilkesley Borehole (Wilson, 1993, fig. 16; Warrington et al., 1980) and in the Prees No. 1 Borehole, and with the Schilfsandstein. Together, they provide an important latest Carnian time-marker throughout north-west Europe (Warrington et al., 1980).

In Well 111/29-1, the **Blue Anchor Formation** (Table 5; formerly the Tea Green Marl, Warrington et al., 1980) is believed to be cut out by minor faulting (throw 38 m), which juxtaposes the Westbury Formation and Elswick Mudstone Formation at about 271 m RKB (Figure 24; see Jackson and Johnson, 1996, pp.13–14, for a description of the formation in the wider Irish Sea area). Neither the characteristic pale green and green-grey dolomitic mudstones (e.g. Poole and Whiteman, 1966; Wilson, 1993), nor the complex spiky log motifs seen in Prees No. 1 Borehole in the Cheshire Basin (Penn, 1987; Jackson and Johnson, 1996, Panel 2A) were recorded.

PENARTH GROUP

The Penarth Group (Table 1) rests with a non-sequence on the Mercia Mudstone Group (Warrington et al., 1980). It was proved offshore for the first time in the Irish Sea, in Well 111/29-1 (from 237 to 271 m RKB, on log correlation), albeit with a faulted lower contact. Occurrences in the surrounding area show a low variation in thickness (Table 5). The marine Westbury Formation was deposited following a transgression encroaching from the south and initiated at the top of the Blue Anchor Formation (Warrington and Ivimey-Cook, 1992; Warrington, 1997). The succeeding lagoonal and subtidal Cotham Member of the Lilstock Formation was deposited during a shallowing of the sea, which subsequently deepened progressively into the Early Jurassic (Bradshaw et al., 1992; Warrington and Ivimey-Cook, 1992). The wireline log profiles of the Penarth Group in Well 111/29-1 can be closely matched with Prees No. 1 Borehole in the Cheshire Basin (Penn, 1987; Jackson and Johnson, 1996, Panel 2A), which in turn can be calibrated with the cored Wilkesley Borehole (Poole and Whiteman, 1966). Revised Penarth Group boundaries in the Wilkesley Borehole were given by Warrington (1997, p.39). In Well 111/29-1 strata between 250 and 262.5 m RKB have been dated as Rhaetian, mostly using sidewall cores. First downhole occurrences of the dinoflagellate cyst *Rhaetogonyaulax rhaetica* and abundant fish teeth were identified at 250 m RKB (the biostratigraphy of the interval 237–250 m is alluded to below).

The **Westbury Formation** has been identified (this account) in Well 111/29-1 between 252 and 271 m RKB by the moderately high gamma-ray values and the very low velocity over part of the section (Figure 24). A thickness of 19 m was proved but the lower contact was probably faulted. Dark grey to black pyritic non-calcareous mudstone is described from cuttings. If correct, this thickness comfortably exceeds those in adjacent, mostly basin margin, areas, but is presumed to be typical of basinal settings (Table 5).

The **Lilstock Formation** is tentatively assessed as occurring from about 237 to 252 m RKB in Well 111/29-1 (15 m, Figure 24). Wireline log profiles reveal a spiky gamma-ray trace with an overall upward decrease in gamma-ray values over much of the interval, and an exceptionally spiky and erratic sonic log. The high velocity, lower gamma-ray value spikes derive from the thin-bedded, grey, argillaceous calcareous siltstone and sandy limestone, and the very low velocity, higher gamma-ray value horizons from poorly indurated beige and yellowish brown to green-grey, dolomitic mudstone (Figure 24). In lithologically similar sequences in the Wilkesley Borehole (Poole and Whiteman, 1966; Warrington, 1997) and the Carlisle Basin (Ivimey-Cook et al., 1995) only the Cotham Member of the formation is thought to be present. A thin grey micritic limestone (0.8 m thick in the Carlisle Basin, and less than 0.15 m in the Wilkesley Borehole) was regarded by Ivimey-Cook et al. (1995, p.310; see also Warrington, 1997) as the topmost bed of the Cotham Member, and thus the calcareous Langport Member (formerly the 'White Lias') is thought to be absent.

JURASSIC

LIAS GROUP

The dominantly marine mudstone and bituminous limestone of the Lias Group were deposited over the entire area, continuing and deepening the northward-advancing transgression of the Rhaetian (Bradshaw et al., 1992; Morton, 1992; Warrington, 1997; Cope, 1997); erosion has since reduced Lower Jurassic occurrences to scattered remnant outliers (albeit in both basinal and marginal settings; Table 5). The preserved Lias and Penarth groups were estimated from

System	Group	Formation	Member	Stage	Ammonite zones	N. Ireland (composite)	111/29-1 Peel Basin	Solway FB (centre)	112/15-1 Solway (N)	Carlisle Basin	Keys Basin	Berw Basin	Cheshire Basin	Kish Bank Basin	Mochras (Cardigan Bay Basin)	
Jurassic	Lias Group			Toarcian	levesquei										>57	l
					thouarsense										23.93	t
					variabilis										44.04	v
					bifrons										42.07	b
					falciferum										62.02	f
					tenuicostatum										*c.*32.62	t
				Pliensbachian	spinatum								*c.*30		*c.*39.93	s
					margaritatus										*c.*107.29	m
					davoei										*c.*25.6	d
					ibex	>12.47(F)									*c.*83.82	i
					jamesoni	>103.11(F)									*c.*129.54	j
				Upper Sinemurian	raricostatum	>56.89(S)							*c.*457		82.3	r
					oxynotum	Igneous Sill								*c.*2700	51.81	o
					obtusum	Igneous Sill									84.74	o
				Lower Sinemurian	turneri	>11.51(S)	??*c.*400				⋆				50.29	t
					semicostatum	>65(S)		*c.*650-800							142.34	s
					bucklandi	>34(T)							27.28		106.68	b
				Hettangian	angulata	*c.*42(T)				>92			45.16		60.35	a
					liasicus	>49(M)							32.59		58.52	l
					planorbis	>19.5(L)	>6						25.43		18.29	p
Triassic		'Pre-Planorbis' Beds		Rhaetian		9.8(L)	15		?9.75	18.11	*c.*600	*c.*200	9.37		1.78	
	Penarth Group	Lilstock Formation	Langport Member			11.96(L)	15			0 (?0.8)			0 (??<0.15)		?>16.86	
			Cotham Member							5.03 (?4.23)			5.75			
		Westbury Formation				8.59(L)	>19(F)		ND	8.11			7.8	ND		
	Mercia Mudst. Group	Blue Anchor Formation				10.82(L)	?F	ND		5.92-6.55	ND	ND	15.14		?0	

Table 5 Distribution and thicknesses (in metres) of the latest Triassic (Blue Anchor Formation, Penarth Group) and Early Jurassic (Lias Group) rocks in the Isle of Man area and adjacent regions (based partly upon Warrington, 1997, fig. 3 and Jackson et al., 1995, fig. 61, with additional information from references quoted in the text, and from Cope et al., 1980, and references therein). In the Northern Ireland column, the thicknesses for the *semicostatum* to *ibex* zones inclusive are taken from the Port More Borehole (Wilson and Manning, 1978), and for the interval from the Blue Anchor Formation to the *planorbis* Zone inclusive from the Larne No. 1 Borehole (Manning and Wilson, 1975). The age of the youngest Lias Group in the columns for the Solway Firth, Peel, Berw and Kish Bank basins is conjectural. The thick black line in each column is the base of the Jurassic. The base of the Penarth Group is a non-sequence.

Abbreviations

S thickness reduced by igneous sill; L Larne No. 1 Borehole; M Magilligan Borehole; T Tyrone (Mire House) Borehole

F Fault; ND no data; ⋆ zone, unit identified

seismic profiles to have a total thickness of 650 m in the Solway Firth Basin and 200 m in the Berw Basin of the East Irish Sea, in each case overlying the disconformity at the base of the Penarth Group (Chapter 4; Jackson et al., 1995, p.80). Newman (1999) subsequently revised the thickness of Lower Jurassic strata in the Solway Firth Basin to 800 m, but this is poorly constrained, and the travel-time thickness suggests a lower figure. Lower Jurassic claystones, 52 m thick and of Rhaetian to Hettangian age, were reported for the first time in the Isle of Man area from Well 111/29-1 in the Peel Basin by Newman (1999). Provisional seismic re-interpretation, following the recognition in this account of the major *décollement* in Well 111/29-1 that almost juxtaposes the Elswick Mudstone Formation with the Calder Sandstone Member (Figure 24), now suggests that a well-developed Lower Jurassic succession (perhaps more than 400 m thick) may be present over large parts of the western Peel Basin.

As in surrounding offshore areas (northern North Sea, Partington et al., 1993, p.377; the southern North Sea, Johnson et al., 1994; East Irish Sea Basin, Jackson and Johnson, 1996, p.10), the base of the Jurassic in this account is defined using Jurassic microfauna and palynomorphs, and is taken at the base of the Lias Group, rather than at the incoming of the ammonite *Psiloceras planorbis* as in onshore areas (Cope et al., 1980; Ivimey-Cook et al., 1995). In Well 111/29-1 the Lias Group consists mostly of medium and dark grey, calcareous, pyritic, bituminous shelly mudstone and, as elsewhere in the Isle of Man area and north-west England (e.g. Ivimey-Cook et al., 1995), no lithological change occurs at the top of the 'Pre-Planorbis' Beds. Strata from 220 to 250 m RKB in Well 111/29-1 are dated by palynology as Hettangian to ?Rhaetian and the beds assigned correspondingly to the Lias Group–?Penarth Group. The first downhole occurrences of key taxa in sidewall cores, on which this determination was based, are included in Jackson (in press).

Wireline log correlations for Well 111/29-1 suggest that the **'Pre-Planorbis' Beds** occur from approximately 222 to 237 m RKB, with undivided lowermost Lias Group mudstone from approximately 216 to 222 m RKB (Figure 24). A low gamma-ray value, high velocity feature between 229 and 233.5 m RKB in Well 111/29-1 (item 21, Figure 24) is regarded here as the correlative of a broad, prominent, low gamma-ray, very high velocity spike in Prees No. 1 Borehole (about 615–620 m). The spike in Prees No. 1 Borehole was equated with the Langport Member by Penn (1987), and with the Lilstock Formation by Jackson and Johnson (1996, Panel 2A), but a revised correlation by Ivimey-Cook (in Warrington, 1997, p.39) implies that the spike occurs within the 'Pre-Planorbis' Beds. Accordingly, the strata from approximately 222 to 237 m RKB in Well 111/29-1 are referred here to the 'Pre-Planorbis' Beds (Figure 24). The spike in Prees No. 1 Borehole can be matched also with the thinly bedded calcareous siltstone and subsidiary limestone of the upper part of the 'Pre-Planorbis' Beds of the Wilkesley Borehole (151.41–153.82 m, Poole and Whiteman, 1966). In Well 111/29-1, the high velocity feature appears to correspond with a well-cemented bed of dolomitic, pyritic siltstone to silty sandstone. In turn, this bed correlates with the limestone-rich horizon from about 71.25 to 74.25 m in the middle of the 'Pre-Planorbis' Beds (18.11 m thick) of Borehole SB1 in the Carlisle Basin (Ivimey-Cook et al., 1995, fig. 3), and with Unit P1 limestone of the Penda Formation (Lias Group) of the southern North Sea (Lott and Knox, 1994).

Planorbis Zone and younger

The strata that occur between 216 and 222 m RKB in Well 111/29-1 are assessed as the basal part of the *planorbis* Zone of the Lias Group, since this zone occurs in all basal Jurassic successions around the Isle of Man area (Table 5; Ivimey-Cook et al., 1995), and a Hettangian age is confirmed from biostratigraphy. Dark grey to black mudstones, 9.19 m thick, of the Lias Group were proved in BGS Borehole 89/11A (Figures 1, 2) in the Keys Basin at the top of an approximately 600 m-thick seismic package lying disconformably on the Triassic (Table 5; Jackson et al., 1995). These mudstones have been dated as Lower Sinemurian, *turneri* Zone, or possibly Upper Sinemurian, *obtusum* Zone by Warrington (1997), who provided a full taxonomic listing, including an age update by Ivimey-Cook).

In Well 112/15-1, a 9.75 m-thick section of the Lias Group supposedly resting directly on the Mercia Mudstone Group at 110.34 m RKB has been recorded (Figure 24), though no further lithological details or biostratigraphical information were provided in the well report, nor were the intervening Penarth Group or Blue Anchor Formation recognised. It is possible that the record relies partly on the mapped limits of the large Lower Jurassic outlier depicted in the Solway Firth Basin (BGS, 1994). However, if the log is correct, the proven 70 per cent of the Warton Halite Formation identified in this account near the top of the well suggests that either the outlier is slightly smaller than mapped by BGS (1994), or, by comparison with Well 111/29-1, that a fault juxtaposes the Lias and Mercia Mudstone groups.

8 Post-Jurassic — Palaeogene igneous rocks

With the exception of a veneer of Quaternary deposits (Chapter 9), no post-Jurassic sedimentary rocks are preserved in the Manx region, principally as a result of uplift and erosion during Palaeogene and Neogene times (Chapter 4). However, development of the 'Iceland Plume' in the early Cainozoic led to the formation of the North Atlantic Igneous Province (e.g. White, 1988). This extensive area of igneous activity, centred on Iceland, affected localities as far afield as eastern Greenland, the Faroes and the north-western parts of the British Isles. In onshore Britain, igneous rocks comprising extensive lava flows, sills, dyke swarms and larger intrusive bodies are found, chiefly in the Inner Hebrides, western Scotland and Northern Ireland.

In the Manx region, early Cainozoic (Palaeogene) igneous rocks have a scattered but widespread distribution. Offshore, they comprise a suite of mafic minor intrusions most evident from their magnetic signature within the Permo–Triassic sedimentary cover. Onshore, east-south-east-trending olivine dolerite dykes are best exposed on the coasts of the Isle of Man, particularly within the southern outcrop of the Carboniferous rocks where they appear to be most abundant (Lamplugh, 1903). They vary in thickness from a few centimetres to six metres and are generally found in swarms which probably traverse the Island, though within the swarms individual dykes rarely extend for more than a short distance.

Igneous rocks of the Manx region can be mapped from their magnetic signature as they are typically far more magnetic than the surrounding strata (Figure 25). Detailed aeromagnetic data (Figures 6b, 26) reveal a distinctive pattern of linear anomalies caused by Palaeogene dykes. The majority of these anomalies have negative polarity, indicating magnetisation in the opposite direction to the Earth's present magnetic field. Such magnetisation occurs because the dykes were intruded at a time when the Earth's field had reversed polarity and they acquired a remanent magnetisation component at that time that is significantly stronger than the magnetisation induced by the Earth's present field. The dykes appear to radiate from Northern Ireland, which was an important centre of Palaeogene igneous activity. The Antrim lavas and Mourne, Slieve Gullion and Carlingford complexes were emplaced during the period 61 to 53 Ma (Mussett et al., 1988; Gamble et al., 1999), with recent U–Pb dating of the Mourne and Slieve Gullion rocks giving ages of around 56 Ma (Meighan et al., 1999). This was a time of predominantly reversed field polarity (Cande and Kent, 1995), consistent with the anomalies observed over most of the Palaeogene dykes of the Manx region. There are also, however, a number of positively magnetised dykes (Figure 25). These might have been intruded during the relatively short normal polarity intervals (chrons C26N, C25N) that occurred during this igneous episode. Alternatively, positive anomalies may arise if the reversed remanent magnetisation component is weak compared with the induced magnetisation.

One of the most prominent Palaeogene dykes in the Manx region is the Fleetwood Dyke (Kirton and Donato, 1985; Arter and Fagin, 1993), a large and complex intrusion comprising a number of separate dykes arranged *en échelon*. The Fleetwood Dyke traverses the northern part of the Isle of Man, where a component of the suite is exposed on the east coast as a dyke 12 m wide, and extends farther east-south-east across the Irish Sea towards the Lancashire coast (Figure 25). The dykes generally dip steeply to the north-north-east, though in places they assume a more sill-like geometry. Seismic reflection data close to the eastern edge of the Manx region provide good images of the Fleetwood Dyke (Figure 27), showing a number of moderately to gently inclined intrusive bodies with a probable steep feeder system. Seismic modelling of the dyke in this area suggests that the larger intrusion is at least 250 m thick (Chadwick and Evans, In press). Elsewhere, magnetic modelling of the southernmost major dyke indicates thicknesses of about 100 m in the Manx region and 600 m farther east (Kirton and Donato, 1985). Well 113/27-1, situated just east of the Manx region, penetrated the Fleetwood Dyke, proving 365 m of dolerite. K–Ar whole-rock dating of core samples gives ages in the range 61.4 ± 0.8 Ma (Jackson et al., 1995) to 65.6 ± 1.0 Ma (Arter and Fagin, 1993). If these dates are reliable, the implication would be that the Fleetwood Dyke is older than most of the igneous rocks of Northern Ireland. It is perhaps more likely that the K–Ar dates are in error, and the dykes of the Manx region were closely associated with emplacement of the Northern Irish igneous rocks.

The location of at least some of the dykes in the Manx region appears to be influenced by faulting. This is perhaps exemplified by the Fleetwood Dyke (Figure 27), whose steep feeder dyke, at least locally, seems to be intruded along a near vertical fault, whilst shallower sills appear to propagate from a gently dipping listric fault. Similarly, a prominent shallow intrusion at the western margin of the Peel Basin lies in the hanging wall block of the St Patrick Fault, its steep feeder dyke possibly sourced along the fault at depth (Figure 14b). On a smaller scale, dolerite bodies identified in some of the wells (e.g. 111/15-1 and 111/29-1) are interpreted as corresponding with normal faults.

In addition to the dyke anomalies, magnetic images (Figure 26) reveal areas of magnetic disturbance that are indicative of igneous bodies with a flat-lying, sheet-like geometry. Some of the more conspicuous of these are shown schematically in Figure 25. The probable explanation for these is that they represent areas where Palaeogene igneous rocks have been intruded as sills. There is a clear correlation between the development of areas of magnetic disturbance and the thicker sedimentary sequences in the Peel and North Channel basins, presumably because the bedding planes within these basins provided preferential sites for the development of sills. Many of the sills occur at very shallow depth and locally form spectacular erosional

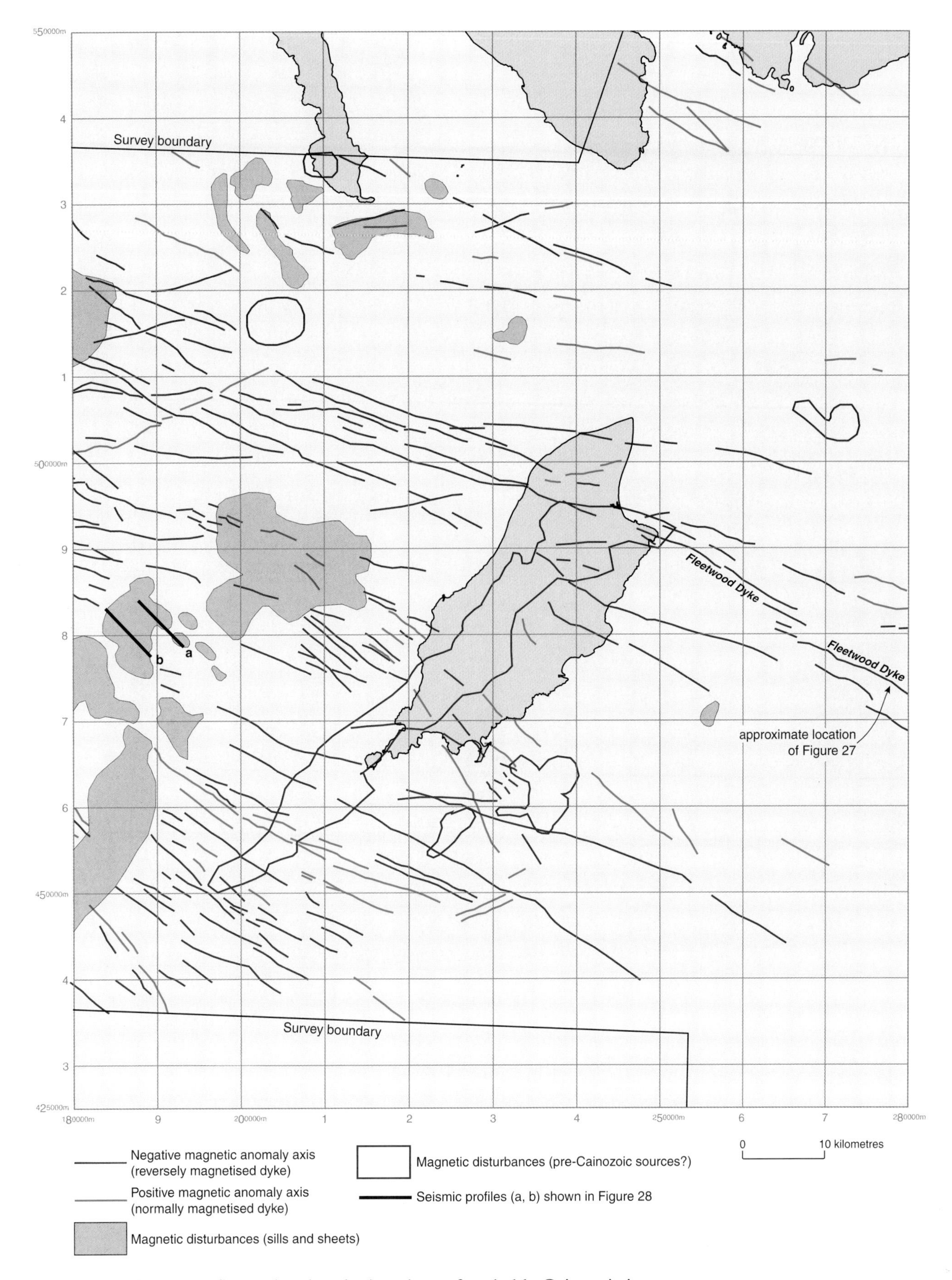

Figure 25 Summary figure showing the locations of probable Cainozoic igneous features identified from detailed aeromagnetic data (see Figures 6b, 26).

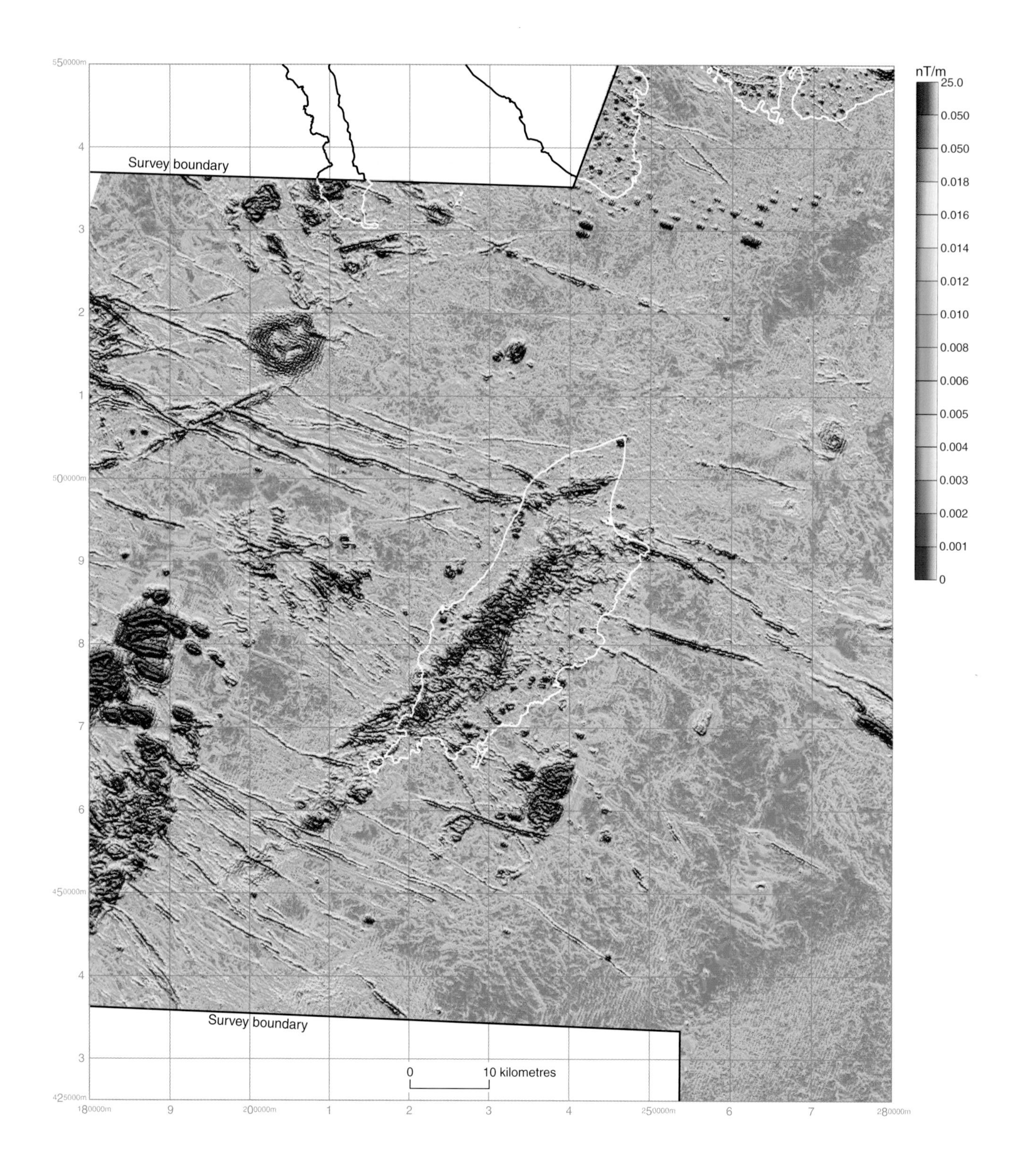

Figure 26 Image of the horizontal gradient of the residual total magnetic field (compare with Figure 6b). Non-linear colour scale. This display accentuates magnetic features due to shallow sources. (Data acquired by World Geoscience, UK Ltd.)

features at, or closely beneath, the sea bed (Figure 28). The maximum elevation of the features approaches 0.150 seconds of two-way travel time (about 150 m depth), with a spectacular sea bed 'cliff' feature, some 20 m high, notable towards the south-east end of one of the seismic lines (Figure 28b). The thickness of these sills is uncertain, as only their tops are clearly imaged by the seismic data, but general indications suggest that they are between about 50 and 200 m thick. On the other hand they may be considerably thinner than their topographic expression, forming tough erosion-resistant 'caps' above softer strata. Although these particular sills have not been drilled, wells 111/29-1 and 111/25-1A, elsewhere in the basin, do penetrate doleritic units, intruded into the Mercia Mudstone Group. The geometry of these bodies is uncertain, but in well section they typically span some 10 to 15 m.

The intrusive relationships of these bodies can only constrain their age as being syn- or post-late Triassic.

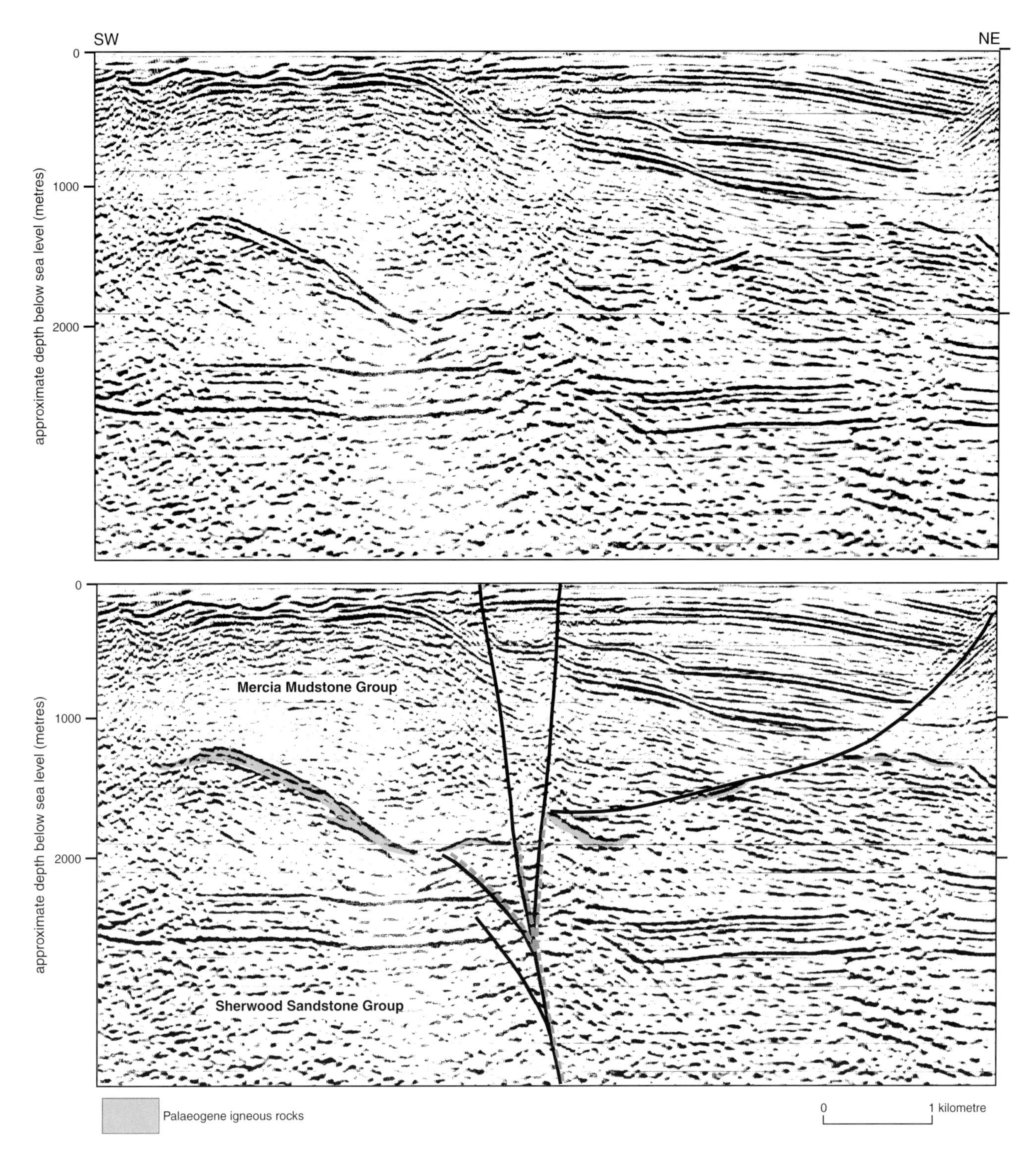

Figure 27 Seismic line illustrating the Fleetwood Dyke in the east of the Isle of Man area. See Figure 25 for location.

It is likely, however, that their emplacement was closely linked to intrusion of the Fleetwood Dyke. The erosional topography associated with the sills appears to have largely developed in Quaternary times. Quaternary deposits appear to fill topographic depressions and include locally channelised features onlapping against, and locally burying, the elevated sill features.

Two areas of magnetic disturbance in the offshore area directly south of the Isle of Man (Figure 25) could be caused by Palaeogene igneous rocks. However, a pre-Palaeogene origin is more likely because the anomalies show normal polarity, and the magnetic sources are located in basement rocks in the footwall block of the Eubonia Fault rather than in the adjacent thick sedimentary sequence.

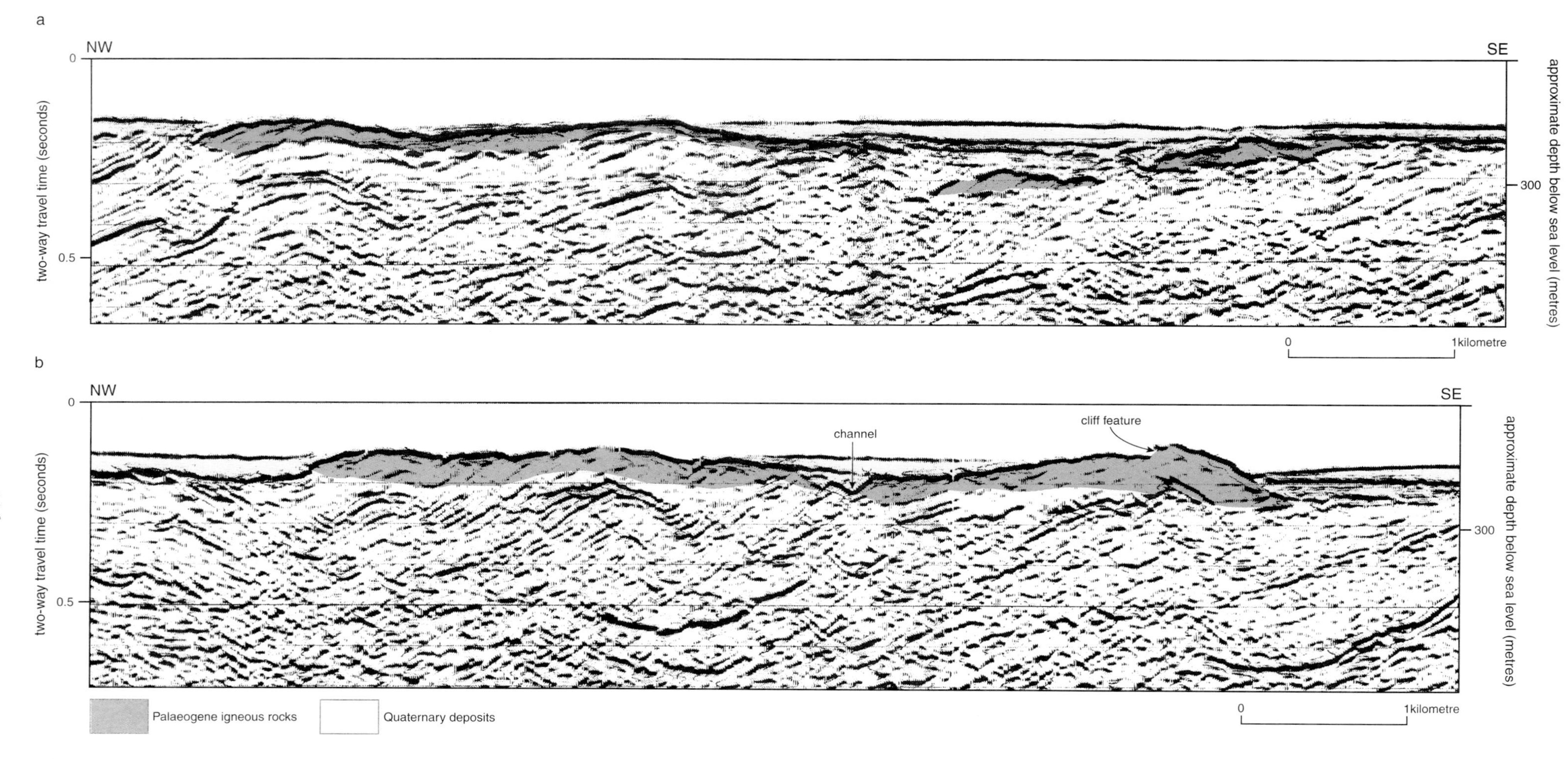

Figure 28 Seismic lines illustrating shallow sills in the Peel Basin, some giving rise to prominent sea floor features. See Figure 25 for location.

9 Quaternary

From its location astride successive ice advances from major source areas in western Scotland, Lamplugh (1903, p.332) regarded the Isle of Man as 'an unrivalled field for the study of the conditions that ruled in the northern part of the Irish Sea basin during the Glacial Period'. Although the greater part of the Island has a thin drift cover, the area underlying the northern plain records one of the thickest Quaternary sequences in Britain, with glacial deposits to at least 145 m below OD (Lamplugh, 1903). The maximum thickness, including that exposed above sea level, is in the order of 250 m. Much of the upper part is exposed in the 25 km of almost continuous cliff section bounding the northern plain; these sections exhibit a glacial sequence of such diverse character they are probably unsurpassed in Britain (Kendall, 1894, p.397).

Traditionally, the Quaternary deposits of the Island have been divided into two major suites (Cumming, 1846; Horne, 1874; Kendall, 1894; Lamplugh, 1903; Thomas, 1976, 1977). A high-level suite, of local composition, is restricted to the area underlain by the Manx Group rocks and is responsible for the characteristic upland scenery of gently rolling hill slopes, heavily drift covered and with little rock exposure. The deposits thicken rapidly down slope and commonly give rise to pronounced asymmetric terraces (Thomas, 1976). Originally interpreted as the product of a glaciation that swept over the Island to its summit (Kendall, 1894; Lamplugh, 1903), the deposits were later regarded as periglacial and having formed during the last glaciation when the Island was thought to have been a nunatak (Wirtz, 1953; Cubbon, 1957; Mitchell, 1965; Thomas, 1976, 1977). The current consensus is that the deposits are locally derived glacial diamicts reworked by periglacial processes during and immediately after deglaciation (Bowen, 1973; Thomas, 1985; Dackombe and Thomas, 1985, 1989; Chiverrell et al., 2001).

The low-level suite, occupying the whole of the northern plain, parts of the plain of Malew and the Peel embayment, is predominantly composed of material foreign to the Island. These deposits have been derived by glacial transport from onshore and offshore outcrops to the north, especially southern and western Scotland, during successive glacial stages. They comprise a wide variety of glacigenic sediments, including diamict, sand, gravel and massive and laminated clay, and they are associated with a very prominent glacial morphology. This culminates in the multiple ridges of the Bride Moraine, one of the largest and most complex moraine structures in Britain (Thomas, 1984) (Figure 29). The moraine strikes east–west across the northern plain and is fronted by a complex assemblage of sandur, ice-front alluvial fans, lake floor and ice-disintegration topography. To the rear, the moraine is cut by a prominent Holocene raised cliff and associated beach ridges, dunes and lagoonal basins. Although traditionally interpreted as a response to onshore glaciation of the Irish Sea Basin during periods of eustatically lowered sea level (Mitchell, 1965; Thomas, 1976, 1977, 1985; Thomas et al., 1985; Dackombe and Thomas, 1989), recent investigations have proposed a glaciomarine origin during periods of isostatically depressed sea level (Eyles and Eyles, 1984; Eyles and McCabe, 1989, 1991; McCabe et al., 1998).

Quaternary history of the Isle of Man

Some forty or so major cold stages have been identified worldwide during the 1.8 million years of the Quaternary (Shackleton and Opdyke, 1973, 1976) and at least eight cold stages have been recognised in onshore sequences in Britain (Bowen, 1999). The Manx glacial succession, however, largely reflects a response to the last or Late Devensian cold stage (oxygen isotope stage 2), and very little is known of earlier glacial or interglacial stages.

Pre-Late Devensian

Sediments predating the exposed Late Devensian (oxygen isotope stage 2) deposits on the Isle of Man are known only from boreholes and offshore seismic data. Using borehole descriptions published by Lamplugh (1903) and Smith (1930), Thomas (1999) subdivided the pre-Late Devensian glacial sediments beneath the northern plain into three formations. The lowest, the Ayre Lighthouse Formation, consists of diamicts, sands and gravels of northern origin overlying Permo–Triassic bedrock to depths of 146 m below OD at the Point of Ayre [NX 440 035]. The age of the formation is unknown but has been provisionally identified as older than oxygen isotope stage 7 (Thomas, 1999). This formation is overlain by the Ayre Formation, which lies at depths of 73 to 65 m below OD and consists of silts and sands with an abundant shell fauna (Lamplugh, 1903). These marine deposits, of presumed interglacial origin, have been attributed to oxygen isotope stages 5, 7 or 9 (Thomas, 1999). The uppermost Kiondroughad Formation overlies both the Ayre Formation and a prominent buried rock platform at depths of 41 to 53 m below OD, and underlies the Shellag Formation, the lowest exposed Late Devensian formation. It consists of sand, gravel and diamicts of northern origin. The age of the formation is also unknown, but probably corresponds to oxygen isotope stages 4, 6 or 8 (Thomas, 1999).

At Ballure [SC 459 934] a distinctive buried cliff with sea-stacks and caves, cut in Manx Group slates, is fronted by a rock platform a few metres below sea level. Overlain by Late Devensian glacigenic formations, it probably represents an interglacial sea level at approximately the same level as the modern sea level and has been tentatively assigned to oxygen isotope stage 5e (Ipswichian Interglacial) around 128 to 115 ka BP (Thomas, 1985, 1999). Possible beach gravels, overlying bedrock and overlain by Late

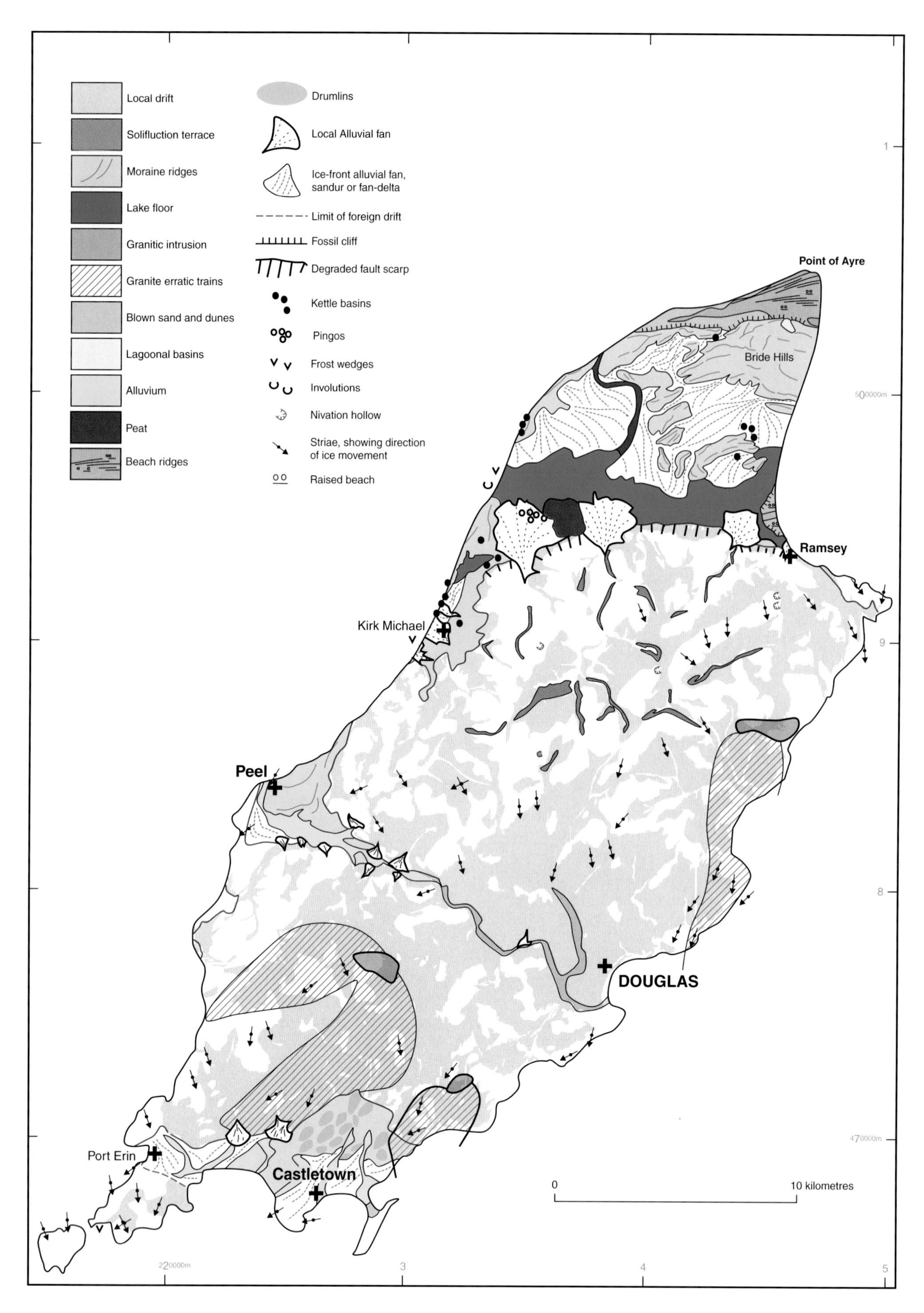

Figure 29 Map of Quaternary features and deposits in the Isle of Man.

Devensian glacigenic formations, at Gob-ny-Creggan Glassey [SC 297 988] may be of similar age.

Although expansion of glaciers in Scotland has been identified in oxygen isotope stage 4 of the Devensian (about 75–50 ka BP) (Sutherland, 1984; Boulton et al., 1991), it is not known if they extended into the northern Irish Sea Basin and encroached onto the Isle of Man. No deposits of this stage have been identified on the Island though they may be included with the buried Kiondroughad Formation. Similarly, no deposits representing oxygen isotope stage 3 (about 50–30 ka BP), before the main Late Devensian glacial expansion, have been recorded, though local scree and head overlying the buried cliff at Ballure may represent this interval and suggest an ice-free, dominantly periglacial environment.

Late Devensian glaciation

The main Late Devensian glaciation in Britain (oxygen isotope stage 2) began after 30 ka BP with extensive growth of glaciers in the mountains of the Western Highlands and Southern Uplands of Scotland. These centres of ice accumulation expanded until the dominant, southerly flowing, Highland ice stream became confluent on its margins with Southern Upland, Lake District and Northern Irish ice in a large lobe moving south through the northern Irish Sea Basin. At its maximum at around 28 to 22 ka BP this lobe extended as far south as the Celtic Sea and was confluent with Welsh and southern Irish ice caps (Bowen, 1991). There is no evidence, in the form of cirque basins or moraines, that the Isle of Man nurtured its own glaciers during the build up and passage of this ice sheet. Estimates of ice thickness in the northern Irish Sea Basin ice sheet at this time vary from 500 to 1000 m (Boulton et al., 1985; Boulton et al., 1991; Lambeck, 1996) and an ice sheet of this thickness would have buried the Isle of Man to its summit (i.e. Snaefell is 621 m).

Evidence of the passage of ice across the Island during the Late Devensian is provided by striations and the distribution of erratic trains running south from the outcrops of the Dhoon, Foxdale and Oatland granitic intrusions (Lamplugh, 1903) (Figure 29). During passage of this ice, thick basal diamict of northerly origin was deposited as a large wedge across the northern plain and against the rock margins of the Island by deposition from basal, debris-rich ice. The prominent degraded fault scarp, marking the northern exposed limit of the Manx Group between Ramsey [SC 460 935] and Kirk Michael [SC 318 903], caused upper-level, clean ice to shear across the higher parts of the Island and emplace extensive sheets of locally derived diamict during its passage.

The foreign glacigenic sediments deposited during advance to the Late Devensian maximum are identified in the Isle of Man as the Shellag Formation. This consists of a number of widespread members particularly well exposed on both coasts of the northern plain, but also around the Island margins. Characteristically, the diamict component comprises a stiff, over-consolidated, red clay with relatively few, far-travelled northern erratics. On the Island rock margin, however, and especially in the plain of Malew, the diamicts include considerable quantities of locally derived clasts, notably limestone and slate, as well as a variable far-travelled northern erratic component, derived by mixing of low- and high-level ice in the lee of ice movement across the Island. Around Ballasalla [SC 280 700] much of this diamict was drumlinised. Other members of this formation include extensive suites of coarse-grained proglacial outwash sediment and laminated silts and clays. At Kirk Michael, a prominent sand bed includes numerous complete shells of *Turritella communis* (Lamplugh, 1903). It is not known if this bed represents penecontemporaneous glaciomarine sedimentation, a rafted portion of pre-existing sea floor or a fossil assemblage derived by washout from earlier sediment.

North of the Bride Moraine, the deposits of the Shellag Formation are highly deformed; to the south they are undeformed. The moraine itself forms a tight, asymmetric anticline with an amplitude of some 100 m, slightly overturned to the north (Thomas, 1984). Superimposed upon the southern limb are a series of congruent, isoclinal overfolds and attendant thrust faults, steeply inclined to the south and breaking along fold crests into series of diapirs. This structure is bounded, in both the up- and down-ice direction, by a series of low-angle, north-dipping thrusts. Members of the Orrisdale Formation unconformably overlie the deformed members of the Shellag Formation. To the north of the Bride Moraine the Orrisdale Formation consists of a stacked sequence of glacigenic sediments offlapping one another in a wedge that thickens to the north. To the south it forms a shallow basin of diamict, sand and laminated and massive mud that thickens off the front face of the moraine. The Orrisdale Formation can be traced westwards towards Kirk Michael, where thick diamict unconformably overlies further deformed Shellag Formation diamicts (Lamplugh, 1903; Thomas, 1976, 1977). Above it are sequences of ice-marginal sandur and ice-front alluvial fan sediments (Thomas et al., 1985), associated with complex ice disintegration topography.

Thomas (1984) interpreted both the succession and structure of the Bride Moraine as a response to a minor onshore re-advance episode during the retreat of Late Devensian ice. He argued that loading and compression of a variable substrate of partly frozen Shellag Formation sediments by the re-advancing ice margin generated a series of rooted, diapiric folds, which, with continued compression, caused overthrusting. To the rear of the ice margin a sheet of sub-horizontal Orrisdale Formation basal diamict was emplaced, terminating to the rear of the moraine. Forward of the moraine, sheets of diamict were released by debris flow from the ice margin and large ice front alluvial fans were deposited. At The Dog Mills [SC 454 978], these fans grade into a series of laminated and massive silts and clays that underlies much of the area at and inland from Ramsey and which Lamplugh (1903) regarded as lacustrine.

An alternative explanation for the origin of the Bride Moraine is provided by Eyles and Eyles (1984) and Eyles and McCabe (1991) who argued that it represents a deformed glaciomarine 'morainal bank' deposited immediately in front of a grounded ice-sheet margin at a time when, due to isostatic depression, regional sea level was relatively high. No indisputable biostratigraphical or sedimentological indicators of contemporaneous marine influence are recorded in the northern Isle of Man, however, and the degree of glacio-isostatic depression required (100–200 m) seems at variance with the models of Lambeck (1996) that calculate only a relative maximum sea level rise to 10 m above OD during the last 20 ka. The extent of marine influence has been further questioned recently (McCarroll, 2001).

Across Jurby Head [SC 343 982] a further sequence of diamict, gravel, sand and extensive massive and laminated mud is grouped together as the Jurby Formation. This lies disconformably upon the Orrisdale Formation and is associated with a prominent linear moraine running parallel to the Jurby coast and a fronting set of ice-marginal sandur, alluvial and subaqueous fans and flat lake floors. The latter crop out between Killane and The Cronk and extend inland towards the Curragh and may form part of later extension to the lake deposits at The Dog Mills near Ramsey. A cartoon depicting the environment in the northern Isle of Man at this time is shown in Figure 30. Thomas (1976, 1977) regarded the Jurby Formation as another response to minor ice-front marginal oscillation during the retreat of the Late Devensian ice sheet.

Dates obtained by the ^{14}C method from organic kettle-hole sediments overlying both the Orrisdale and Jurby formations at Jurby Head and Glen Balleira [SC 314 914] indicate that the retreating Late Devensian ice margin had cleared the north of the Island by 18.6 to 17.6 cal ka BP (Joachim, 1978; Chiverrell et al., 1999). In this report 'cal' means a calibrated radiocarbon year BP and the age is an actual radiocarbon date. Calibration is based on calibration curves derived from tree rings and marine corals. It corrects for variations in production of ^{14}C in the atmosphere as a result of variations in global carbon cycling. All other ages were derived from other methods (e.g. ice cores, correlation, luminescence studies) and are given as ka BP. Recent research on Greenland ice cores and North Atlantic marine cores indicates that the retreat of the Late Devensian glacial stage was punctuated by millennial-scale climate shifts that generated significant stadial ice advances (Dansgaard et al., 1993; Bond and Lotti, 1995). Stratigraphical evidence for the latest of these, Heinrich Event 1 (18.0–15.0 ka BP), has been dated to between 18.2 and 14.4 cal ka BP on the east coast of Ireland and correlated with an extensive ice re-advance across the floor of the northern Irish Sea Basin. Its limit ran from Killard Point in Northern Ireland, through the Bride Moraine to St Bees Head in Cumbria (McCabe et al., 1998). It was during this brief episode that the Bride Moraine was probably built and the re-advance sediments of the Orrisdale and Jurby formations deposited.

Late Devensian deglaciation

As the Late Devensian ice sheet retreated north across the Island the locally derived suite of upland glacial deposits formed during its advance were uncovered. Lying on relatively steep, probably meltwater-saturated slopes, they were rapidly remobilised down-slope by solifluction processes acting in a cold, periglacial climate to produce the thick soliflucted diamicts of the Snaefell Formation. These deposits now display rapid down-slope thickening, a consistent down-slope stratification and fabric, a preferential development on slopes orientated towards the north-west through north to the north-east, and pronounced asymmetric terracing (Thomas, 1977; Chiverrell et al., 2001); all are indicators of a former periglacial depositional environment. The precise age of periglacial reworking is not known but probably occurred from the time of deglacial recovery to at least the beginning of the Late-glacial interstadial episode at approximately 14.8 ka BP, together with possible further periglacial reworking during subsequent Late-glacial stadial episodes.

During the Late-glacial interstadial (14.8–13.5 ka BP) temperatures rose (Björck et al., 1998), the influence of periglacial process declined and fluvial process increased, and much of the soliflucted diamict was incised and removed. Upland river systems, adjusting to these changes, transferred considerable quantities of sediment downstream to produce large mountain-front alluvial fans fringing the uplands (Figure 30). Similar, though smaller, fans were also built at main tributary

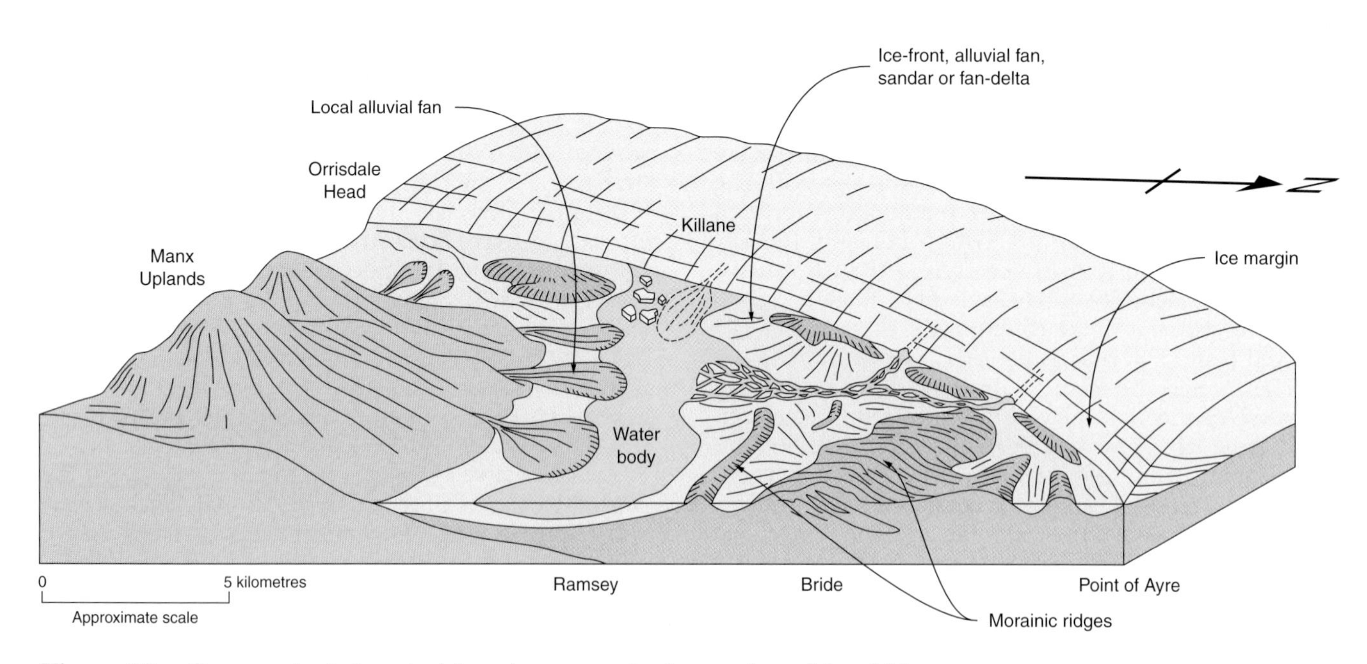

Figure 30 Cartoon depicting glacial environments in the northern Isle of Man at the time of deposition of the Jurby Formation.

junctions within the uplands. During this time (18.5–13.5 cal ka BP) organic sediments of the Glen Balleira Formation were deposited in enclosed, open-water kettle basins formed by melting of dead ice within the Orrisdale Formation glacigenic sediment around Kirk Michael and Jurby Head (Mitchell, 1965; Dickson et al., 1970; Joachim, 1978; Tooley, 1985).

Palaeo-ecological data (coleopteran and pollen) and ^{14}C dating indicate that these organic sediments span the Greenland Interstadial 1 (GI-1; 14.8–12.5 ka BP) and Greenland Stadial 1 (GS-1; 12.5–11.5 ka BP) (Björck et al., 1998), and identify a sequence of climatic changes that is in accord with other sites in north-west Europe (Joachim, 1978; Lowe et al., 1994; Coope and Lemdahl, 1995; Coope et al., 1998; von Grafenstein et al., 1996, 2000). The alluvial fan gravels, grouped together as the Ballaugh Formation, overlie the organic Glen Balleira Formation at Kirk Michael, implying that incision by rivers into the diamict-filled valleys of the Manx uplands and prograding alluvial fan accumulation in the lowlands occurred until at least 11.5 cal ka BP. Pingos on the surface of the Ballaugh fan have yielded *Megalocerus giganteus* (Irish Elk) antler remains that have been ^{14}C dated at 10.7 to 10.2 cal ka BP (Gonzalez et al., 2000), indicating that alluvial fan accumulation ceased during the early Holocene (Chiverrell et al., 2001).

Holocene

From a low of 55 m below OD in the northern Irish Sea Basin at the end of the Devensian (Wingfield, 1995) sea level rose rapidly with the onset of warmer climatic conditions in the Holocene. Part of the record of rising sea level, and consequent coastal change, is recorded in the Point of Ayre Formation. At Point of Ayre itself a complex sequence of fresh and brackish water lagoonal basins, prograding beach ridges (up to 5–6 m above OD) and linear and barchan dunes are backed by a very prominent abandoned cliff line running east from Blue Point. Other similar abandoned cliffs occur at Ramsey and Douglas. Biogenic sediments in one lagoonal basin at Lough Cranstal [NX 450 026] record a high sea level event, which reached between 0.59 m below OD and 2.17 m above OD at 9.0 to 8.4 cal ka BP (Tooley, 1985). After this date, the beach has accreted rapidly, fed by a dominantly northward long-shore drift from eroding cliffs on the east and west coasts, and the coast has prograded some 3 km northwards.

Peat accumulation in the Island began during the early Holocene and has continued in places to the present day. The most extensive peat sequences occur in the lowlands, with 5 to 6 m in the Curragh and over 3 m in the Lhen Trench. Peat accumulation at Ballaugh Curragh and Curragh-y-Cowle began during the early Holocene, approximately 10.5 to 9.5 cal ka BP. The most extensive accumulations in the uplands occur on the flanks of Beinn-y-Phott [SC 375 868], where peat inception occurred approximately between 7.2 and 7.0 cal ka BP. Elsewhere in the uplands the date of peat inception varies, starting between approximately 10.5 to 10.2 cal ka BP at Montpellier Mire in Druidale [SC 363 883] and 3.1 to 2.9 cal ka BP on the flanks of Mullagh Ouyr [SC 396 867] (Russell, 1978; Chiverrell et al., 2001). Together these peats are grouped as the Curragh Formation.

Though low in erosional and depositional capability in today's climate, Manx rivers have continued to incise into the thick diamicts of the uplands, particularly in the catchment headwaters. In the downstream reaches of many of the larger valleys, particularly those draining into the northern plain, the central valley and the plain of Malew, the rivers have aggraded a series of terraces. River terrace gravels and alluvium of Holocene age are grouped into the Sulby Formation; so named because Sulby Glen [SC 382 914] contains a well-preserved sequence of terraces (Chiverrell et al., 2001). The highest terraces are no more than 5 m above the present-day river; they probably began forming during the Late Devensian and were occupied by rivers into the early to mid-Holocene. During the late Holocene, the rivers began to incise again, producing up to three lower and younger terraces. The onset of periods of fluvial incision are dated to the last 3000 years, with further incision 2410 to 640 years ago and during the last 300 years (Chiverrell et al., 2001). Increased scale of human activity and changes in the climate are the most likely triggers for these phases of increased fluvial activity, given that the fluvial incision is coincident with substantial woodland clearances and major shifts to wetter climatic conditions recorded in peat sequences (Barber et al., 1994).

OFFSHORE QUATERNARY STRATIGRAPHY

The Neogene and early Pleistocene were times of uplift and erosion across the Irish Sea Basin. This period was followed by more extensive erosion and deposition in the mid- to late Pleistocene as a result of repeated glacial advance and retreat. Pleistocene and Holocene sediments are recognised on seismic profiles within the basin both by their unconformable relationship with pre-Quaternary strata and their commonly subhorizontal stratification (Figure 28). Together they provide evidence for successive glaciation over a greater time period than that represented by the exposed onshore sequence, and reflect changes, frequently rapid, in sea level.

The thickness of offshore Quaternary sediments mirrors that onshore with the greatest thickness (approximately 150 m) occurring off the Point of Ayre where a deep channel infilled with glacial sediment is orientated north-west–south-east. Elsewhere around the Island, Quaternary deposits rarely reach 50 m in thickness and are commonly thin or absent close inshore, particularly to the south of the Island. It is only at about 30 to 40 km offshore (to the east, the west and south-west of the Island) that Quaternary deposits consistently exceed 50 m in thickness and may be more than 100 m thick, although rockhead is sometimes obscured by gas blanking on seismic records (Jackson et al., 1995).

The main offshore Quaternary formations include a lower, Cardigan Bay Formation and an upper, Western Irish Sea Formation (Figure 31). The Cardigan Bay Formation comprises three members: a Lower Till Member, a discontinuous Bedded and Infill Member and an Upper Till Member (Figure 31). Although found extensively farther south in the Irish Sea, the presence of the Lower Till member offshore from the Isle of Man is not certain but it may occur as patches above the rockhead, particularly

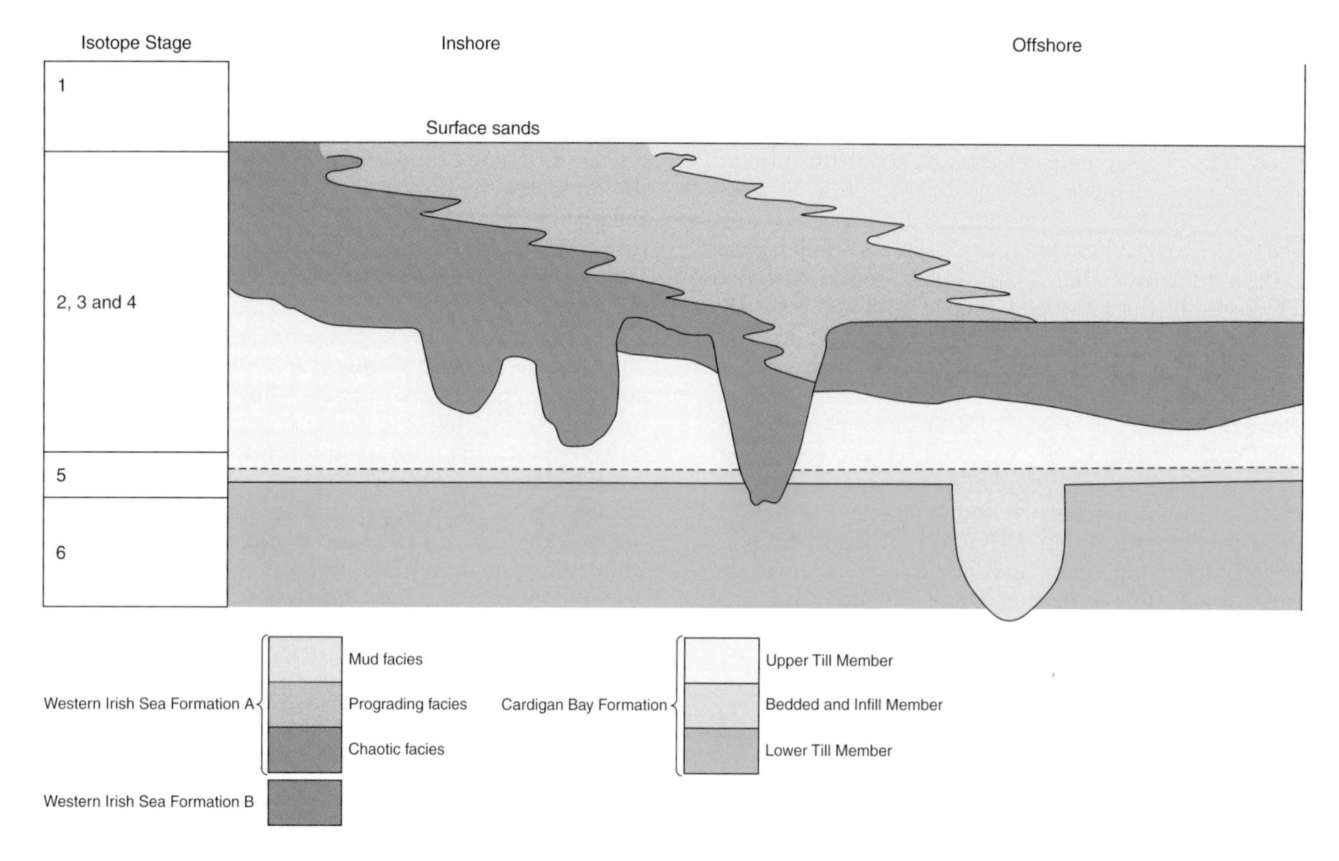

Figure 31 Schematic diagram illustrating the stratigraphical relationship, age and composition of Quaternary formations offshore from the Isle of Man. Vertical scale represents time and horizontal scale is position with respect to the Isle of Man (i.e. away from the Island on either the western or southern coasts).

south of the Island (Wingfield et al., 1990). Over most of the Irish Sea Basin the Lower Till Member is separated from the Upper Till Member by an indistinct unconformity. Locally, however, the unconformity becomes distinct, occurring as deep channels infilled by the Bedded and Infill Member (Figure 31). The channels are subglacial meltwater channel systems which, on retreat, were filled with proglacial outwash sediment and subsequently by interglacial marine sediment. The Bedded and Infill Member exhibits two acoustic facies: a lower lenticular infill and an upper tabular stratification. The lenticular infill facies is interpreted as fining-upwards glacial sediment. The tabular facies has been sampled in several offshore boreholes and represents sediments of cold or boreal, marine interglacial conditions. These probably correlate with the marine silts of the onshore Ayre Formation (Lamplugh, 1903) and probably date to oxygen isotope stage 5 (Ipswichian Interglacial). The underlying glacial sediments of the Lower Till Member must therefore date to at least oxygen isotope stage 6, or earlier.

The Upper Till Member of the Cardigan Bay Formation crops out extensively at the sea bed south and east of the Island where it comprises a hard clay diamicton with clasts ranging from sand to cobble-size and boulders up to one metre in diameter. It is most probably of Late Devensian age and equates with the Shellag Formation and later formations of the Island onshore stratigraphy.

The Western Irish Sea Formation unconformably overlies the Cardigan Bay Formation and is divisible into two units. The Western Irish Sea Formation B (Figure 31) is only locally developed and may be equivalent to the upper parts of the Upper Till Member of the Cardigan Bay Formation. The Western Irish Sea Formation A overlies the Cardigan Bay Formation with a well defined unconformity marked by channels deeply incised into the underlying Cardigan Bay Formation and is divisible into three facies. A *chaotic facies* occurs in much of the area east of the Island and forms the lower infill of the channels marking the unconformity. Samples yield gravel-rich diamictons formed in glaciolacustrine and glaciomarine, ice-proximal conditions. The succeeding *prograding facies* forms the bulk of the channel infill and comprises a prograding wedge of sand-dominated sediments that also occurs in more open areas both east and west of the Isle of Man and may be up to 50 m thick. It passes laterally into a *mud facies*. Boreholes indicate these muds are a prodeltaic glaciomarine unit representing the changes from ice-proximal chaotic facies to a distal mud facies as the ice retreated. Delta topsets seen on seismic profiles indicate a sea level 75 m below present OD at the time of deposition (Jackson et al., 1995).

Upon the retreat of Late Devensian ice from the eastern Irish Sea an irregular surface of hollows and channels was exposed across the sea floor. As sea level rose at the end of the Devensian and into the early Holocene, these features became infilled by proglacial and lagoonal sediments, largely comprising laminated muds with minor sands. East of the Isle of Man these deposits include sediments from Vannin Sound

(Pantin, 1978), a sequence that may be correlated with similar, lacustrine sediment of the Dog Mills Member exposed onshore. The mud facies has a near transparent acoustic character and gas blanking is present at various horizons within the unit, often totally obscuring lower units and the rockhead. Sampling indicates that these sediments are predominantly silts, commonly sulphide- or glauconite-rich, which record an upward change from cold, boreal conditions to modern temperate Holocene conditions. Scattered pebbles are interpreted as having been deposited from floating ice.

The present day sea floor has areas of net erosion and net deposition. These reflect the general trend of fining of surface sediment away from the Island. Gravel-rich sediments predominate within 10 to 20 km of the coast, passing into sand-dominated sediments and finally mud east and west of the Island. In sand-rich areas, the sea bed shows evidence of sediment movement in the form of sand waves, which reflect sediment transport from north and south of the Island towards the east (Belderson and Stride, 1969). The finest grained material is currently accumulating in the mud-belt offshore from Cumbria, and between Ireland and the Isle of Man. Sedimentation rates of 20 to 80 cm per 1000 years have been reported in the former area (Kershaw et al., 1988). Sand ridges occur offshore from the Point of Ayre, but only the shallowest are active, with those below 7 m water depth formed when sea level was lower than present.

ONSHORE QUATERNARY STRATIGRAPHY

The geological map accompanying this report uses the formation as the principal mapping unit though many of the formations identified in the stratigraphy are not exposed at the surface. The relationship between these formations in the northern part of the Island is given in Figure 32. Superimposed upon the exposed formations are a set of significant sediment–landform assemblages. These assemblages have discrete surface expression, and broadly equate both with members within the formations and with distinctive glacigenic processes. A brief description of each is given below.

ICE-MARGINAL MORAINES Areas of prominent, linear moraine ridges, underlain by complex sequences of diamict and fluvioglacial sediment, commonly tectonised. They represent ice margin sedimentation during still-stand, re-advance or minor snout oscillation (Shellag, Orrisdale and Jurby formations).

ICE DISINTEGRATION TOPOGRAPHY Areas of disorganised topography, including small-scale ridges, mounds and basins (many water-filled) commonly in wide linear belts. Complex sequences of diamict and fluvioglacial sediment underlie this topography. Melting of buried ice at the margin of the glacier caused the disintegration of the original ice-marginal topography (Orrisdale Formation).

ICE-FRONT ALLUVIAL FANS, SUBAQUEOUS FANS AND SANDUR Either cone-shaped topography sloping away from and normal to ice-marginal moraine systems or wide, flat channels or troughs running parallel to ice-marginal moraine systems. These features are underlain by sand and gravel sequences. They include ice-front alluvial fans deposited by water draining directly from tunnels in the ice margin, subaqueous fans deposited by water draining from tunnels into water bodies, and outwash sandur that were laid down parallel to the ice margin directed by the occurrence of large, abandoned moraines forward of the ice-margin (Shellag, Orrisdale and Jurby formations).

LACUSTRINE BASINS Extensive flat areas underlain by laminated or massive mud deposited by streams draining the ice margin. They represent glacial lake floor infill (Orrisdale and Jurby formations).

DIAMICT FLOORS Areas of low amplitude, subdued topography underlain by thick diamict. These are areas of basal lodgement till that were deposited under thick, advancing active ice (Shellag Formation).

DRUMLIN FIELDS Areas of thick diamict showing characteristic 'basket of eggs' topography consisting of elongate, smooth ridges on a scale of up to a kilometre in length. They represent areas of basal lodgement till moulded by fast advance of thick ice (Shellag Formation).

SOLIFLUCTION TERRACES Linear terraces flanking main river valleys in the uplands, composed of local diamict, and showing a pronounced facing direction towards the north-west, north or north-east. They represent a response to micro-climate control during Late Devensian and Late-glacial episodes of permafrost and periglacial slope process (Snaefell Formation).

WIND-BLOWN SAND Areas of irregular or linear sand dunes along the margin of the present coast between Jurby Head and the Point of Ayre. Sand was eroded by wind from the glacial drift cliffs and transported north-east or east by the prevailing wind during Holocene and modern times (Point of Ayre Formation).

PROGRADING BEACH RIDGES Areas of low-amplitude gravel-beach ridges running eastwards to the Point of Ayre. They represent coastal progradation during the Holocene, from material derived by longshore drift from erosion of glacial drift cliffs in the Jurby Head area (Point of Ayre Formation).

LAGOONAL BASINS Small areas of salt, brackish and fresh-water sedimentation formed behind prograding Holocene beach ridges (Point of Ayre Formation).

LITHOSTRATIGRAPHICAL CLASSIFICATION

A formal lithostratigraphy for the Quaternary of the Isle of Man was first devised by Thomas (1977) and revised by Thomas (1999). Recent work for the revision of the map necessitated further revision and these changes are incorporated into Table 6 and Figure 32. A brief description of each unit within the lithostratigraphy is given below.

Ayre Lighthouse Formation

Stratotype: Borehole VI, Point of Ayre [NX 440 035] Known only from boreholes (Lamplugh, 1903; Smith,

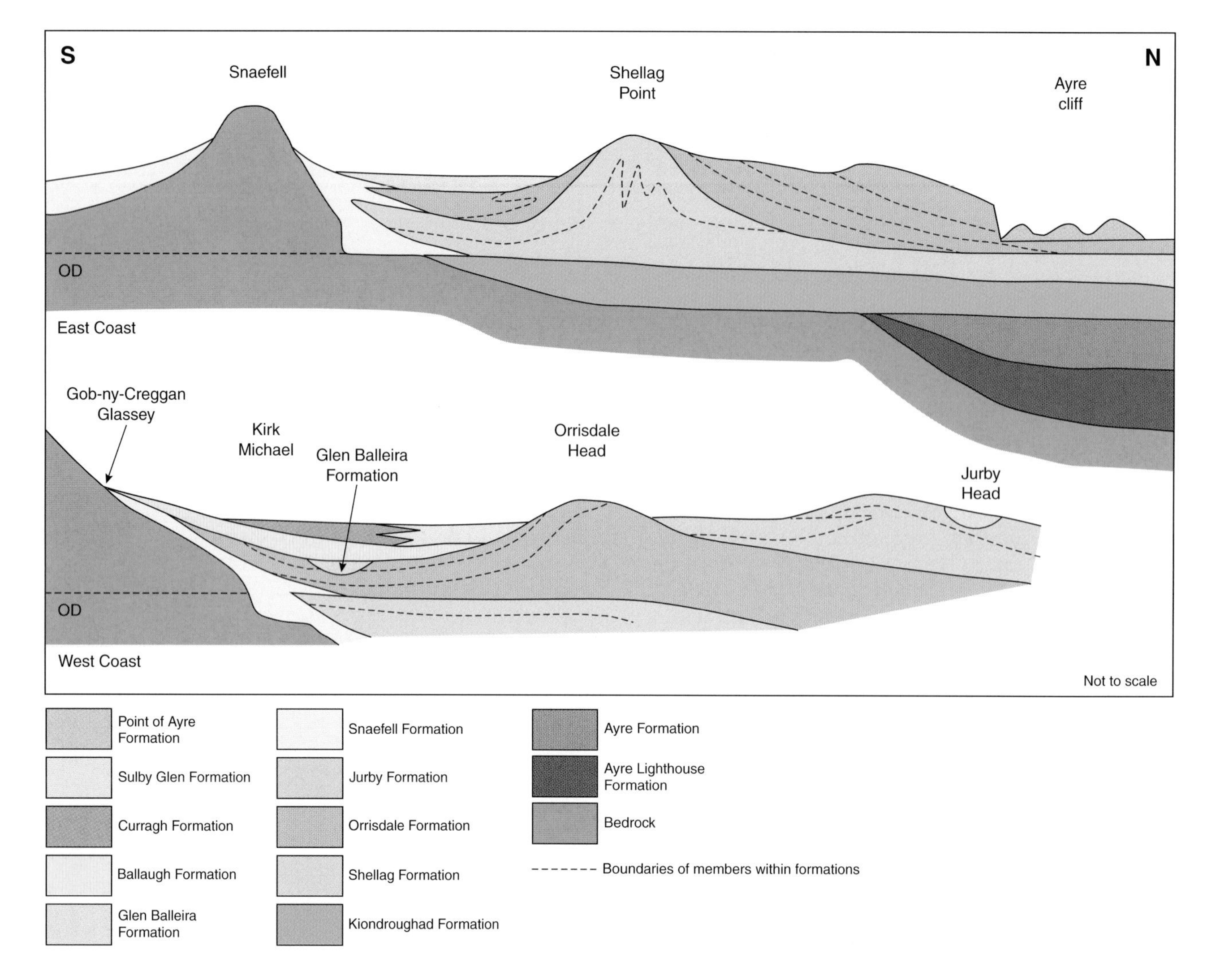

Figure 32 Schematic cross-section north–south through the northern part of the Isle of Man showing relationships between formations in the Manx Quaternary stratigraphy.

1930). Overlying Permo–Triassic bedrock at a maximum depth of 140 m below OD it comprises about 70 m of sand, gravel and diamict of northern origin. The age of the formation is indeterminate, but on the basis of the overlying succession it may be correlated with cold oxygen isotope stages 8, 10 or 12. Previously named the Isle of Man Formation (Thomas, 1999); a name of more local significance is now used.

Ayre Formation

Stratotype: Borehole IV, Point of Ayre [NX 465 050]. Known only from boreholes (Lamplugh, 1903; Smith, 1930) it consists of up to 8 m of shelly silts and sands at depths between 65 and 73 m below OD, and overlies the Ayre Lighthouse Formation. Lamplugh (1903) described the bed as marine. Its age is unknown but it is provisionally correlated with temperate oxygen isotope stages 5, 7 or 9 (Thomas, 1977, 1985).

Kiondroughad Formation

Stratotype: Borehole 16, Kiondroughad [NX 395 015]. Also known only from boreholes (Lamplugh, 1903; Smith, 1930) it comprises about 60 m of sand, gravel and diamict of northern origin. It rests partly on an extensive level rock platform between 41 and 53 m below OD and partly on the Ayre Formation (Thomas, 1985) and is overlain by the Shellag Formation. Its age is unknown but probably corresponds to cold oxygen isotope stages 4, 6 or 8.

Shellag Formation

Stratotype: Shellag Point [NX 460 000]. Glacitectonically deformed and complex glacigenic formation of foreign origin overlain unconformably by the Orrisdale Formation. On the north-east coast, the *Bride Member* [NX 460 000] is a massive, fine-grained basal diamict that is overlain by the *Cronk ny Arrey Laa Member* [NX 460 000], a coarse, cryoturbated, ice-front, alluvial fan gravel. On the north-west coast, the *Wyllin Member* [SC 309 906] is a deformed, massive, fine-grained diamict correlated with the Bride Member (Thomas, 1977), and succeeded by the *Kirk Michael Member* [SC 309 906]. This is composed of sand and contains abundant shells of *Turritella communis*. This fossil assemblage may represent in situ glaciomarine sedimentation, a raft from the former sea floor, or shells derived by washout from earlier sediments. In the south of the Island, the *Ballasalla Member* comprises extensive basal diamicts of mixed local and foreign composition, locally drumlinised. It

Table 6 Classification of the Quaternary stratigraphy of the Isle of Man (modified after Thomas, 1999).

Formation	Member	Isotope Stage
Point of Ayre		1
Sulby Glen		1
Curragh		1
Ballaugh		1 and 2
Glen Balleira		2
Snaefell	Druidale Ballure Mooar	2
Jurby	Killane St Patrick's Ballateare	2
Orrisdale	Orrisdale Head Bishop's Court Trunk Ballaleigh Ballavarkish Ballacottier Ballaquark Cranstal Kionlough Dog Mills	2
Shellag	Bride Cronk ny Arrey Laa Wylllin Kirk Michael Ballasalla Plain of Malew	2
Kiondroughad		4, 6 or 8
Ayre		5, 7 or 9
Ayre Lighthouse		8, 10 or 12

is overlain by the *Plain of Malew Member*, a series of proglacial outwash deposits.

Orrisdale Formation

Stratotype: Orrisdale Head [SC 319 930]. A stratigraphically very complex glacigenic formation of foreign origin that unconformably overlies the Shellag Formation on the north-west and north-east coasts.

On the north-west coast, the *Orrisdale Head Member* [SC 319 930] is a stratified coarse diamict formed subglacially (Dackombe and Thomas, 1991) or by glaciomarine density underflow and pelagic rainout (Eyles and Eyles, 1984). The *Bishop's Court Member* [SC 319 930] is a thick sequence of sands and gravels formed in a series of diachronous marginal sandurs on an unstable, ice-cored supraglacial topography (Thomas et al., 1985). The *Trunk Member* [SC 317 923] shows rapid vertical and lateral facies variation and extensive flow folding; it is interpreted as a resedimented debris flow from a stagnating ice margin (Dackombe and Thomas, 1991). This member, previously assigned to the Jurby Formation, has been reassigned to the Orrisdale Formation following recent mapping. The *Ballaleigh Member*, formerly identified as part of the Late-glacial Ballaugh Formation (Thomas, 1999), is now included in the Orrisdale Formation as its gravels are derived from a foreign, glacial outwash fan source.

On the north-east coast, to the north of the Bride Moraine, the *Ballavarkish Member* [NX 462 007], the *Ballacottier Member* [NX 462 007], the *Ballaquark Member* [NX 465 013] and the *Cranstal Member* [NX 468 020] all offlap one another to the north and consist of stratified coarse diamict deposited subglacially. The Ballaquark, Ballacottier and Cranstal members were all previously assigned to the Jurby Formation (Thomas, 1999), but recent mapping identifies them as older and part of the Orrisdale Formation. To the south of the Bride Moraine, the *Kionlough Member* [SC 455 987] comprises debris flow and ice front alluvial fan sands and gravels, regarded as a breakdown product of the deformation of the moraine (Thomas, 1984). The member passes distally into the *Dog Mills Member* [SC 456 988], a sequence of massive and laminated sands, silts and clays with extensive soft-sediment and dewatering structures, containing a rich microfauna that may be in situ or derived.

Jurby Formation

Stratotype: Jurby Head [SC 343 980]. A stratigraphically complex glacigenic formation that disconformably overlies the Orrisdale Formation across the north-west coast. Remapping of the area across Jurby Head has resulted in a complete revision of the stratigraphy and the previous classification of Thomas (1999) has been abandoned. The *Killane Member* [SC 339 968] comprises a thick succession of laminated and massive mud with dropstones and other ice-rafted debris, and is interpreted as the distal deposits of the floor of an ice-contact lake. The *St Patrick's Member* [SC 344 982] consists of a complex series of gravel, sand and mud deposited in subaqueous fans and proximal lake floors. The *Ballateare Member* [SC 342 972] consists of an offlapping sequence of muddy diamict.

Snaefell Formation

Stratotype: Druidale [SC 355 878]. Extensive head, scree and slope wash deposits covering the upland area and of exclusively local origin (Thomas, 1976). The *Druidale Member* [SC 355 850] comprises coarse scree overlying bedrock, succeeded by units of solifluctate intercalated with redeposited diamict and some gravels. The lower units probably date from the Early Devensian, but the majority are probably Late Devensian periglacially reworked local diamict (Evans and Arthurton, 1973; Bowen, 1973; Thomas, 1985; Chiverrell et al., 2001). The *Ballure* [SC 458 934] and *Moaar* members [SC 303 894] comprise local head and scree that intercalate with Orrisdale Formation glacigenic sediments at low elevations around the Island margin (Thomas, 1976).

Glen Balleira Formation

Stratotype: Glen Balleira [SC 314 915]. The formation comprises peat, organic mud and calcareous marl deposited in kettle basins overlying the Jurby and Orrisdale formations. Five kettle sequences have been recorded at Glen Balleira and two sequences at Jurby. The sediments range from Greenland Interstadial 1 to the beginning of the Greenland Stadial 1 (18.5–12.5 ka BP) (Joachim, 1978; Dackombe and Thomas, 1985; Chiverrell et al., 1999). In Thomas (1999) the deposits were identified informally as the Jurby Head and Glen Balleira beds, but their palaeoecological significance warrants their being raised to formation status.

Ballaugh Formation

Stratotype: Ballaugh [SC 348 935]. The formation comprises the large gravel-dominated mountain-front alluvial fans that fringe the northern uplands. They include fans at Glen Wyllin, Glen Balleira, Ballaugh, Sulby Glen, Glen Auldyn and Ballure, together with minor fans in the central valley. All overlie the Orrisdale Formation. The Glen Wyllin and Glen Balleira fans overlie Late-glacial organic sediments and are younger than 12.8 to 11.3 cal ka BP (Mitchell, 1965; Dickson et al., 1970). The Ballaugh, Sulby and Glen Auldyn fans began accumulating earlier, and the Ballure fan interdigitates with members of the Orrisdale Formation glacigenic sediments, suggesting that the fans began accumulating immediately after the uplands were deglaciated (Thomas, 1976; Chiverrell et al., 2001),

Curragh Formation

Stratotype: The Curragh [SC 365 950]. Extensive peat sequences that have accumulated in lowland basins, valleys and upland plateaux, with dates of peat inception varying from the base of the Holocene to about 3000 years BP (Russell, 1978; Chiverrell et al., 1999, 2001). The formation now includes the Bungalow Formation of Thomas (1999) on the grounds that there is little distinction between upland and lowland peat.

Sulby Glen Formation

Stratotype: Sulby Glen [SC 385 924]. Extensive fills of fluvial gravel, sands and alluvium occur in the Sulby, Auldyn, Dhoo, Baldwin, Neb and Silverburn valleys. Holocene fluvial activity has left a series of river terraces and alluvial fans in the valleys of the Manx uplands (Chiverrell et al., 2001) and along the lowland rivers (Lamplugh, 1903).

Point of Ayre Formation

Stratotype: Point of Ayre [NX 440 035]. Extensive shingle beach ridges, underlain by lagoonal basins, and backed by a degraded raised cliff. The *Ayre Member* [NX 440 035] comprises offlapping gravel ridges with overlying blown sand and dunes. The earliest beach accumulation began at 8.985 to 8.365 cal ka BP with a sea level between 0.6 m below and 2.2 m above OD (Tooley, 1978). The *Lough Cranstal Member* [NX 455 025] (formerly the Cranstal Member of Thomas, 1999) comprises diatomite, fen peat, fresh water lake muds and brackish water clays showing a marine connection at 8.985 to 8.365 cal ka BP (Phillips, 1967; Tooley, 1978). The *Phurt Member* [NX 467 027] comprises laminated silt, peat, palaeosol and a forest bed dated at 8.005 to 7.555 cal ka BP capped by marine silty peat mud formed between 7.82 to 7.59 and 5.580 to 5.075 cal ka BP (Innes et al., 2000). Its upper part is a sandy organic soil containing Neolithic artefacts.

10 Economic geology

MINERALS

Historical records of mineral extraction on the Isle of Man date back to at least the 13th century, though it has been suggested (Ford, 1993) that the Island contains evidence of Bronze Age mining. The earliest records relate to the working of copper, iron and lead ores. These, together with zinc ores, became important elements in the Island's economy in the 19th century, with some production continuing into the first half of the 20th century. More recent investigations into the possibility of renewed metal working (Mackay and Schnellman, 1963) have proved fruitless and all such mining has long been abandoned. Features of the mining industry remain conspicuous in the landscape with the Lady Isabella water wheel at Laxey Mine forming one of the Island's best known tourist attractions (Plate 15).

Recorded production of metal ores, between 1845 and 1938, was 268 000 tons of lead concentrates, 256 000 tons of zinc concentrates, 14 000 tons of copper concentrates and 25 000 tons of iron ore (Ford, 1993). Substantial amounts of silver were recovered as a by-product of lead smelting. The Isle of Man mines have thus contributed approximately 5 per cent of the total British output of lead ores and around 20 per cent of the total output of zinc ores. Mineral extraction on the Island today is confined to the working of bulk minerals such as sand and gravel, crushed rock and limestone, with smaller amounts of building stone and slate.

Lamplugh (1903) provided very detailed contemporary descriptions of the Island's economic geology, together with a wealth of historical information on mining. Descriptions of a number of mineral deposits were also published by Dewey (1920), Carruthers and Strahan (1923) and Dewy and Eastwood (1925). More recent, though much briefer, accounts of the Island's mining, mainly of a historical nature, include those by Skelton (1956), Pearce and Rose (1979), von Arx (1994, 1996, 1998), Dobson and Hollis (1993), Warriner and Gillings (1983), Hollis (1986, 1987a, b, 1988, 1989) and Ford (1993). A study by Mackay and Schnellman (1963) on the economic potential of lead–zinc mining on the Island includes a list of known mining sites.

Plate 15 Lady Isabella water wheel at Laxey. The wheel was built in 1854 to drain mines higher up the valley [SC 4326 8533] (P 108718).

VEIN MINERALISATION

Despite the large number of known mineral deposits, and the very considerable former economic importance of several of these, the mineralogy and metallogenesis of the Isle of Man have attracted surprisingly little research interest. Apart from the references already cited, and a comparatively recent study on hydrogeochemical lead, zinc and copper anomalies by Gaciri and Ineson (1981), Lamplugh's (1903) text remains the most detailed descriptive account of the Isle of Man veins. The brief outline of the vein deposits given below is compiled from information contained in these published sources.

The significant vein deposits are restricted to a strike-parallel zone along the axis of the outcrop of Lower Palaeozoic rocks (Figure 33). The vein deposits also correlate well with the broad belt of higher metamorphic grade determined using white mica 'crystallinity' techniques (Roberts et al., 1990). Typically they are associated with steeply inclined faults in the lower to middle Arenig metasedimentary rocks of the Manx Group, although veins in the Foxdale area are known to pass into a granite host at depth (Lamplugh, 1903, p.500). Relatively little mineralisation is apparent in the younger rocks. An extensive trial at Glen Maye (Lamplugh, 1903, p.545) explored lead-bearing veins that occur close to the faulted boundary of the Silurian Niarbyl Formation. No productive veins are known within the Carboniferous rocks which crop out in the south of the Island, although traces of lead and copper mineralisation occur in association with dolerite dykes at Castletown and Langness (Lamplugh, 1903, p.537). No mineralisation is recorded in the Peel Sandstone Group.

Most of the Island's veins strike roughly north–south, though some veins in the Foxdale area trend east–west. The productive veins are locally broken and displaced by later transverse faults. Lamplugh (1903) noted that very many small north-east-trending quartz veins occur along the planes of cleavage in the Manx Group rocks but they are invariably barren of ore minerals. Vein widths of up to 11 m have been reported from the Foxdale mines and widths of 8 m at Laxey and Beckwith's mines, though widths of around 1.5 m or less seem to have been more normal. The most prominent veins, at the Foxdale and Laxey mines, have been traced over strike lengths of around 4 km and 1.6 km, respectively, and

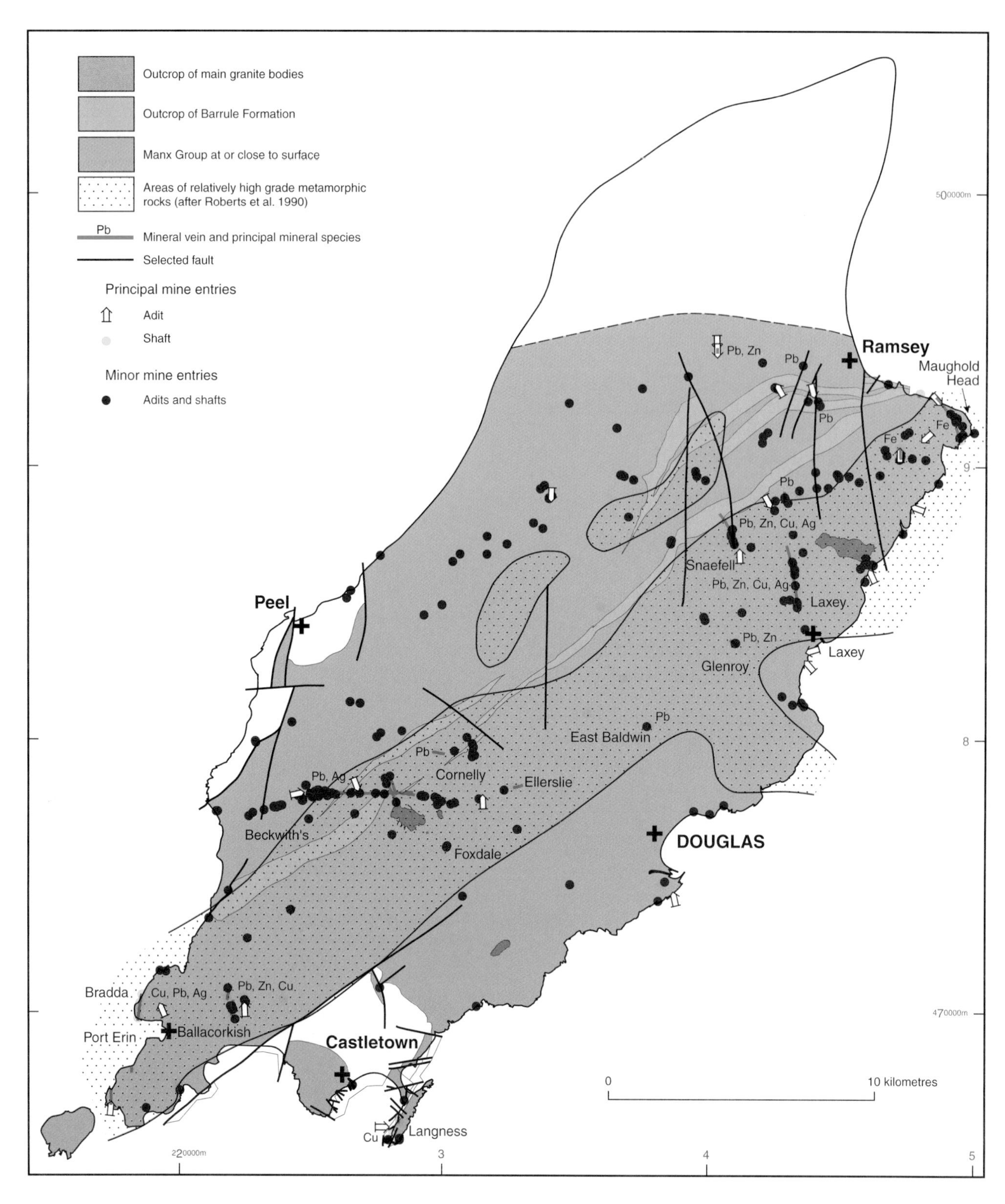

Figure 33 Map of mineral veins, mines and adits.

worked to depths up to 610 m below the surface. Other veins may be traced over much shorter distances.

So far as can be established from the available published descriptions, the mineral veins of the Island may be summarised and grouped according to their principal metalliferous constituents: lead–zinc–copper veins, iron ore (hematite) veins and miscellaneous metalliferous veins.

Lead–zinc–copper veins

The great majority of veins carry dominant lead–zinc mineralisation, with galena and sphalerite as the principal ore minerals, though the relative proportions of these minerals in individual deposits is extremely variable. Lamplugh (1903, p.520) recorded sphalerite as the most abundant ore at the Laxey mines, where it was an important product, whereas galena is the dominant ore at Foxdale, where sphalerite was not found in workable quantity. Other ore minerals include minor amounts of chalcopyrite, pyrite, pyrrhotite and, locally, copper sulphosalts such as tetrahedrite (referred to by Lamplugh, 1903, p.501 as 'polytelite' or 'silberfahlerz') and jamesonite (referred to as 'plumosite' by Smyth, 1887). The limited available evidence suggests that some, perhaps most, of the veins that have been worked primarily for copper may simply represent copper-rich expressions of the suite of veins dominated by lead and zinc minerals. There is currently insufficient information to distinguish a separate suite of copper-dominated veins from veins dominated by lead and zinc mineralisation, as can be done in the nearby Lake District. Gangue minerals include quartz, calcite, dolomite and siderite, the latter having been recorded in substantial quantities at Foxdale. Some baryte and fluorite occur locally. Brecciated and decomposed wallrock is common in some veins. Supergene minerals, which seem not to have been abundant, include atacamite, native copper, cuprite, malachite, tenorite, melanterite, cerussite and pyromorphite.

In common with most British lead ores, much, if not all Isle of Man galena is typically argentiferous. Comprehensive assay or recovery figures are not available for all Isle of Man lead mines, though records quoted by Lamplugh (1903, p.520) reveal average silver values of around 40 ounces per ton of lead from the Laxey orebodies. More modest values of around 14 to 16 ounces per ton of lead are reported from the Snaefell, Rushen and Ballacorkish mines, though values as low as 3 to 4 ounces per ton of lead were recorded from parts of the Rushen Mine. Lamplugh (1903, pp.502–511) noted that at the Foxdale mines the galena was much richer in silver with values ranging from 50 to 400 ounces per ton. The presence of highly argentiferous tetrahedrite, with up to 13.57 per cent silver, in the Foxdale ores was noted by Lamplugh (1903, p.502). The highly argentiferous ore may well have contained a significant proportion of this silver-rich tetrahedrite. Similar silver-rich tetrahedrite has been reported from lead–zinc veins in the English Lake District (Stanley and Vaughan, 1981). It is possible that much of the Isle of Man galena may also contain an abundance of silver-bearing copper sulphosalts, similar to those described from the Lake District.

Very little has been published on the origins of the Isle of Man lead–zinc veins. Their structural and regional setting and their mineralogy invite comparison with the nearest similar veins in the Lake District (Stanley and Vaughan, 1982), or south-west Scotland (Rice, 1993). Despite this, it must be stressed that in view of the lack of modern data on the Isle of Man deposits any such comparison should be regarded as extremely tentative and provisional. The abundance of galena and sphalerite, together with the apparently widespread occurrence of comparatively minor amounts of copper sulphides, particularly the presence of silver-rich sulphosalts such as tetrahedrite, supports this comparison. However, published descriptions of veins in which copper minerals are in relatively greater abundance, and from which significant productions of copper ore have been obtained, such as those of the Bradda and Langness mines, are different from the copper-rich veins of the Lake District. The apparent absence of arsenopyrite and chlorite and an abundance of iron sulphides, including pyrrhotite, together with the common occurrence of galena and sphalerite, are more suggestive of these being a rather more copper-rich expression of the Island's lead–zinc mineralisation. Lamplugh (1903, p.520) noted that chalcopyrite occurs either in fine strings or in disseminations on the margins of the Laxey orebodies. This suggests that, at least locally, the introduction of copper minerals may predate that of lead–zinc mineralisation, though it does not preclude the possibility of the lead–zinc veins, plus or minus copper minerals, being the product of one mineralising episode.

Evidence for the age of the Island's lead–zinc mineralisation is very limited. Ineson and Mitchell (1979) determined K–Ar dates on 30 samples of clay gouges from veins or altered wallrocks on the Isle of Man. Dates of 310 to 320 Ma (mid- to late Carboniferous), 250 Ma (Permian) and 220 Ma (Triassic) were interpreted as evidence of several phases of mineralisation. Lamplugh (1903, p.488) described relationships which might suggest that some of the Isle of Man veins postdate Palaeogene basic dykes. This is unlikely to be a realistic date for the main mineralisation. Rather, it may lend support to Ineson and Mitchell's (1979) suggestion of some Palaeogene remobilisation of previously emplaced mineralisation.

Detailed descriptions of the Island's numerous individual mines are given by Lamplugh (1903) and are not repeated here. However, a brief account of important features of the three principal groups of workings in these deposits is provided below.

LAXEY The main vein at Laxey Mine [SC 432 856] strikes north–south and dips steeply to the east (Lamplugh, 1903; Ford, 1993, 1998). Vein widths of up to 8 m were recorded. Post-mineralisation faults disrupt the vein and the northern limit of workings seems to have been determined by such a fracture, beyond which the vein was not relocated. A roughly parallel vein approximately 3 km west of the Laxey Vein was worked at Snaefell Mine [SC 408 875]. Both galena and sphalerite are abundant in these veins, in a gangue composed mainly of quartz, calcite and dolomite. Sphalerite was especially plentiful in the Laxey workings. Uranium-bearing hydrocarbons, referred to by Lamplugh (1903, p.520) as 'anthracite' were also found in the veins. Mining at Laxey reached depths of over 335 m below surface, with the vein being traced along strike for around 1.6 km. Mining at Snaefell ended in 1898 and at Laxey in 1919. Ford (1993) noted intermittent attempts at re-opening in the years leading up to 1938. The spoil heaps were reprocessed for lead and copper between 1953 and 1958. The uranium-rich hydrocarbons were the subject of investigation during the 1950s under the UKAEA (Hollis, 1987b).

The history of mining at Laxey has been the subject of several studies in industrial archaeology (e.g. Warriner and Gillings, 1983; Hollis, 1986, 1987a, b; Scarfe, 1987, 1990).

FOXDALE AND GLEN RUSHEN The Foxdale and Glen Rushen group of mines worked an east–west-trending vein structure with a strike length of up to 5 km, together with several parallel veins and cross-courses (Ford, 1993). At the Foxdale mines, the veins lie within granite wallrocks of the Foxdale intrusion. At the Beckwith's and Glen Rushen mines, the veins were first encountered in Manx Group wallrocks but pass downwards into granite. The deepest working in this area, Beckwith's Mine, reached a depth of 613 m below the surface (Ford, 1993). Mining in this area ended in 1911.

BRADDA HEAD A number of veins have been worked and tried in the neighbourhood of Bradda Head [SC 185 698], where several large veins are conspicuous in the sea cliffs. Lead and copper ores have been raised from these mines. Mining in this area ended in 1883.

Iron ore (hematite) veins

A small group of veins on Maughold Head were explored and, in some cases worked, for hematite. Lamplugh (1903, p.539) gave details of these deposits under the heading of the 'Northern hematite group', pointing out that such mineralisation is restricted to this part of the Island. Two main groups of workings, the Maughold Head mines [SC 486 924] and the Drynane Mine [SC 493 910], appear to have accounted for the main output of around 25 000 tons of iron ore credited to the Island between 1845 and 1938 (Ford, 1993). Hollis (1987a, 1988) has described the results of recent investigations by mine explorers in these deposits.

The veins occur within the Lonan and Maughold formations of the Manx Group. Hematite appears to be the main mineral, accompanied by much smaller amounts of quartz, dolomite and calcite. Lamplugh (1903, p.540) recorded that the vein exposed in the cliff at Stack Mooar, on the north side of Maughold Head, was about 12 m wide and was composed of fault breccia and quartz with cavities containing hematite. At Drynane Mine a 'bunch' of ore (presumably hematite) up to 3 m wide was cut (Lamplugh, 1903, p.540). At the Ballajora Iron Mine, in addition to hematite, the veins locally contained substantial amounts of iron carbonate (presumably siderite) which, according to Lamplugh, contained insufficient iron to be workable.

Lamplugh (1903, p.539) drew attention to similarities between the hematite deposits of the Isle of Man and those of the Lake District and west and south Cumbria. In support of this he cited the proximity of the Manx hematite veins to red Permo–Triassic rocks, adding that the Carboniferous limestone of the Island, where overlain by these rocks, is stained and veined with hematite. In both areas hematite seems to be the dominant iron mineral with a very limited range of gangue minerals. Other iron minerals in Cumbria include very minor amounts of pyrite, goethite and siderite, though in no case is there any evidence that the hematite has been derived from them by supergene alteration; the hematite within the Cumbria deposits is everywhere a primary constituent of the deposits. Numerous authors, including Smith (1924), Rose and Dunham (1977), Shepherd and Goldring (1993) and Akhurst et al. (1997), have reviewed the nature and origins of the Cumbrian hematite deposits, with suggestions for the age of emplacement varying between Permian, Early Triassic and post-Triassic. Whereas there is little or no evidence available for the age of the Manx deposits, in view of their apparent close similarity to the well-studied Cumbrian deposits it is likely that they are part of this mineralised province and thus are of the same age.

MISCELLANEOUS METALLIFEROUS VEINS

Lamplugh (1903) made reference to a small number of occurrences of other minerals in veins that clearly do not belong to either the lead–zinc or hematite vein suites. Trials have been made on some of these though none has been of economic importance.

Antimony

At Niarbyl Bay, trial workings [SC 214 773] undertaken in the mid 19th century, apparently in search of the western extension of the Foxdale Vein, revealed the presence of a small pocket of antimony ore, though no workable deposit was found. A further investigation here in 1893–1894 also failed to reveal further mineralisation. Whereas it is possible that the vein at Niarbyl is an unusual antimony-rich expression of the Island's lead–zinc mineralisation, it seems more probable that it may represent a separate phase of mineralisation. Antimony (stibnite)-bearing veins are known from the Lake District (Young, 1987) and southern Scotland (Dewey, 1920; Gallagher et al., 1983, 1989) and it is possible that the Niarbyl vein may be a counterpart of this mineralisation. K–Ar ages of around 390 Ma from the Niarbyl Vein (Ineson and Mitchell, 1979) are significantly older than most dates obtained from other Manx veins. This is consistent both with the separate nature of this mineralisation and its association with the antimony mineralisation of the Lake District and southern Scotland.

Gold

The presence of gold in the Isle of Man was discussed briefly by Lamplugh (1903, p.549) and has been discussed more recently by Hollis (1989). In this latter account reference is made to small trial workings on veins reported to contain gold in Sulby Glen and near Maughold. Another trial at Onchan Mine, Douglas Bay [SC 394 774] on a quartz vein containing galena and baryte is said to have revealed ore containing several pennyweights per ton of gold. Lamplugh (1903) also recorded the presence, within the Cummings Collection at King William's College, Castletown, of two specimens of slate showing specks of free gold labelled simply as originating from Langness. There is no record of any commercial production of gold from the Island.

Molybdenum

Molybdenite occurs as a coating on joints in the Dhoon granodiorite (Lamplugh, 1903, p.550). It is not present in sufficient quantity to have attracted commercial interest.

Nickel

Very small trial workings in the Rhenas area were discussed by Lamplugh (1903, p.547) under the name of Laurel Bank or Wheal Michael [SC 316 868]. It seems that small quartz veins carrying traces of millerite (NiS) were the object of the exploration (Smyth, 1863), perhaps associated with lead-bearing veins.

Uranium

The local abundance in some veins, notably those at Laxey and Snaefell, of solid hydrocarbons, then referred to as 'anthracite', was noted by Lamplugh (1903, p.520). The high uranium content of this material, described by Davison and Bowie (1951), attracted interest in the 1950s when these mines were investigated as a potential source of uranium ore, though no workable deposit was found (Hollis, 1987b).

BULK AND INDUSTRIAL MINERALS

Building stone

Whereas most of the Island's rocks have been used for building at some period, good quality stone is available only from a limited range of sources. A variety of rock types may be seen in domestic and farm buildings and stone walls across the Island. Their characteristics, and the sources of these in contemporary use, have been described by Lamplugh (1903, p.561).

Flaggy sandstone and blocks of laminated mudstone and siltstone from most of the Lower Palaeozoic formations have been used widely for building purposes.

The Peel Sandstone Group was formerly quarried north-east of Peel near Creg Malin [SC 251 844 and 254 855], as a source of red 'freestone'. However, Lamplugh (1903, p.563) noted that thin or irregular bedding, the presence of shaly and conglomeratic layers, and its poor resistance to weathering, renders much of the unit unsuitable for the production of good quality blocks. However, the stone may be seen in the ruins of Peel Castle and in many other buildings in and around Peel.

The Carboniferous limestone of the Island has been a source of building stone, both as rough and dressed blocks. Lamplugh (1903, p.563) cited Castle Rushen at Castletown [SC 265 675] as a testimony to the durability of carefully chosen limestone, although he commented on its 'somewhat dingy' colour. Flaggy dark grey limestone from the flaggy and shaly Bowland Shale Formation on the eastern shore at Poyllvaaish [SC 246 672] was formerly worked as an ornamental stone for use in chimney pieces, tombstones and mantelpieces and marketed as a 'black marble' (Lamplugh, 1903, p.564). Some limestone is still worked today for dimension stone at Poyllvaaish.

The granitic rocks on the Isle of Man have also been quarried for building stone. In addition, paving setts were formerly produced from the Foxdale granite and the Dhoon granodiorite was used to make agricultural rollers. The Foxdale granite is quarried today at Stoney Mountain [SC 291 771] to provide crushed rock aggregate, building stone and armour stone for coastal protection work.

Crushed rock aggregate and roadstone

A variety of rocks have, in the past, provided a source of crushed rock aggregate for building and roadstone. Crushed rock aggregate is today worked from a range of sources. The quartz arenite-dominated Creg Agneash Formation in the Manx Group is exploited at Dreemskerry [SC 476 911]). Granite is worked at Stoney Mountain [SC 291 771] and dolerite at Poortown [SC 271 832] near Peel. The Carboniferous limestone is worked at Turkeyland [SC 295 689] and Billown [SC 269 101]. Bitumen-coated roadstone is produced at the quarries at Billown, Stoney Mountain and Poortown.

Slate

Although previously known collectively as the 'Manx Slates' the Lower Palaeozoic rocks of the Isle of Man yield comparatively little true slate. The Barrule and Glen Rushen formations have been the main source of slate, and quarries and trials are widespread along the outcrops of these formations. However, the occurrence of two cleavages prevents the rock from being split evenly and thinly. With the advent of cheap transport in the 19th century, competition from the Cambrian slates of north Wales effectively destroyed the market for Manx slate as a roofing product. Some material is worked today for various purposes, notably from South Barrule quarries [SC 269 769].

Limestone

In past centuries the quarrying and burning of comparatively small amounts of limestone for use as a soil conditioner, and in the preparation of mortar, was a widespread practice. The majority of the limestone so used was obtained from the Carboniferous limestone of the Island. Lamplugh (1903, p.653) commented on the historical uses of limestone, noting the local use of erratic boulders of Carboniferous limestone in the north of the Island, of a cornstone band in the Peel Sandstone Group at The Stack [SC 254 850], and the presence of an early mortar prepared from burnt sea shells in the fabric of the chapel on St Michael's Island, Langness [SC 295 673].

Limestone working is today confined to the Carboniferous limestone. The quarries at Turkeyland [SC 295 689] and Billown [SC 269 701] produce agricultural lime in addition to crushed aggregate and roadstone. The production of building stone from the Carboniferous limestone at Poyllvaaish [SC 246 672] has also been noted above.

Salt

The upper Triassic deposits, proved by drilling beneath the Point of Ayre, contain thick beds of halite. A brine-pumping industry was established here towards the end of the 19th century with an evaporation works at Ramsey. However, the industry was short-lived, and ended when the brine pipeline was destroyed by storms (Ford, 1993).

Sand and gravel

The Quaternary and Recent deposits of the Island have long provided local sources of sand and gravel. Present-day workings extract sand, gravel and concreting sand from the raised beach deposits of the Point of Ayre [NX 460 043], sand from blown sand deposits at Ballagarraghyn, near Jurby [SC 362 005], and sand and gravel of glacial origin from Lhergydhoo, near Peel [SC 267 850] and Ballaharra [SC 264 824]. At Ballaharra, the material is used in the manufacture of concrete products and bricks.

MISCELLANEOUS MINERAL PRODUCTS

Lamplugh's (1903) summary of the Island's geology makes reference to several other minor mineral products. These are of historical interest and not likely to attract future economic interest.

Asbestos

The working of 'asbestos' or 'dun earth' for the making of polishing powder, from veins in the Dhoon granodiorite [SC 458 867], was described by Lamplugh (1903, p.556). The precise nature of the mineral is not clear. Lamplugh referred to it as 'fibrous tourmaline' though cited an unidentified report that named the mineral as fibrous actinolite. The workings date from the early years of the 19th century.

Beryl

Dawson (1966) drew attention to the presence of beryl in significant amounts in two pegmatites associated with the Foxdale granite and although he suggested further investigation of the economic potential no further work on this occurrence is known.

Fuller's earth

Lamplugh (1903, p.556) referred to the use of a fine glacial clay from Glen Wyllin, near Kirk Michael [SC 318 898] as a fulling agent. Although the true mineralogical nature of this material is not known, it is unlikely to resemble a true fuller's earth (calcium montmorillonite).

Graphite

Under the heading of 'plumbago', Lamplugh (1903, p.550) referred to the localised occurrence of graphite, both within graphitic slates and as a constituent of metalliferous veins. The occurrence of graphite at Beary was noted by Greg and Lettsom (1858). An unsuccessful attempt to locate workable graphite here was recorded by Lamplugh (1903, p.548), who also commented briefly on the discovery of a block of good quality 'plumbago', apparently derived from a nearby vein, on the foreshore at Douglas.

Quartz

Lamplugh (1903, p.557) commented on the working of vein quartz for 'ornamental rock-work' from a wide vein on the north-east side of the Foxdale granite [SC 288 773] and from a similar vein on the north slope of Kerrowgarroo, near St Johns [SC 294 806].

Rottenstone

Lamplugh (1903, p.556) recorded the preparation of a small amount of 'rotten-stone' for use as a polishing agent. This was made from a fine silt, apparently formed by rain-wash, in a depression [SC 245 753] on the moorland between South Barrule and Cronk Fedjag.

Ochre and umber

Earthy ferruginous deposits suitable for use as pigments were described by Lamplugh (1903, p.555) from several places. Ochre was encountered in some abundance in the upper oxidised portions of some mineral veins, particularly those at the Bradda and Ballacorkish mines. Ochre derived from the decomposition of partially dolomitised Carboniferous limestone was being worked at Ballasalla during the time of Lamplugh's survey. Other sources were associated with decomposed olivine dolerite dykes, for example at Maughold Head [SC 494 913] (Lamplugh, 1903, p.541).

ENERGY SOURCES

Coal

Attempts to identify coal on the Isle of Man date back to at least 1699 when the Lord of Mann, Charles, 8th Earl of Derby, initiated a search for workable deposits. Brief summaries of these and numerous unsuccessful attempts, have been described by Lamplugh (1903, p.557). The youngest Carboniferous rocks known on the Island are of early Namurian age and have been proved in borings beneath the extensive cover of Quaternary deposits in the north of the Island. Whereas there are some similarities between the Carboniferous rocks proved in these borings and the Carboniferous succession of Cumbria, no workable coal has been found in any of these investigations and no Coal Measures rocks are known, or are likely to occur, on the Island.

Oil and gas

The search for hydrocarbons, beneath the sea around the Isle of Man, is largely a consequence of the discovery and successful exploitation of significant, commercial oil and gas fields in neighbouring areas to the south-east in central and southern parts of the East Irish Sea Basin (Colter, 1997; Quirk, Roy et al., 1999). As in these adjacent areas, hydrocarbon prospects in the Manx region are to be expected principally in 'cover' strata of Carboniferous and Permo–Triassic age. Since many of the elements that have led to major hydrocarbon entrapment in the East Irish Sea Basin are also present in the area around the Isle of Man, it was hoped that commercial accumulations would be found in this area. However, despite the drilling of several wells, no commercial discoveries have been made so far. There are many reasons for this, the most important of which appears to be the absence, or restricted occurrence, of suitable source rocks (Newman, 1999).

The present-day structure of the Isle of Man area is largely the result of Cainozoic inversion superimposed on the effects of several earlier extensional and compressional tectonic events (Chapter 4). As a result of erosion following this inversion, the Permo–Triassic rocks of the region are now restricted to three main areas: the Solway Firth, Peel and Eubonia–Lagman basins (Figures 12b, 16a). Of particular significance is the relatively small area where rocks of the Mercia Mudstone Group are preserved (Figure 16b), since these argillaceous and evaporitic strata are the main potential trap-sealing rocks for any Permo–Triassic reservoirs. Carboniferous rocks are more widespread in their extent, but were severely eroded during Variscan earth movements and only in two areas (Solway Firth and Eubonia–Lagman basins) are Upper Carboniferous rocks extensively preserved (Figure 12a). Within these somewhat limited areas, the complex tectonic post-Caledonian history has led to the formation of several fault block and anticlinal closures that have been identified and mapped from the seismic reflection data. These closures follow the main north-east–south-west and north–south structural trends. Within the Carboniferous strata many of these potential traps were initiated during the Variscan inversion, whereas those in Permo–Triassic rocks developed in post-early Lias Group times (Chapter 4).

Source rocks and burial (thermal) history

If any Jurassic source rocks (e.g. lower Jurassic strata or upper Jurassic Kimmeridge Clay) were ever present in the region it is unlikely that they were sufficiently deeply buried to have generated oil and they have long since been eroded away. The red-bed and evaporite-bearing Permo–Triassic rocks have no significant source potential. However, evidence from adjacent areas suggests that there are at least two main units of possible source rock of Carboniferous age in the region (Fraser et al., 1990; Hardman et al., 1993; Armstrong et al., 1997; Newman, 1999). These are the marine shales in the Namurian (Pendleian to Yeadonian) Bisat Group, which could potentially yield both oil and gas, and the Westphalian Kidston Group (Coal Measures), which could potentially yield gas.

Source potential is also possible in older, Dinantian, Garwood Group rocks, but so little is known of these strata that this suggestion cannot be tested. Data presented by Newman (1999) suggest that the Dinantian rocks so far sampled are organically lean (total organic content generally less than 1 per cent), with the exception of some sporadic thin gas-prone shales and coals. Except in those restricted areas where significant thicknesses of Upper Carboniferous strata are preserved, any Dinantian source rocks were probably at their maximum depth of burial in Late Carboniferous times when any hydrocarbons formed would have dispersed before or during the Variscan uplift.

Deep-marine oil-prone Namurian shales have proved to be important oil and gas source rocks in the East Irish Sea Basin and adjacent areas (Armstrong et al., 1997; Newman, 1999) and in the East Midlands of England (Fraser et al., 1990). Onshore, in northern England, these pass northwards into shallow marine and deltaic sedimentary rocks with much less or no source potential. A similar northwards facies change is likely in the Irish Sea though little detailed information is available. Thus, several authors have suggested that, in the Eubonia, Peel and Solway basins, oil-prone Namurian shales are likely to be lacking or of limited occurrence, even in the restricted areas where strata of this age have been preserved (e.g. Newman, 1999; Quirk, Roy et al., 1999). This negative assessment has, in part, been challenged by Racey et al. (1999). They have shown that Namurian shales from boreholes and outcrops in the Isle of Man, on the margins of the Solway and Eubonia basins, contain poor to moderate quantities (total organic content generally less than 5 per cent) of gas-prone organic matter presently in the oil-window.

The coal-bearing, gas-prone Westphalian Coal Measures are the source for much of the gas in the southern North Sea Basin, but do not appear to have played any significant role in the generation of the East Irish Sea Basin gasfields (Hardman et al., 1993). In the Manx region they are limited in occurrence, and are likely to have been extensively eroded and oxidised during Late Carboniferous to Early Permian erosion, accompanying and following Variscan inversion. In those areas where rocks of this age are still preserved, little or nothing is known of the maturity of the organic matter. It is thought, as in the East Irish Sea Basin, that they were probably insufficiently deeply buried in Mesozoic or more recent times to have yielded significant amounts of gas.

Reservoir rocks

Potential reservoir rocks are present at several stratigraphical levels in the Manx region:

- fractured Lower Palaeozoic rocks
- limestone and sandstone units in the Garwood Group
- sandstone bodies in the Bisat and Kidston groups
- Collyhurst Sandstone Formation
- Sherwood Sandstone Group (principally Ormskirk Sandstone Formation)

However, in the East Irish Sea Basin, only the Sherwood Sandstone Group reservoir is of importance, and this is likely to be the situation in the Manx region also. Fractured Lower Palaeozoic and Garwood Group rocks in structural closures in certain favourable locations close to suitably mature source rocks could prove to be useful reservoirs. The intergranular porosity of these rocks is generally very low. In all probability, such rocks are likely to be poorly or inadequately sealed. No major hydrocarbon shows have yet been found in such rocks though they have not been specifically targeted.

Upper Carboniferous sandstones form an important reservoir rock in the East Midlands of England and the southern North Sea, although their porosity and permeability values are commonly relatively low (Fraser et al., 1990). Similar sandstone has been proved in the northern part of the Isle Man (Racey et al., 1999). Porosity values up to 15 per cent have been recorded in these rocks, but in general much lower values (around 5 per cent) are to be expected. Details of their distribution and lateral variation are unknown, and no significant shows have yet been found in such rocks within the Manx region.

Onshore equivalents of the aeolian facies of the Collyhurst Sandstone Formation commonly exhibit good porosity and permeability values. However, rocks of this formation are restricted in occurrence and thickness around the Isle of Man, being absent in most of the wells so far drilled. No significant occurrences of oil or gas have been found in these rocks in the Isle of Man area or in the East Irish Sea Basin.

The main reservoir rocks in the East Irish Sea Basin are in the Sherwood Sandstone Group, notably in its upper part and in the Ormskirk Sandstone Formation in particular (Jackson et al., 1995; Colter, 1997). In the exploration boreholes drilled around the Isle of Man average porosity values in this formation have proved to be generally 15 to 17 per cent, with an average permeability of around 0.45 mD. The porosity in the underlying Calder Sandstone Member is similar (13 to 16 per cent). As in other adjacent areas, the lowest part of the group (i.e. Rottington Member) has much less favourable characteristics with porosity values typically around 7 per cent.

Conclusions

- i Structural traps are present in Carboniferous and Permo–Triassic rocks.
- ii No widespread, reliable potential source rocks of suitable maturity have been proved, though some gas potential from Namurian shales is likely.
- iii The best reservoir rocks are likely to belong to the higher part of the Sherwood Sandstone Group; reservoir potential at other stratigraphical levels (e.g. Upper Carboniferous strata and Collyhurst Sandstone Formation) is less certain.
- iv Sealed traps in Upper Carboniferous strata are only possible in the restricted areas where significant thicknesses of such rocks have been preserved.
- v Sealed traps in Sherwood Sandstone Group reservoirs are only possible in the restricted area where they are overlain by a significant thickness of Mercia Mudstone Group sealing cover.

WATER RESOURCES

Groundwater is present in varying amounts within all rock groups and most superficial deposits on the Isle of Man. Traditionally, it has been important as a source of supply to many isolated domestic dwellings. Figure 34 shows the distribution of wells and springs across the Island. The map indicates clearly the distribution of population on the northern glacial plain and coastal fringes, with the higher moorland of the centre of the Island largely unpopulated. The absence of any highly permeable aquifers has meant that exploitation of the resource using deep boreholes and classic hydrogeological assessment techniques has not occurred. As a consequence, there is very little information on the hydrogeological characteristics of the Island's rocks.

Lower Palaeozoic rocks

Most of the Lower Palaeozoic rocks, which occupy approximately 75 per cent of the land surface of the Island, are highly lithified and generally of low porosity and permeability. They can store and transmit only very small amounts of groundwater, except in regions containing void spaces. These take the form of fractures and are generally associated with fault zones and cavities adjacent to mineralised veins. The groundwater flow paths through bedrock are thus complex and structurally controlled, and lead to many isolated outbreaks of water at ground level, particularly on hill slopes. A relatively large amount of groundwater also moves at very shallow depths within the zone of weathered rock that occurs at rockhead.

Mining operations at Laxey encountered water at many levels, and down to more than 360 m depth. Flooding by surface water in the mines was a major problem in the early part of the 19th century because most of the mine shafts were situated in the valley floor at Glen Mooar. The river was always a danger and retaining wall collapses caused the deaths of several miners. By 1846, diversion tunnels had been constructed and mining could progress to greater depths. However, inflows of groundwater from bedrock cross-faults, or 'slides' continued to hamper progress. This led to the construction of the Lady Isabella water wheel, completed in 1854, which is still the largest surviving example of its type in Europe (Plate 16). After commissioning of the wheel, dewatering took place at the rate of 20 litres per second. Waste water was discharged into the river via the main adit where water still flows at the present day. However, the potential for sudden inflows of groundwater from storage along fracture zones remained. This problem was exemplified in 1901 when a mine heading that was being developed over 200 m below surface intercepted a fault. This produced an inflow of groundwater so great that the whole mine complex quickly flooded, drowning several miners (personal communication, F Cowin, 2001). The 1901 incident was the most extreme example of groundwater inflow at Laxey, but many other cross-faults and water inflows were encountered throughout the history of the mine.

Recharge to the groundwater system occurs partly along fracture zones in the Manx Group rocks where they are in contact with rivers and streams. This was significant at the Laxey mines because the main mineral veins follow the line of the main streams, providing ample opportunity for leakage to the fault planes. Local infiltration to the workings and, hence, to the local groundwater system occurred at the shallow headings in the south of the complex. These workings were the only ones of the whole mine complex to encounter soft, weathered ground. Here, waste-contaminated water originating from overhead farm buildings was observed to enter the workings

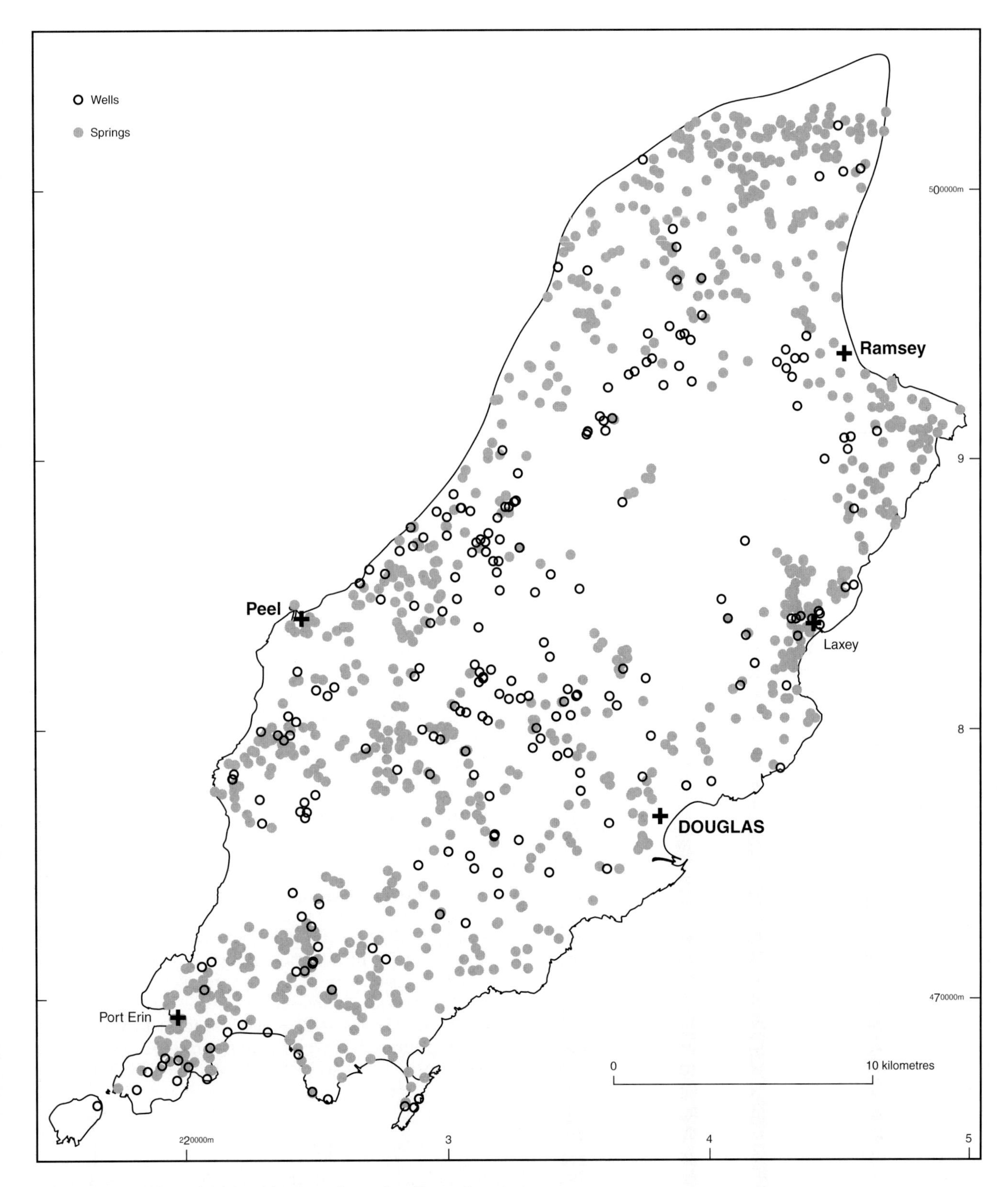

Figure 34 Map showing the location of wells and springs.

through the mine roof (personal communication, F Cowin, 2001).

Other metalliferous mines on the Island also experienced problems with water inflow from permeable fault planes. These include the Snaefell Mine, 3 km to the north-west of the Laxey complex, and the mines near Foxdale, in the south of the Island. Here, at Beckwith's Mine, the lowest of the three in the area, polluted iron-rich mine drainage water continues to flow today from an adit into Glen Maye.

Peel Sandstone Group

The sandstone strata of the Peel Sandstone Group are well cemented and moderately dipping in coastal exposures. There are no data on their hydrogeological characteristics, but the rocks are expected to be moderately permeable. The limited area of outcrop of the Peel Sandstone Group and widespread cover of Quaternary deposits means that the potential for recharge is low.

Carboniferous rocks in the Castletown area

The Carboniferous Ballasalla Group occupies an area of approximately 20 km^2 of low-lying ground around Castletown and has coastal borders to the south and east. The hydraulic properties of the limestone are largely unknown as no deep abstraction boreholes have been drilled. In spite of the relative thinness of the strata, the group is thought to have the highest general permeability for bedrock on the Island. However, the group is still only classed as moderately permeable on the Groundwater Vulnerability Map of Isle of Man (Palmer and Holman, 2000). The nature of groundwater flow and storage is thought to be similar to that in Carboniferous limestone aquifers in England with fissure flow predominating.

Concealed Upper Palaeozoic–Mesozoic rocks

The Carboniferous and Permo–Triassic rocks buried beneath the northern plain are described in chapters 5, 6 and 7. The westernmost part of the Permo–Triassic subcrop, beneath The Lhen, consists of fine-grained red sandstone belonging to the Lower Triassic Sherwood Sandstone Group, overlying Carboniferous limestone. The sandstone has a generally low porosity of around 5 per cent (Racey et al., 1999) and is likely to have a moderate permeability. The blanket cover of Quaternary deposits, over 50 m in thickness, restricts recharge in spite of being a mainly granular sequence because rockhead is over 50 m below sea level. Farther east, the sandstone is replaced by a mainly mudstone sequence, the Mercia Mudstone Group, where saliferous groundwater is present within beds of salt and gypsum. Deep boreholes at the Point of Ayre encountered brine at depths below 180 m. During the first half of the 20th century it was pumped to the surface and sent via pipeline to Ramsey, 11 km to the south (see below).

Quaternary deposits

On middle and lower ground slopes across the Island, clayey till and solifluction deposits commonly contain small amounts of groundwater within their basal layers where they are in contact with weathered Manx Group rocks. Surface water infiltrating through the superficial deposits collects in the layer of broken rock at rockhead and moves down slope to reappear at the surface in the form of springs and seepages. Many wells have been dug into this layer which, in the past, was an important source of water for farm and domestic use.

The northern plain of the Island contains thick glacial and raised beach deposits, which include large thicknesses of sandy and gravelly material. Groundwater occurs in complex, localised shallow aquifers, commonly bounded by clay layers, which help to form shallow, discontinuous groundwater bodies within sandy or gravelly lenses. The position of clay layers in the Quaternary sequence commonly determines the depth to the water table (Lamplugh, 1903). Where shallow clays exist, temporary flooding can occur at the surface where water tables intercept ground level. Large areas of sandy material at the surface, as at Jurby, form a deeper water table and account for the absence of dug wells and older dwellings in this area except where spring lines have developed above clay barriers.

Recent raised beach material along the north coast is predominantly composed of well-sorted coarse gravel. The permeability and porosity of this material is very high and there is a strong hydraulic link between fresh groundwater within it and the sea. Investigations at the landfill site near the Point of Ayre confirmed that the shallow groundwater surface within the raised beach gravel has a gradient approximately perpendicular to the coast, with discharge to the sea (personal communication, D O'Riordan, 2001).

Groundwater chemistry

Groundwater within the Manx Group is typically poorly mineralised, but in certain areas it may contain elevated concentrations of iron and other materials. In comparison, groundwater within the limestone of the Ballasalla Group is thought to have a higher pH and a higher content of calcium carbonate. Under the northern plain, little is known about the chemical quality of the Sherwood Sandstone Group, but the Mercia Mudstone Group to the east contains highly mineralised groundwater which, considering its depth below sea level, is likely to be much older than other Manx groundwaters.

Groundwater usage

The public supply on the Island is exclusively surface water at present as the lack of any highly productive aquifers on the Island precludes the use of groundwater for large-scale distribution. However, as in other rural communities, shallow wells (up to a few metres deep) and springs were in common use outside the main towns up to the middle of the 20th century. The raised beach gravel along the northern coasts contains water of good quality and was once exploited for use by lighthouses.

Traditionally, a small number of wells were thought to have holy significance and special properties such as healing powers and charms against witchcraft. St Maughold's Well, located high on Maughold Head in the north-east, was supposed to enhance fertility in young women, particularly if the waters were taken on the summer solstice. Another well was said to provide a cure for sore eyes. Other holy wells were also visited at this time of the year, according to Celtic practice. Apart from brewery wells, the only documented use of groundwater for industrial purposes is at the Point of Ayre where highly saline water was pumped from deep boreholes in the Permo–Triassic to the saltworks at Ramsey. There, it was evaporated to produce granular salt and exported. The industry closed in the 1950s. The brines also aided the development of tourism in Victorian times as a spur off the main pipeline was installed just to the north of Ramsey and a hotel hydro built for the purpose of taking the waters.

References

Allen, J R L, and Crowley, S F. 1983. Lower Old Red sandstone fluvial dispersal systems in the British Isles. *Transactions of the Royal Society of Edinburgh*, Vol. 74, 61–68.

Akhurst, M C, and 24 others. 1997. The geology of the west Cumbria district. *Memoir of the British Geological Survey*, Sheets 28, 37 and 47 (England and Wales).

Akhurst, M C, McMillan, A A, Kimbell, G S, Stone, P, and Merriman, R J. 2001. Silurian subduction-related assembly of fault-defined tracts at the Laurieston Fault, Southern Uplands accretionary terrane, Scotland, UK. *Transactions of the Royal Society of Edinburgh*, Vol. 91, 435–446.

Armstrong, H A, and Purnell, M A. 1987. Dinantian conodont biostratigraphy of the Northumberland Trough. *Journal of Micropalaeontology*, Vol. 6, 97–112.

Armstrong, J P, Smith, J, d'Elia, V A A, and Trueblood, S P. 1997. The occurrence and correlation of oils and Namurian source rocks in the Liverpool Bay — North Wales area. 195–211 *in* Petroleum geology of the Irish Sea and adjacent areas. Meadows, N S, Trueblood, S P, Hardman, M, and Cowan, G (editors). *Geological Society of London, Special Publication*, No. 124.

Arter, G, and Fagin, S W. 1993. The Fleetwood Dyke and the Tynwald fault zone, Block 113/27, East Irish Sea Basin. 835–843 in: *Petroleum Geology of north-west Europe: Proceedings of the 4th Conference*. Parker, J R. (editor). (London: Geological Society of London.)

Arthurton, R S, and Hemingway, J E. 1972. The St Bees Evaporites — a carbonate-evaporite formation of Upper Permian age in West Cumberland, England. *Proceedings of the Yorkshire Geological Society*, Vol. 38, 565–592.

Arthurton, R S, Burgess, I C, and Holliday, D W. 1978. Permian and Triassic. 189–206 *in* The geology of the Lake District. Moseley, F (editor). *Yorkshire Geological Society, Occasional Publication*, No. 3.

Audley-Charles, M G. 1970. Triassic palaeogeography of the British Isles. *Quarterly Journal of the Geological Society of London*, Vol. 126, 49–90.

Badley, M E, Price, J D, and Backshall, L C. 1989. Inversion, reactivated faults and related structures: seismic examples from the southern North Sea. 201–219 in *Inversion Tectonics*. Cooper, M A, and Williams, G D, (editors). *Geological Society of London, Special Publication*, No. 44.

Barber, K E, Chambers, F M, Maddy, D, Stoneman, R, and Brew, J S. 1994. A sensitive high-resolution record of late Holocene climatic change from a raised bog in northern England. *The Holocene*, Vol. 4, 198–205.

Barclay, W J, Riley, N J, and Strong, G E. 1994. The Dinantian rocks of the Sellafield area, West Cumbria. *Proceedings of the Yorkshire Geological Society*, Vol. 50, 37–50.

Barnes, R P, and Stone, P. 1999. Trans-Iapetus contrasts in the geological development of southern Scotland (Laurentia) and the Lakesman terrane (Avalonia). 307–324 *in* 'In sight of the suture' the Palaeozoic geology of the Isle of Man in its Iapetus Ocean context. Woodcock, N H, Quirk, D G, Fitches, W R, and Barnes, R P (editors). *Geological Society of London, Special Publication*, No. 160.

Barnes, R P, Ambrose, K, Holliday, D W, and Jones, N S. 1994. Lithostratigraphical subdivision of the Triassic Sherwood Sandstone Group in west Cumbria. *Proceedings of the Yorkshire Geological Society*, Vol. 50, 51–60.

Barnes, R P, Lintern, B C, and Stone, P. 1989. Timing and regional implications of deformation in the Southern Uplands of Scotland. *Journal of the Geological Society of London*, Vol. 146, 905–908.

Barnes, R P, Power, G M, and Cooper, D C. 1999. The definition of sandstone-bearing formations in the Isle of Man and correlation with adjacent areas — evidence from sandstone chemistry. 139-154 *in* 'In sight of the suture' the Palaeozoic geology of the Isle of Man in its Iapetus Ocean context. Woodcock, N H, Quirk, D G, Fitches, W R, and Barnes, R P (editors). *Geological Society, London, Special Publication*, No. 160.

Beamish, D, and Smythe, D B. 1986. Geophysical images of the deep crust: the Iapetus suture. *Journal of the Geological Society of London*, Vol. 143, 489–497.

Belderson, R H, and Stride, A H. 1969. Tidal currents and sand wave profiles in the north-eastern Irish Sea. *Nature*, London, Vol. 222, 74–75.

Berger, J J. 1814. Mineralogical account of the Isle of Man. *Transactions of the Geological Society of London*, Vol. 2, 29–65.

Besly, B M. 1987. Sedimentological evidence for Carboniferous and Early Permian palaeoclimates of Europe. *Extrait des Annales de la Societe Geologique du Nord*, Vol. 151, 131–143.

Bisat, W S. 1934. The goniatites of the *Beyrichoceras* zone (Carboniferous) in the north of England. *Proceedings of the Yorkshire Geological Society*, Vol. 22.

Björk S, Walker M J C, Cwynar L C, Johnsen S, Knudsen K L, Lowe J J, Wohlfarth B, and Intimate Members. 1998 An event stratigraphy for the Last Termination in the North Atlantic region based on the Greenland ice-core record: a proposal by the INTIMATE group. *Journal of Quaternary Science*, Vol. 13, 283–292.

Blake, J F. 1905. On the order of succession of the Manx Slates in their northern half, and its bearing on the origin of the schistose breccia associated therewith. *Quarterly Journal of the Geological Society of London*, Vol. 61, 358–373.

Bolton, H. 1899. Observations on the Skiddaw Slates of the north of the Isle of Man. *Report of the British Association for 1893*. 770–771.

Bond, G C, and Lotti, R. 1995. Iceberg discharges into the north-Atlantic on millennial time scales during the last glaciation. *Science*, Vol. 267, (5200) 1005–1010.

Bond, G, Broecker, W, Johnsen, S, McManus, J, Labeyrie, L, Jouzel, J, and Bonani, G. 1993. Correlations between climate records from North-Atlantic sediments and Greenland ice. *Nature*, Vol. 365, (6442) 143–147.

Bott, M H P. 1964. Gravity measurements in the north-eastern part of the Irish Sea. *Quarterly Journal of the Geological Society of London*, Vol. 120, 369-396.

Bott, M H P, Long, R E, Green, A S P, Lewis, A H J, Sinha, M C, and Stevenson, D L. 1985. Crustal structure south of the Iapetus Suture beneath northern England. *Nature*, Vol. 314, 724–727.

Boulton, G S, Peacock, J D, and Sutherland, D G. 1991. Quaternary. 503–542 in *The Geology of Scotland*. Craig, G Y (editor). (London: The Geological Society.)

Boulton, G S, Smith, G D, Jones, A S, and Newsome, J. 1985. Glacial geology and glaciology of the mid-latitude ice sheets. *Journal of the Geological Society of London*, Vol. 142, 447–474.

Bowen, D Q. 1978. *Quaternary Geology: A stratigraphic framework for multidisciplinary work.* (Oxford: Pergamon Press.)

Bowen, D Q. 1991. Time and space in the glacial sediment systems of the British Isles. 3–11 in *Glacial deposits in Great Britain and Ireland.* Ehlers J, Gibbard, P L, and Rose, J (editors). (Rotterdam: A A Balkema.)

Bowen, D Q (editor). 1999. A revised correlation of Quaternary Deposits in the British Isles. *Geological Society of London, Special Report*, No. 23.

Boyd Dawkins, W. 1894. On the geology of the Isle of Man. Part I — the Permian, Carboniferous and Triassic rocks and the New Saltfield of the North. *Transactions of the Manchester Geological Society,* Vol. 22, 590–613.

Boyd Dawkins, W. 1902. The red sandstone rocks of Peel (Isle of Man). *Quarterly Journal of the Geological Society of London*, Vol. 58, 633–646.

Bradshaw, M J, Cope, J C W, Cripps, D W, Donovan, D T, Howarth, M K, Rawson, P F, West, I M, and Wimbledon, W A. 1992. Jurassic. 107–129 *in* Atlas of palaeogeography and lithofacies. Cope, J C W, Ingham, J K, and Rawson, P F (editors). *Memoir of the Geological Society of London*, No. 13.

Brandon, A, Aitkenhead, N, Crofts, R G, Ellison, R A, Evans, D J, and Riley, N J. 1998. Geology of the country around Lancaster. *Memoir of the British Geological Survey*, Sheet 59 (England and Wales).

Brewer, J A, Matthews, D H, Warner, M R, Hall, J, Smythe, D K, and Whittington, R J. 1983. BIRPS deep seismic reflection studies of the British Caledonides — the WINCH profile. *Nature*, Vol. 305, 206–210.

British Geological Survey. 1994. East Irish Sea. Special Sheet Edition, Solid Geology. 1:250 000. (Edinburgh: British Geological Survey.)

British Geological Survey. 2001. Isle of Man, solid and drift geology. 1:50 000 map series. British Geological Survey, Nottingham.

Brodie, J, and White, N. 1994. Sedimentary basin inversion caused by igneous underplating: northwest European continental shelf. *Geology*, Vol. 22, 147–150.

Brookfield, M E. 1978. Revision of the stratigraphy of Permian and supposed Permian rocks of Southern Scotland. *Geologische Rundschau*, Vol. 67, 110–149.

Brown, P E, Miller, J A, and Grasty, R L. 1968. Isotopic ages of late Caledonian granitic intrusions in the British Isles. *Proceedings of the Yorkshire Geological Society*, Vol. 36, 251–276

Burnett, D J. 1999. The stratigraphy, geochemistry and provenance of the Lower Palaeozoic Manx Group, Isle of Man. Unpublished PhD thesis, Oxford Brookes University.

Burnett, D J, Barnes, R P, Harvey, M L, and Barron, H F. 2001 An integrated geological map and database: an example from the Isle of Man. Abstract in: New insights into basin studies from collaborative research, 15th March 2001, Programme and Abstract. (London: The Geological Society.)

Butterworth, M A, and Butcher, C E. 1983. Basal Dinantian miospores from the Cockermouth area. *Journal of Micropalaeontology*, Vol. 2, 13–16.

Cande, S C, and Kent, D V. 1995. Revised calibration of the geomagnetic polarity timescale for the Late Cretaceous and Cenozoic. *Journal of Geophysical Research*, Vol. 100, 6093–6095.

Carruthers, R, and Strahan, A. 1923. Lead and zinc ores of Durham, Yorkshire, Derbyshire and the Isle of Man. *Special reports on the Mineral Resources of Great Britain. Memoir of the Geological Survey of Great Britain,* No. 26.

Chadwick, R.A.1993. Aspects of basin inversion in southern Britain. *Journal of the Geological Society of London,* Vol. 150, 311-322.

Chadwick, R A. 1997. Fault analysis of the Cheshire Basin, NW England. 297–313 *in* Petroleum geology of the Irish Sea and adjacent areas. Meadows, N S, Trueblood, S, Hardman, M, and Cowan, G (editors). *Geological Society of London, Special Publication,* No. 124.

Chadwick, R A, and Evans, D J. 1995. The timing and direction of Permo–Triassic extension in southern Britain. 161–192 *in* Permian and Triassic rifting in NW Europe. Boldy, S R, and Hardman, R F P (editors). *Geological Society of London, Special Publication,* No. 91.

Chadwick, R A, and Holliday, D W. 1991. Deep crustal structure and Carboniferous basin development within the Iapetus convergence zone, northern England. *Journal of the Geological Society of London*, Vol. 148, 41–53.

Chadwick, R A, Evans, D J, and Holliday, D W. 1993. The Maryport Fault: the post-Caledonian tectonic history of southern Britain in microcosm. *Journal of the Geological Society of London,* Vol. 150, 247–250.

Chadwick, R A, Kirby, G A, and Baily, H E. 1994. The post-Triassic structural evolution of north-west England and adjacent parts of the East Irish Sea. *Proceedings of the Yorkshire Geological Society,* Vol. 50, 91–102.

Chadwick, R A, Holliday, D W, Holloway, S, and Hulbert, A G. 1995. The structure and evolution of the Northumberland–Solway Basin and adjacent areas. *Subsurface Memoir of the British Geological Survey.* (London: HMSO.)

Chiverrell, R C, Davey, P J, Gowlett, J A J, and Woodcock, J J. 1999. Radiocarbon dates for the Isle of Man. 321–336 in *Recent Archaeological Research on the Isle of Man.* Davey, P J (editor). (Oxford: BAR British Series 278).

Chiverrell, R C, Thomas, G S P, and Harvey, A M. 2001a. Late-Devensian and Holocene landscape change in the uplands of the Isle of Man. *Geomorphology*, Vol. 40, 219–236.

Chiverrell, R C, Thomas, G S P, and Dackombe, R V (editors.). 2001b. *A New History of the Isle of Man.* Volume 1 Evolution of the natural landscape. (Liverpool: Liverpool University Press.)

Cocks, L R M, and Fortey, R A. 1982. Faunal evidence for oceanic separations in the Palaeozoic of Britain. *Journal of the Geological Society of London*, Vol. 139, 465–478.

Cocks, L R M, and Fortey, R A. 1990. Biogeography of Ordovician and Silurian faunas. 97–104 *in* Palaeozoic palaeogeography and biogeography. *Memoir of the Geological Society of London*, No. 12.

Colter, V S. 1978. Exploration for gas in the Irish Sea. 503–516 *in* Key-notes of the MEGS-II (Amsterdam, Netherlands, 1978). Loon, A J van (editor). *Geologie en Mijnbouw*, Vol. 57.

Coope, G R, and Lemdahl, G. 1995. Regional differences in the Lateglacial climate of northern Europe based on coleopteran analysis. *Journal of Quaternary Science*, Vol. 10, 391–395.

Coope, G R, Lemdahl, G, Lowe, J J, and Walkling, A. 1998. Temperature gradients in northern Europe during the last glacial-Holocene transition (14-9 C-14 kyr BP) interpreted from coleopteran assemblages. *Journal of Quaternary Science*, Vol. 13, 419–433.

Cooper, A H, Fortey, N J, Hughes, R A, Molyneaux, S G, Rushton, A W A, and Stone, P. In press. The Skiddaw Group of the English Lake District. *Memoir of the British Geological Survey.*

Cooper, A H, Rushton, A W A, Molyneux, S G, Hughes, R A, Moore, R M, and Webb, B C. 1995. The stratigraphy, correlation, provenance and palaeogeography of the Skiddaw Group (Ordovician) in the English Lake District. *Geological Magazine*, Vol. 132, 185–211.

Cooper, D C, Lee, M K, Fortey, N J, Cooper, A H, Rundle, C C, Webb, B C, and Allen, P M. 1988. The Crummock Water aureole: a zone of metamorphism and source of ore metals in the English Lake District. *Journal of the Geological Society of London*, Vol. 145, 523–540.

Cope, J C W. 1994. A latest Cretaceous hotspot and the southeasterly tilt of Britain. *Journal of the Geological Society of London*, Vol. 151, 905–908.

Cope, J C W. 1997. The Mesozoic and Tertiary history of the Irish Sea. 47-59 *in* Petroleum geology of the Irish Sea and adjacent areas. Meadows, N S, Trueblood, S P, Hardman, M, and Cowan, G (editors). *Geological Society of London, Special Publication*, No. 124.

Cope, J C W, Getty, T A, Howarth, M K, Morton, N, and Torrens, H S. 1980. A correlation of Jurassic rocks in the British Isles. Part One: Introduction and Lower Jurassic. *Special Report of the Geological Society of London*, No. 14.

Corcoran, D, and Clayton, G. 1999. Interpretation of vitrinite reflectance profiles in the Central Irish Sea area — implications for the timing of organic maturation. *Journal of Petroleum Geology*, Vol. 22, 261–286.

Cornwell, J D. 1972. A gravity survey of the Isle of Man. *Proceedings of the Yorkshire Geological Society*, Vol. 39, 93–106.

Colter, V S. 1997. The East Irish Sea Basin — from caterpillar to butterfly, a thirty-year metamorphism. 1–9 *in* Petroleum geology of the Irish Sea and adjacent areas. Meadows, N S, Trueblood, S P, Hardman, M, and Cowan, G (editors). *Geological Society of London, Special Publication*, No. 124.

Cowan, G. 1993. Identification and significance of aeolian deposits within the dominantly fluvial Sherwood Sandstone Group of the East Irish Sea Basin, UK. 231–245 *in* Characterization of fluvial and aeolian reservoirs. North, C P, and Prosser, D J (editors). *Geological Society of London, Special Publication*, No. 73.

Cowan, G, Burley, S D, Hoey, A N, Holloway, P, Bermingham, P, Beveridge, N, Hamborg, M, and Sylta, O. 1999. Oil and gas migration in the Sherwood Sandstone of the East Irish Sea Basin. 1383–1398 in *Petroleum Geology of Northwest Europe: Proceedings of the 5th Conference*. Fleet, A J, and Boldy, S A R (editors). (London: The Geological Society.)

Cowan, G, Ottesen, C, and Stuart, I A. 1993. The use of dip meter logs in the structural interpretation and palaeocurrent analysis of Morecambe Fields, East Irish Sea Basin. 867-882 in *Petroleum geology of Northwest Europe: Proceedings of the 4th conference*. Parker, J R (editor). (London: The Geological Society of London.)

Coward, M P. 1995. Structural and tectonic setting of the Permo-triassic basins of northwest Europe. 7–40 *in* Permian and Triassic rifting in northwest Europe. Boldy, S R, and Hardman, R F P (editors). *Geological Society of London, Special Publication*, No. 91.

Crowley, S F. 1981. Facies, environments and diagenesis of the Peel sandstones, Isle of Man. Unpublished MSc Thesis, University of Reading.

Crowley, S F. 1985. Lithostratigraphy of the Peel Sandstones, Isle of Man. *Mercian Geologist*, Vol. 10, 73–76.

Crowley, S, and Power, G. 1998. Petrography, geochemistry and isotopic composition of the Foxdale granite and its relationship to the geotectonic evolution of the Isle of Man. 14–16 in *'In sight of the Suture' Conference, Isle of Man, March–April 1998, Abstract Volume.*

Cubbon, A M. 1957. The Ice Age in the Isle of Man. *Proceedings Isle of Man Natural History and Antiquarian Society*, Vol. 5, 499–512.

Cumming J G. 1846. On the geology of the Isle of Man. Part 2: The Tertiary Formations. *Quarterly Journal of the Geological Society of London*, Vol. 2, 335–348.

Dackcombe, R V, and McCarroll, D. 1990. The Manx landscape. 10–17 in *The Isle of Man — celebrating a sense of place.* Robinson, V, and McCarroll, D (editors). (Liverpool: Liverpool University Press.)

Dackombe, R V, and Thomas, G S P (editors). 1985. *Field Guide to the Quaternary of the Isle of Man.* (Cambridge: Quaternary Research Association.)

Dackombe, R V, and Thomas, G S P. 1989. Glacial deposits and Quaternary stratigraphy of the Isle of Man. 333–344 in *Glacial deposits of Great Britain and Ireland.* Ehlers, J, Gibbard, P L, and Rose, J (editors). (Rotterdam: A A Balkema.)

Dansgaard, W, Johnsen, S J, Clausen, H B, Dahljensen, D, Gundestrup, N S, Hammer, C U, Hvidberg, C S, Steffensen, J P, Sveinbjornsdottir, A E, Jouzel J, and Bond, G. 1993. Evidence for general instability of past climate from a 250-kyr ice-core record. *Nature*, Vol. 364 (6434), 218–220.

Davison, C F, and Bowie, S H U. 1951. Thucolite-pitchblende, hydrocarbon, and moisture — at Laxey lead mine. *Bulletin of the Geological Survey of Great Britain*, No. 3, 4.

Dawson, J. 1966. Beryllium in the Foxdale Granite, Isle of Man. *Bulletin of the Geological Survey of Great Britain*, No. 25, 55–58.

Day, J B W. 1970. Geology of the country around Bewcastle. *Memoir of the Geological Survey of Great Britain (England and Wales)*. Sheet 12.

Deegan, C.E. 1973. Tectonic control of sedimentation at the margin of a Carboniferous basin in Kirkcudbrightshire. *Scottish Journal of Geology*, Vol. 9, 1–28.

Dewey, H. 1920. Arsenic and antimony ores. *Special reports on the Mineral Resources of Great Britain. Memoir of the Geological Survey of Great Britain,* No. 15.

Dewey, H, and Eastwood, T. 1925. Copper ores of the Midlands, Wales, the Lake District and the Isle of Man. *Special reports on the Mineral Resources of Great Britain. Memoir of the Geological Survey of Great Britain,* No. 30.

Dickson, C A, Dickson J H, and Mitchell G F. 1970. The Late Glacial flora of the Isle of Man. *Philosophical Transaction of the Royal Society London*, Vol. 259, 31–79.

Dickson, J A D, Ford, T D, and Swift, A. 1987. The stratigraphy of the Carboniferous rocks around Castletown, Isle of Man. *Proceedings of the Yorkshire Geological Society*, Vol. 46, 203–229.

Dobson, M, and Hollis, D B. 1993. Lead mines and trials in Glen Auldyn, Isle of Man. *Bulletin of the Peak District Mines Historical Society*, Vol. 12, 31–37.

Downie, C, and Ford, T D. 1966. Microfossils from the Manx Slate Series. *Proceedings of the Yorkshire Geological Society*, Vol. 35, 307–322.

Durant, G P, and Grant, C. 1985. The Scarlett Volcanic Complex, Isle of Man. Shallow-water submarine volcanic pile. *Geological Society of London Newsletter*, Vol. 14, 46.

Earp, J R, and Taylor, B J. 1986. Geology of the country around Chester and Winsford. *Memoir of the British Geological Survey*, Sheet 109 (England and Wales).

Eastwood, T, Dixon, E E L, Hollingworth, S E, and Smith, B. 1931. The geology of the Whitehaven and Workington district. *Memoir of the Geological Survey of Great Britain*, Sheet 28 (England and Wales).

Eastwood, T, Hollingworth, S E, Rose, W C C, and Trotter, F M. 1968. Geology of the country around Cockermouth and Caldbeck. *Memoir of the Geological Survey of Great Britain*, Sheet 23 (England and Wales).

England, R W, and Soper, N J. 1997. Lower crustal structure of the East Irish Sea from deep seismic reflection data. 61–72 in Petroleum geology of the Irish Sea and adjacent areas. Meadows, N S, Trueblood, S P, Hardman, M, and Cowan, G (editors). *Special Publication of the Geological Society of London*, No. 124.

Evans, D J, Rees J G, and Holloway, S. 1993. The Permian to Jurassic stratigraphy and structural evolution of the central Cheshire Basin. *Journal of the Geological Society of London*, Vol. 150, 857–870.

EYLES, C H, and EYLES, N. 1984. Glaciomarine sediments of the Isle of Man as a key to late Pleistocene stratigraphic investigations in the Irish Sea Basin. *Geology*, Vol. 12, 359–364.

EYLES, N, and MCCABE, A M. 1989. The late Devensian (<22 000 BP) Irish Sea basin: the sedimentary record of a collapsed ice sheet margin. *Quaternary Science Reviews*, No. 8, 307–351.

EYLES, N, and MCCABE, A M. 1991. Glaciomarine deposits of the Irish Sea Basin: The role of Glacio-Isostatic disequilibrium. 311 330 in *Glacial deposits of Great Britain and Ireland.* EHLERS, J, GIBBARD, P L, and ROSE, J (editors). (Rotterdam: A A Balkema.)

FITCHES, W R, BARNES, R P, and MORRIS, J H. 1999. Geological structure and tectonic evolution of the Lower Palaeozoic rocks of the Isle of Man. 258–288 *in* 'In sight of the suture' the Palaeozoic geology of the Isle of Man in its Iapetus Ocean context. WOODCOCK, N. H., QUIRK, D G, FITCHES, W R, and BARNES, R P (editors). *Geological Society of London, Special Publication*, No. 160.

FORD, T D. 1972. Slump structures in the Peel Sandstone Series, Isle of Man. *Proceedings of the Isle of Man Natural History and Antiquarian Society, New Series*, Vol. 7, 440–448.

FORD, T D. 1993. The Isle of Man. Greensmith, J T. (editor). *Geologists' Association Guide*, No. 46. (PSS Group of Companies, England.)

FORD, T D. 1998. The geology of the Laxey Lode. *Mercian Geologist*, Vol. 14, 125–134.

FORD, T D, BURNETT, D J, and QUIRK, D G. 2001. The geology of the Isle of Man. GREENSMITH, J T (editor). *Geologists' Association Guide*, No. 46.

FORD, T D, WILSON, E, and BURNETT, D J. 1999. Previous ideas and models of the stratigraphy, structure and mineral deposits of the Manx Group, Isle of Man. 11–21 *in* 'In sight of the suture' the Palaeozoic geology of the Isle of Man in its Iapetus Ocean context. WOODCOCK, N H, QUIRK, D G, FITCHES, W R, and BARNES, R P (editors). *Geological Society of London, Special Publication*, No. 160.

FRASER, A J, and GAWTHORPE, R L. 1990. Tectono-stratigraphic development and hydrocarbon habitat of the Carboniferous in northern England. 49–86 *in* Tectonic events responsible for Britain's oil and gas reserves. HARDMAN, R F P, and BROOKS, J (editors). *Geological Society of London, Special Publication,* No. 55.

FRASER, A J, NASH, D F, STEELE, R P, and EBDON, C C. 1990. A regional assessment of the intra-Carboniferous play of northern England. 417–440 *in* Classic petroleum provinces. BROOKS, J (editor). *Geological Society of London, Special Publication*, No. 50.

FYFE, J A, LONG, D, and EVANS, D. 1993. *United Kingdom offshore regional report: the geology of the Malin–Hebrides sea area.* (London: HMSO for British Geological Survey.)

GACIRI, S J, and INESON, P R. 1981. Hydrogeochemical lead-zinc-copper anomalies on the Isle of Man. *Transaction of the Institution of Mining and Metallurgy (Section B: Applied Earth Sciences),* Vol. 90, B120–125.

GALLAGHER, M J, KEMP, A E S, HILLS, M G, JONES, R C, SMITH, R T, PEACHEY, D, VICKERS, B P, PARKER, M E, ROLLIN, K E, and SKILTON, B R H. 1983. Stratbound arsenic and vein antimony mineralisation in Silurian greywackes at Glendinning, south Scotland. *British Geological Survey Mineral Reconnaissance Programme Report,* No. 59.

GALLAGHER, M J, STONE, P, and DULLER, P R. 1989. Gold-bearing arsenic-antimony concentrations in Silurian greywackes, south Scotland. *Transactions of the Institution of Mining and Metallurgy (Section B: Applied Earth Sciences)*, Vol. 98, B58–60.

GAMBLE, J A, WYSOCZANSKI, R J, and MEIGHAN, I G. 1999. Constraints on the age of the British Tertiary Volcanic Province from ion microprobe U-Pb (SHRIMP) ages for acid igneous rocks from NE Ireland. *Journal of the Geological Society of London*, Vol. 156, 291–299.

GAWTHORPE, R L, GUTTERIDGE, P, and LEEDER, M R. 1989. Late Devonian and Dinantian basin evolution in northern England and North Wales. 1–23 *in* The role of tectonics in Devonian and Carboniferous sedimentation in the British Isles. ARTHURTON, R S, GUTTERIDGE, P, and NOLAN, S C (editors). *Yorkshire Geological Society, Occasional Publication*, No. 6.

GEOLOGICAL SURVEY. 1898. Isle of Man. Sheet 36, 45, 46, 56 and 57. Solid and Drift geology. 1:63 360 scale. Reprinted at 1:50 000 scale by Institute of Geological Sciences 1975. (Southampton: Ordnance Survey.)

GILLOTT, J E. 1956. Breccias in the Manx Slates: their origin and stratigraphic relationships. *Liverpool and Manchester Geological Journal*, Vol. 1, 370–380.

GLENNIE, K W. 1998. Lower Permian — Rotliegend. 137–173 in *Petroleum Geology of the North Sea: basic concepts and recent advances* (4th edition). GLENNIE, K W (editor). (Oxford: Blackwell Science Ltd.)

GONZALEZ, S, INNES, J B, HUDDART, D, DAVEY, P J, and PLATER, A J. 2000. Holocene coastal change in the north of the Isle of Man: stratigraphy palaeoenvironment and archaeological evidence. 343–363 *in* Coastal and estuarine environments: sedimentology, geomorphology and geoarchaeology. PYE K, and ALLEN, J R L (editors). *Geological Society of London, Special Publication,* No. 175.

GONZALEZ, S, KITCHENER, A C, and LISTER, A M. 2000. Survival of the Irish elk into the Holocene. *Nature*, Vol. 405, 753–754.

GRADSTEIN, F M, and OGG, J G. 1996. A Phanerozoic timescale. *Episodes*, Vol. 19, 3–5.

GREEN, P F, DUDDY, I R, and BRAY, R J. 1997. Variation in thermal history styles around the Irish Sea and adjacent areas: implications for hydrocarbon occurrence and tectonic evolution. 73–93 *in* Petroleum Geology of the Irish Sea and adjacent areas. MEADOWS, N S, TRUEBLOOD, S, HARDMAN, M, and COWAN, G (editors). *Geological Society of London, Special Publication,* No. 124.

GREG, R P, and LETTSOM, W G. 1858. *Manual of the mineralogy of Great Britain and Ireland.* John van Voorst, London, reprinted 1977 by Lapidary Publications, Broadstairs, Kent.

GREGORY, J W. 1920. The Red Rocks of a deep bore at the north end of the Isle of Man. *Transactions of the Institution of Mining Engineers,* Vol. 59, 156–168.

GREIG, D C. 1971. *British regional geology: the south of Scotland* (third edition). (Edinburgh: HMSO for Institute of Geological Sciences.)

GUION, P D, and FIELDING, C R. 1988. Westphalian A and B sedimentation in the Pennine Basin, UK. 153–177 in *Sedimentation in a synorogenic basin complex: the Upper Carboniferous of northwest Europe.* BESLY, B M, and KELLING, G (editors). (Glasgow and London: Blackie.)

GUION, P D, FULTON, I M, and JONES, N S. 1995. Sedimentary facies of the coal-bearing Westphalian A and B north of the Wales–Brabant High. 45–78 *in* European Coal Geology. WHATELEY, M K G, and SPEARS, D A (editors). *Geological Society of London, Special Publication,* No. 82.

GUION, P D, GUTTERIDGE, P, and DAVIES, S J. 2000. 14. Carboniferous sedimentation and volcanism on the Laurussian margin. 227–270 in *Geological History of Britain and Ireland.* WOODCOCK, N, and STRACHAN, R (editors). (Oxford: Blackwell Science Ltd.)

HARDMAN, M, BUCHANAN, J, HERRINGTON, P, and CARR, A. 1993. Geochemical modelling of the East Irish Sea Basin: its influence on predicting hydrocarbon type and quality. 809–821 in *Petroleum geology of northwest Europe.* Proceedings of the fourth conference. PARKER, J R (editor). (London: Geological Society of London.)

HALL, J, BREWER, J A, MATTHEWS, D H, and WARNER, M R. 1984. Crustal structure across the Caledonides from the 'WINCH' seismic reflection profile: influences on the evolution of the Midland Valley of Scotland. *Transactions of the Royal Society of Edinburgh,* Vol. 75, 97–109.

HARKNESS, R, and NICHOLSON, H A. 1866. On the Lower Silurian rocks of the Isle of Man. *Quarterly Journal of the Geological Society of London,* Vol. 22, 488–491.

HERRIES, R D, and COWAN, G. 1997. Challenging the 'sheetflood' myth: the role of water-table-controlled sabkha deposits in redefining the depositional model for the Ormskirk Sandstone Formation (Lower Triassic), East Irish Sea Basin. 253–276 *in* Petroleum geology of the Irish Sea and adjacent areas. MEADOWS, N S, TRUEBLOOD, S P, HARDMAN, M, and COWAN, G (editors). *Geological Society of London, Special Publication,* No. 124.

HOLLIDAY, D W. 1993a. Geophysical log signatures in the Eden Shales (Permo–Triassic) of Cumbria and their regional significance. *Proceedings of the Yorkshire Geological Society,* Vol. 49, 345–354.

HOLLIDAY, D W. 1993b. Mesozoic cover over northern England: interpretation of apatite fission-track data. *Journal of the Geological Society of London,* Vol. 150, 657–660.

HOLLIDAY, D W, and REES, J G. 1994. Advances in west Cumbrian geology resulting from the NIREX investigations around Sellafield: convenors' review. *Proceedings of the Yorkshire Geological Society,* Vol. 50, 1–3.

HOLLIS, D B. 1986. The Great Laxey winding engine, Great Laxey mine, Isle of Man. *Bulletin of the Peak District Mines Historical Society,* No. 9. 306–312.

HOLLIS, D B. 1987a. The forgotten iron mines of Kirk Maughold, Isle of Man. British Mining (Memoirs of the Northern mines Research Society) No. 34.

HOLLIS, D B. 1987b. Uranium in the Isle of Man. *British Mining,* No. 34.

HOLLIS, D B. 1988. The forgotten iron mines of Kirk Maughold, Isle of Man. Recent explorations. *British Mining,* No. 37.

HOLLIS, D B. 1989. The search for iron, lead and gold in Douglas Bay, Isle of Man; old mining trials and insights into the geology. *Bulletin of the Peak District Mines Historical Society,* Vol. 10, 291–304.

HORBURY, A D. 1989. The relative roles of tectonism and eustacy in the deposition of the Urswick Limestone in South Cumbria and North Lancashire. 153–169 *in* The role of tectonics in Devonian and Carboniferous sedimentation in the British Isles. ARTHURTON, R S, GUTTERIDGE, P, and NOLAN, S C (editors). *Yorkshire Geological Society, Occasional Publication,* No. 6.

HORNE J. 1874. A sketch of the geology of the Isle of Man. *Transactions of the Edinburgh Geological Society,* Vol. 2, 323–347.

HOWE, M P A. 1999. The Silurian fauna (graptolite and nautiloid) of the Niarbyl Formation, Isle of Man. 177–188 *in* 'In sight of the suture' the Palaeozoic geology of the Isle of Man in its Iapetus Ocean context. WOODCOCK, N H, QUIRK, D G, FITCHES, W R, and BARNES, R P. (editors). *Geological Society of London, Special Publication,* No. 160.

INESON, P R, and MITCHELL, J G. 1979. K–Ar ages from the ore deposits and related rocks of the Isle of Man. *Geological Magazine,* Vol. 116, 117–128.

IVIMEY-COOK, H C, WARRINGTON, G, WORLEY, N E, HOLLOWAY, S, and YOUNG, B. 1995. Rocks of Late Triassic and Early Jurassic age in the Carlisle Basin, Cumbria (north-west England). *Proceedings of the Yorkshire Geological Society,* Vol. 50, 305–316.

JACKSON, D I. In press. The Permian, Triassic and Jurassic rock successions proved in offshore and onshore wells and borehole in the Isle of Man area. *British Geological Survey Internal Open File Report,* IR/01/147.

JACKSON, D I, and JOHNSON, H. 1996. *Lithostratigraphic nomenclature of the Triassic, Permian and Carboniferous of the UK offshore East Irish Sea Basin.* (Nottingham: British Geological Survey.)

JACKSON, D I, and MULHOLLAND, P. 1993. Tectonic and stratigraphical aspects of the East Irish Sea Basin and adjacent areas: contrasts in their post-Carboniferous structural styles. 791–808 in *Petroleum geology of northwest Europe: Proceedings of the 4th Conference.* PARKER, J R (editor). (London: The Geological Society.)

JACKSON, D I, MULHOLLAND, P, JONES, S M, and WARRINGTON, G. 1987. The geological framework of the East Irish Sea Basin. 191–203 in *Petroleum Geology of Northwest Europe.* BROOKS, J, and GLENNIE, K W (editors). (London: Graham and Trotman.)

JACKSON, D I, JACKSON, A A, EVANS, D, WINGFIELD, R T R, BARNES, R P, and ARTHUR, M J. 1995. *United Kingdom offshore regional report: the geology of the Irish Sea.* (London: HMSO for British Geological Survey.)

JACKSON, D I, JOHNSON, H, and SMITH, N J P. 1997. Stratigraphical relationships and a revised lithostratigraphical nomenclature for the Carboniferous, Permian and Triassic rocks of the offshore East Irish Sea Basin. 11–32 *in* Petroleum geology of the Irish Sea and adjacent areas. MEADOWS, N S, TRUEBLOOD, S P, HARDMAN, M, and COWAN, G (editors). *Geological Society of London, Special Publication,* No. 124.

JACOB, A W B, KAMINSKI, W, MURPHY, T, PHILLIPS, W E A, and PRODEHL, C. 1985. A crustal model for a northeast-southwest profile through Ireland. *Tectonophysics,* Vol. 113, 75–103.

JIN YU-GAN, WARDLAW, B R, GLENISTER, B F, and KOTLYAR, G V. 1997. Permian chronostratigraphic subdivisions. *Episodes,* Vol. 20, 10–15.

JOACHIM, M J. 1978. Late-glacial Coleopteran assemblages from the west coast of the Isle of Man. Unpublished PhD Thesis, University of Birmingham.

JOHNSON, H, WARRINGTON, G, and STOKER, S J. 1994. Volume 6. Permian and Triassic of the Southern North Sea. In *Lithostratigraphic nomenclature of the UK North Sea.* KNOX, R W O'B, and CORDEY, W G (editors). (Nottingham: British Geological Survey.)

JONES, N S. 1992. Sedimentology of Westphalian coal-bearing strata and applications to opencast coal mining, west Cumbrian Coalfield, UK. Unpublished PhD thesis, Oxford Brookes University.

JONES, N S, and AMBROSE, K. 1994. Triassic sandy braidplain and aeolian sedimentation in the Sherwood Sandstone Group of the Sellafield area, west Cumbria. *Proceedings of the Yorkshire Geological Society,* Vol. 50, 61–76.

KELLING, G, and WELSH, W. 1970. The Loch Ryan Fault. *Scottish Journal of Geology,* Vol. 6, 266–271.

KEMP, A E S. 1991. Mid-Silurian pelagic and hemipelagic sedimentation and palaeogeography. *Special Papers in Palaeontology, London,* Vol. 44, 261–299.

KENDALL, P F. 1894. On the glacial geology of the Isle of Man. *Yn Lioar Manninagh,* Vol. 1, 397–437.

KENNAN, P S, and MORRIS, J H. 1999. Manganiferous ironstones in the early Ordovician Manx Group, Isle of Man: a protolith of coticule? 109–120 *in* 'In sight of the suture' the Palaeozoic geology of the Isle of Man in its Iapetus Ocean context. WOODCOCK, N H, QUIRK, D G, FITCHES, W R, and BARNES, R P (editors). *Geological Society of London, Special Publication,* No. 160.

KERSHAW, P J, SWIFT, D J, and DENOON, D C. 1988. Evidence of recent sedimentation in the eastern Irish Sea. *Marine Geology,* Vol. 85, 1–14.

KIMBELL, G S, and QUIRK, D G. 1999. Crustal magnetic structure of the Irish Sea region: evidence for a major basement boundary beneath the Isle of Man. 227–238 *in*

'In sight of the suture' the geology of the Isle of Man in its Iapetus Ocean context. Woodcock, N H, Quirk, D G, Fitches, W R, and Barnes, R P (editors). *Geological Society of London, Special Publication,* No. 160.

Kimbell, G S, and Stone, P. 1995. Crustal magnetisation variations across the Iapetus Suture Zone. *Geological Magazine,* Vol. 132, 599–609.

Kirby, G A, and Swallow, P. 1987. Tectonism and sedimentation in the Flamborough Head region of north-east England. *Proceedings of the Yorkshire Geological Society,* Vol. 46, 301–309.

Kirby, G A, Baily, H E, Chadwick, R A, Evans, D J, Holliday, D W, Holloway, S, Hulbert, A G, Pharaoh, T C, Smith, N J P, Aitkenhead, N, and Birch, B. 2000. The structure and evolution of the Craven Basin and adjacent areas. *Subsurface Memoir of the British Geological Survey.* (London: The Stationery Office.)

Kirk, M. 1983. Sedimentology and palaeogeography in the Westphalian A and B coalfields of Scotland. Unpublished PhD Thesis, University of Strathclyde.

Kirton, S R, and Donato, J A. 1985. Some buried Tertiary dykes of Britain and surrounding waters deduced by magnetic modelling and seismic reflection methods. *Journal of the Geological Society of London,* Vol. 142, 1047–1057.

Kneller, B C, Scott, R W, Soper, N J, Johnson, E W, and Allen, P M. 1994. Lithostratigraphy of the Windermere Supergroup, Northern England. *Geological Journal,* Vol. 29, 219–240.

Knipe, R J, Cowan, G, and Balendran, V S. 1993. The tectonic history of the East Irish Sea Basin with reference to the Morecambe Fields. 857–866 in *Petroleum geology of northwest Europe: Proceedings of the 4th Conference.* Parker, J R (editor). (London: The Geological Society.)

Lambeck, K. 1996. Glaciation and sea-level change for Ireland and the Irish Sea since Late-Devensian/Midlandian time. *Journal of the Geological Society of London,* Vol. 153, 853–872.

Lamplugh, G W. 1903. The geology of the Isle of Man. *Memoir Geological Survey of Great Britain.*

Lamplugh, G W, and Watts, W W. 1895. The crush-conglomerates of the Isle of Man. *Quarterly Journal of the Geological Society of London,* Vol. 51, 563–599.

Lee, A G. 1988. Carboniferous basin configuration of central and northern England modelled using gravity data. 69–84 in *Sedimentation in a synorogenic basin complex: the Upper Carboniferous of Northwest Europe.* Besley, B M, and Kelling, G (editors). (Glasgow: Blackie.)

Leeder, M R. 1974. Origin of the Northumberland Basin. *Scottish Journal of Geology,* Vol. 10, 283-296.

Leeder, M R. 1982. Upper Palaeozoic basins of the British Isles — Caledonide inheritance versus Hercynian plate margin processes. *Journal of the Geological Society of London,* Vol. 139, 479–491.

Leeder, M R, and Hardman, M. 1990. Carboniferous geology of the Southern North Sea Basin and controls on hydrocarbon prospectivity. 87–105 *in* Tectonic events responsible for Britain's oil and gas reserves. Hardman, R F P, and Brooks, J (editors). *Geological Society of London, Special Publication,* No. 55.

Leeder, M R, Fairhead, D, Lee, A, Stuart, G, Clemmey, H, El-Haddaheh, B, and Green, C. 1989. Sedimentary and tectonic evolution of the Northumberland Basin. 207–223 *in* The role of tectonics in Devonian and Carboniferous sedimentation in the British Isles. Arthurton, R S, Gutteridge, P, and Nolan, S C (editors). *Yorkshire Geological Society, Occasional Publication,* No. 6.

Lewis, A H J. 1986. The deep seismic structure of northern England and adjacent marine areas from the Caledonian Suture Seismic Project. Unpublished PhD Thesis, University of Durham.

Lewis, C L E, Green, P F, Carter, A, and Hurford, A J. 1992. Elevated late Cretaceous to Early Tertiary palaeotemperatures throughout north-west England: three kilometres of Tertiary erosion? *Earth and Planetary Science Letters,* Vol. 112, 131–145.

Lewis, H P. 1930. The Avonian succession in the south of the Isle of Man. *Quarterly Journal of the Geological Society of London,* Vol. 86, 234–290.

Llewellyn, P G, Mahmoud, S A, and Stabbins, R. 1968. Nodular anhydrite in Carboniferous Limestone, west Cumberland. *Transactions of the Institute of Mining and Metallurgy, Section B,* Vol. 77, B18–25.

Lomas, C G, and Neville, R S W. 1976. The palynology and stratigraphy of the interval 500–4500′ from the Cluff Oil Limited 112/30-1 Irish Sea Well. *Robertson Research International Limited Oilfield Report,* No. 2205.

Lott, G K, and Knox, R W O'B. 1994. Volume 7. Post-Triassic of the Southern North Sea. In *Lithostratigraphic nomenclature of the UK North Sea.* Knox, R W O'B, and Cordey, W G (editors). (Nottingham: British Geological Survey.)

Lowe, J J, Ammann, B, Birks, H H, Björck, S, Coope, G R, Cwynar, L, De Beaulieu, J-L, Mott, R J, Peteet, D M, and Walker, M J C. 1994. Climatic changes in areas adjacent to the North Atlantic during the last glacial-interglacial transition (14–9 ka BP): a contribution to IGCP-253. *Journal of Quaternary Science,* Vol. 9, 185–198.

Machette, M N. 1985. Calcic soils of the southwestern United States. 1–21 *in* Soils and Quaternary geology of the southwestern United States. Weide, D L, and Faber, M L (editors). *Special Paper of the Geological Society of America,* Vol. 203.

Mackay, L, and Schnellman, G A. 1963. *The mines and minerals of the Isle of Man.* Report submitted to the Industrial Officer of the Government of the Isle of Man.

Maddox, S J, Blow, R A, and O'Brien, S R. 1997. The geology and hydrocarbon prospectivity of the North Channel Basin. 95–111 *in* Petroleum geology of the Irish Sea and adjacent areas. Meadows, N S, Trueblood, S P, Hardman, M, and Cowan, G (editors). *Geological Society of London, Special Publication,* No. 124.

Maguire, K, Thompson, J, and Gowland, S. 1996. 163–182 *in* Recent Advances in Lower Carboniferous Geology. Strogen, P, Somerville, I D, and Jones, G L L (editors). *Geological Society of London, Special Publication,* No. 107.

Mange, M, Turner, P, Ince, D, Pugh, J, and Wright, D. 1999. A new perspective on the zonation and correlation of barren strata: an integrated heavy mineral and palaeomagnetic study of the Sherwood Sandstone Group, East Irish Sea Basin and surrounding areas. *Journal of Petroleum Geology,* Vol. 22, 325–348.

Manning, P I, and Wilson, H E. 1975. The stratigraphy of the Larne Borehole, County Antrim. *Bulletin of the Geological Survey of Great Britain,* No. 50, 1–50.

Mansfield, J, and Kennett, P. 1963. A gravity survey of the Stranraer sedimentary basin. *Proceedings of the Yorkshire Geological Society,* Vol. 34, 139–151.

McCabe, M, Knight, J, and McCarron, S. 1998. Evidence for Heinrich event 1 in the British Isles. *Journal of Quaternary Science,* Vol. 13, 549–568.

McConnell, B, Morris, J H, and Kennan, P S. 1999. A comparison of the Ribband Group (southern Ireland) to the Manx Group (Isle of Man) and Skiddaw Group (northwestern England). 337–344 *in* 'In sight of the suture' the Palaeozoic geology of the Isle of Man in its Iapetus Ocean context. Woodcock, N H, Quirk, D G, Fitches, W R, and Barnes, R P (editors). *Geological Society of London, Special Publication,* No. 160.

McLean, D, and Chisholm, J I. 1996. Reworked palynomorphs as provenance indicators in the Yeadonian of the Pennine Basin. *Proceedings of the Yorkshire Geological Society*, Vol. 51, 141–151.

McNestry, A. 1991. Palynological report on a Carboniferous interval in Irish Sea Well 113/27-2. *British Geological Survey Technical Report,* WH/91/31C.

Meadows, N S, and Beach, A. 1993. Structural and climatic controls on facies distribution in a mixed fluvial and aeolian reservoir: the Triassic Sherwood Sandstone Group in the Irish Sea. 247–264 *in* Characterization of Fluvial and Aeolian Reservoirs. North C P, and Prosser D J (editors). *Geological Society of London, Special Publication,* No. 73.

Meadows, N S, Trueblood, S P, Hardman, M, and Cowan, G (editors). 1997. Petroleum geology of the Irish Sea and adjacent areas. *Geological Society of London, Special Publication,* No. 124.

Meighan, I G, Gamble, J A, and Wysoczanski, R J. 1999. New U–Pb (SHRIMP) zircon ages for Tertiary igneous rocks. The North Atlantic Igneous Province: Magmatic Controls on Sedimentation. Geological Society of London (Conference Abstract).

Mitchell, G F. 1965. The late Quaternary of the Ballaugh and Kirk Michael districts. *Quarterly Journal of the Geological Society London,* Vol. 21, 359–381.

Mitchell, M, Taylor, B J, and Ramsbottom, W H C. 1978. Carboniferous. 168–188 *in* The geology of the Lake District. Moseley, F (editor). *Occasional Publication Yorkshire Geological Society*, Vol. 3.

Molyneux, S G. 1979. New evidence for the age of the Manx Group, Isle of Man. 415–421 *in* Caledonides of the British Isles: reviewed. Harris, A L, Holland, C H, and Leake, B E (editors). *Geological Society of London, Special Publication,* No. 8.

Molyneux, S. 1999. A reassessment of Manx Group acritarchs, Isle of Man. 23–32 *in* 'In sight of the suture' the Palaeozoic geology of the Isle of Man in its Iapetus Ocean context. Woodcock, N H, Quirk, D G, Fitches, W R, and Barnes, R P (editors). *Geological Society, London, Special Publication,* No. 160.

Molyneux, S G. 2001. Palynology of the Manx Group, Isle of Man. *British Geological Survey Report,* CR/01/21

Morris, J H, Woodcock, N H, and Howe, M P A. 1999. The Silurian succession of the Isle of Man: the late Wenlock Niarbyl Formation, Dalby Group. 189–212 *in* 'In sight of the suture' the Palaeozoic geology of the Isle of Man in its Iapetus Ocean context. Woodcock, N H, Quirk, D G, Fitches, W R, and Barnes, R P (editors). *Geological Society of London, Special Publication,* No. 160.

Morris, P, and Max, M D. 1995. Magnetic crustal character in central Ireland. *Geological Journal*, Vol. 30, 49–67.

Morrison, C W K. 1989. A study of the anchizone-epizone metamorphic transition. Unpublished PhD Thesis. St Andrews University.

Morton, N. 1992. Late Triassic to Middle Jurassic stratigraphy, palaeogeography and tectonics west of the British Isles. 53–68 *in* Basins on the Atlantic seaboard: petroleum geology, sedimentology and basin evolution. Parnell, J (editor). *Geological Society of London, Special Publication,* No. 62.

Mussett, A E, Dagley, P, and Skelhorn, R R. 1988. Time and duration of activity in the British Tertiary Igneous Province. 337–348 *in* Early Tertiary volcanism and the opening of the NE Atlantic. Morton, A C, and Parson, L M (editors). *Geological Society of London, Special Publication,* No. 39.

Nadin, P A, and Kuznir, N J. 1995. Palaeocene uplift and Eocene subsidence in the northern North Sea Basin from 2D forward and reverse stratigraphic modelling. *Journal of the Geological Society of London,* Vol. 152, 833–848.

Newman, P J. 1999. The geology and hydrocarbon potential of the Peel and Solway Basins, East Irish Sea. *Journal of Petroleum Geology*, Vol. 22, 305–324.

Nockolds, S R. 1931. The Dhoon (Isle of Man) granite. *Mineralogical Magazine*, Vol. 22, 494–509.

Ord, D M, Clemmey, H, and Leeder, M R. 1988. Interaction between faulting and sedimentation during Dinantian extension of the Solway Basin, SW Scotland. *Journal of the Geological Society of London*, Vol. 145, 249–259.

Owens, B. 1988a. Palynological report on Carboniferous sediments from Irish Sea Well 112/30-1. *British Geological Survey Technical Report,* WH/88/389C.

Owens, B. 1988b. Palynological report on Carboniferous sediments in Irish Sea Well 113/26-1. *British Geological Survey Technical Report*, WH/88/387C.

Palmer, R C, and Holman, I P. 2000. Groundwater vulnerability map of the Isle of Man. SSLRC client report No. JF 4253 V for the Isle of Man Department of Local Government and the Environment.

Pantin, H M. 1978. Quaternary sediments from the north-east Irish Sea: Isle of Man to Cumbria. *Bulletin of the Geological Survey of Great Britain,* No. 64.

Parker, J R. (editor). 1993. *Petroleum Geology of Northwest Europe: Proceedings of the 4th Conference.* (London: The Geological Society.)

Partington, M A, Copestake, P, Mitchener, B C, and Underhill, J R. 1993. Biostratigraphic calibration of genetic stratigraphic sequences in the Jurassic–lowermost Cretaceous (Hettangian to Ryazanian) of the North Sea and adjacent areas. 371–386 in *Petroleum geology of Northwest Europe: Proceedings of the 4th Conference.* Parker, J R (editor). (London: The Geological Society of London.)

Pearce, A, and Rose, G M. 1979. Mining in the Isle of Man. *Bulletin of the Peak District Mines Historical Society,* No. 7, 216–230.

Penge, J, Munns, J W, Taylor, B, and Windle, T M F. 1999. Rift-raft tectonics: examples of gravitational tectonics from the Zechstein basins of northwest Europe. 201–213 in *Petroleum geology of northwest Europe: Proceedings of the 5th Conference.* Fleet, A J, and Boldy, S A R (editors). (London: The Geological Society of London.)

Penn, I E. 1987. Geophysical logs in the stratigraphy of Wales and adjacent onshore and offshore areas. *Proceedings of the Geologists' Association,* Vol. 98, 275–314.

Penn, I E, Holliday, D W, Kirby, G A, Kubala, M, Sobey, R A, Mitchell, W I, Harrison, R K, and Beckinsale, R D. 1983. The Larne No. 2 Borehole; discovery of a new Permian volcanic centre. *Scottish Journal of Geology*, Vol. 19, 333–346.

Pickering, K T, Stow, D A V, Watson, M, and Hiscott, R N. 1986. Deep-water facies, processes and models: a review and classification scheme for modern and ancient sediments. *Earth Science Reviews*, Vol. 22, 75–174.

Pickett, E A. 2001. Isle of Man: foundations of a landscape. (Edinburgh: British Geological Survey.)

Piper, J D A, and Crowley, S F. 1999. Palaeomagnetism of (Palaeozoic) Peel Sandstones and Langness Conglomerate Formation, Isle of Man; implications for the age and regional diagenesis of Manx red beds. 213–226 *in* 'In sight of the suture' the Palaeozoic geology of the Isle of Man in its Iapetus Ocean context. Woodcock, N H, Quirk, D G, Fitches, W R, and Barnes, R P (editors). *Geological Society of London, Special Publication,* No. 160.

Piper, J D A, Biggin, A J, and Crowley, S F. 1999. Magnetic survey of the Poortown Dolerite. 155–164 *in* 'In sight of the suture' the Palaeozoic geology of the Isle of Man in its Iapetus Ocean context. Woodcock, N H, Quirk, D G, Fitches, W R, and Barnes, R P (editors). *Geological Society of London, Special Publication,* No. 160.

POOLE, E G, and WHITEMAN, A J. 1966. Geology of the country around Nantwich and Whitchurch. *Memoir of the Geological Survey of Great Britain*, Sheet 122 (England and Wales).

POWER, G M, and BARNES, R P. 1999. Relationships between metamorphism and structure on the northern edge of eastern Avalonia in the Manx Group, Isle of Man. 289–308 *in* 'In sight of the suture' the Palaeozoic geology of the Isle of Man in its Iapetus Ocean context. WOODCOCK, N H, QUIRK, D G, FITCHES, W R, and BARNES, R P (editors). *Geological Society of London, Special Publication*, No. 160.

POWER, G M, and CROWLEY, S F. 1999. Petrological and geochemical evidence for the tectonic affinity of the (?)Ordovician Poortown Basic Intrusive Complex, Isle of Man. 165–175 *in* 'In sight of the suture' the Palaeozoic geology of the Isle of Man in its Iapetus Ocean context. WOODCOCK, N H, QUIRK, D G, FITCHES, W R, and BARNES, R P (editors). *Geological Society of London, Special Publication*, No. 160.

QUIRK, D G (editor). 1999. Hydrocarbon potential of the Irish Sea. *Journal of Petroleum Geology*, Vol. 23.

QUIRK, D G, and BURNETT, D. 1999. Lithofacies of Lower Palaeozoic deep marine sediments in the Isle of Man: a new map and stratigraphic model of the Manx Group. 69–88 *in* 'In sight of the suture' the Palaeozoic geology of the Isle of Man in its Iapetus Ocean context. WOODCOCK, N H, QUIRK, D G, FITCHES, W R, and BARNES, R P (editors). *Geological Society of London, Special Publication*, No. 160.

QUIRK, D G, and KIMBELL, G S. 1997. Structural evolution of the Isle of Man and central part of the Irish Sea. 135–159 *in* Petroleum Geology of the Irish Sea and adjacent areas. MEADOWS, N S, TRUEBLOOD, S, HARDMAN, M, and COWAN, G (editors). *Geological Society of London, Special Publication*, No. 124.

QUIRK, D G, FORD, T D, KING, J A, ROBERTS, I L, POSTANCE, R B, and ODELL, I. 1990. Enigmatic boulders and syn-sedimentary faulting in the Carboniferous Limestone of the Isle of Man. *Proceedings of the Yorkshire Geological Society*, Vol. 48, 99–113.

QUIRK, D G, ROY, S, KNOTT, I, REDFERN, J, and HILL, L. 1999a. Petroleum geology and future hydrocarbon potential of the Irish Sea. *Journal of Petroleum Geology*, Vol. 22, 243–260.

QUIRK, D G, BURNETT, D J, KIMBELL, G S, MURPHY, C A, and VARLEY, J S. 1999b. Geological interpretation of shallow tectonic lineaments in the Isle of Man. 239–257 *in* 'In sight of the suture' the geology of the Isle of Man in its Iapetus Ocean context. WOODCOCK, N H, QUIRK, D G, FITCHES, W R, and BARNES, R P (editors). *Geological Society of London, Special Publication*, No. 160.

RACEY, A, GOODALL, J G S, and QUIRK, D G. 1999. Palynological and geochemical analysis of Carboniferous borehole and outcrop samples from the Isle of Man. *Journal of Petroleum Geology*, Vol. 22, 349–362

RAMSBOTTOM, W H C, and six others. 1978. A correlation of Silesian rocks in the British Isles. *Geological Society of London, Special Report*, No. 10.

RICE, C M. 1993. Mineralization associated with caledonian intrusive activity. 102–186 in *Mineralization in the British Isles*. PATTRICK, R A D, and POLYA, D A (editors). (London: Chapman and Hall.)

RICKARDS, R B, BURNS, V, and ARCHER, J. 1965. The Silurian sequence at Balbriggan, County Dublin. *Proceedings of the Irish Academy*, Vol. 73, 303–316.

RILEY, N J. 1992a. Foraminiferal biostratigraphy of Irish Sea Borehole 112/25A-12, interval 2575–2780 m. *British Geological Survey Technical Report*, WH92/96C.

RILEY, N J. 1992b. Foraminiferal biostratigraphy of Irish Sea Borehole 113/27-2, cores 12 and 13, interval 8250–8725'. *British Geological Survey Technical Report*, WH92/98C.

ROBERTS, B, MORRISON, C, and HIRONS, S. 1990. Low grade metamorphism of the Manx Group, Isle of Man: a comparative study of white mica 'crystallinity' techniques. *Journal of the Geological Society of London*, Vol. 147, 271–277.

ROSE, W C C, and DUNHAM, K C. 1977. Geology and hematite deposits of south Cumbria. *Geological Survey of Great Britain Economic Memoir*, Sheets 58 and 48 part (England and Wales).

RUFFELL, A H, and SHELTON, R G. 2000. Permian to Late Triassic post-orogenic collapse, early Atlantic rifting, deserts, evaporating seas and mass extinctions. 297–313 in *Geological History of Britain and Ireland*. WOODCOCK, N, and STRACHAN, R (editors). (Oxford: Blackwell Science Ltd.)

RUSHTON, A W A. 1993. Graptolites from the Manx Group. *Proceedings of the Yorkshire Geological Society*, Vol. 49, 259–262.

RUSSELL, G. 1978. The structure and vegetation history of the Manx hill peats. Man and environment in the Isle of Man. DAVEY, P J (editor). *British Archaeological Reports, British Series*, Vol. 54, 39–50.

SCARFE, A. 1987. The building of the Laxey Wheel. *Bulletin of the Peak District Mines Historical Society*, No. 10, 129–140.

SCARFE, A. 1990. Shipping the Great Laxey ores. *Bulletin of the Peak District Mines Historical Society*, No. 11, 85–90.

SCOTESE, C R, BAMBACH, R K, BARTON, C, VAN DER VOO, R, and ZIEGLER, A M. 1979. Palaeozoic base maps. *Journal of Geology*, Vol. 87, 217–278.

SHACKLETON, N J, and OPDYKE, N D. 1973. Oxygen isotope and palaeomagnetic stratigraphy of equatorial Pacific core V28-238: oxygen isotope temperatures and ice volume on a 10^5 and 10^6 year scale. *Quaternary Research*, Vol. 3, 39–55.

SHACKLETON, N J, and OPDYKE, N D. 1976. Oxygen isotope and palaeomagnetic stratigraphy of Pacific core V28-238: late Pliocene to Holocene. *Memoir of the Geological Society of America*, No. 145, 449–464.

SHELTON, R. 1997. Tectonic evolution of the Larne Basin. 113–133 *in* Petroleum geology of the Irish Sea and adjacent areas. MEADOWS, N S, TRUEBLOOD, S, HARDMAN, M, and COWAN, G (editors). *Geological Society of London, Special Publication*, No. 24.

SHEPHERD, T J, and GOLDRING, D C. 1993. Cumbrian hematite deposits, north-west England. 419–445 in *Mineralization in the British Isles*. PATTRICK, R A D, and POLYA, D A (editors). (London: Chapman and Hall.)

SIMPSON, A. 1963a. The stratigraphy and tectonics of the Manx Slates Series. *Quarterly Journal of the Geological Society of London*, Vol. 119, 367–400.

SIMPSON, A. 1963b. Quartz veining in the Manx Slate Series. *Nature*, Vol. 199, 900–901.

SIMPSON, A. 1964a. The metamorphism of the Manx Slate Series. *Geological Magazine*, Vol. 101, 20–36.

SIMPSON, A. 1964b. Deformed acid intrusions in the Manx Slate Series, Isle of Man. *Geological Journal*, Vol. 4, 189–206.

SIMPSON, A. 1965. The syn-tectonic Foxdale–Archallagan granite and its metamorphic aureole. Isle of Man. *Geological Journal*, Vol. 4, 415–434.

SIMPSON, A. 1968. The Caledonian history of the north-eastern Irish Sea region and its relation to surrounding areas. *Scottish Journal of Geology*, Vol. 4, 135–163.

SKELTON, R H. 1956. The Manx Mines. *Mining Magazine*, Vol. 92, 9–18.

SMITH, B. 1924. Iron ores: haematites of west Cumberland, Lancashire and the Lake District (second edition). *Special Report on the Mineral Resources of Great Britain. Memoir of the Geological Survey of Great Britain*, Vol. 8.

SMITH, B. 1931. Borings through the glacial drifts of the northern part of the Isle of Man. *Summary of Progress of the Geological Survey of Great Britain*, Vol. 3, 14–23.

SMITH, D B, and TAYLOR, J C M. 1992. Permian. 87–96 *in* Atlas of palaeogeography and lithofacies. COPE, J C W, INGHAM, J K, and RAWSON, P F (editors). *Memoir of the Geological Society of London*, No. 13.

SMITH, D B, BRUNSTROM, R G W, MANNING, P I, SIMPSON, S, and SHOTTON, F W. 1974. A correlation of Permian rocks in the British Isles. *Geological Society of London, Special Report*, No. 5.

SMITH, R A. 1986. Permo–Triassic and Dinantian rocks of the Belfast Harbour Borehole. *Report of the British Geological Survey*, Vol. 18, No. 6.

SMITH, R A, JOHNSTON, T P, and LEGG, I C. 1991. Geology of the country around Newtownards. *Memoir of the Geological Survey of Northern Ireland*, Sheets 37 and part of sheet 38 (Northern Ireland).

SMITH, S A, and HOLLIDAY, D W. 1991. The sedimentology of the Middle and Upper Border groups (Visean) in the Stonehaugh Borehole, Northumberland. *Proceedings of the Yorkshire Geological Society*, Vol. 48, 435–446.

SMYTH, W W. 1863. List of Manx minerals. *Isle of Man Historical and Antiquarian Society*, Vol. 1.

SMYTH, W W. 1887. On the occurrence of Feather Ore (Plumosite) in Foxdale Mine, Isle of Man. *Transactions of the Royal Geological Society of Cornwall*, Vol. 10, 82–89.

SOPER, N J. 1986. The Newer Granite problem: a geotectonic view. *Geological Magazine*, Vol. 123, 227–236.

SOPER, N J, ENGLAND, R W, SNYDER, D B, and RYAN, P D. 1992. The Iapetus suture zone in England, Scotland and eastern Ireland: a reconciliation of geological and deep seismic data. *Journal of the Geological Society of London*, Vol. 149, 697–700.

SOPER, N J, WEBB, B C, and WOODCOCK, N H. 1987. Late Caledonian (Acadian) transpression in north-west England: timing, geometry and geotectonic significance. *Proceedings of the Yorkshire Geological Society*, Vol. 46, 175–192.

STANLEY, C J, and VAUGHAN, D J. 1981. Native antimony and bournonite intergrowths in galena from the English Lake District. *Mineralogical Magazine*, Vol. 44, 257–260.

STANLEY, C J, and VAUGHAN, D J. 1982. Copper, lead, zinc and cobalt mineralisation in the English Lake District: classification, conditions of formation and genesis. *Journal of the Geological Society of London*, Vol. 139, 568–579.

STONE, P. 1988. The Permian successions at Ballantrae and Loch Ryan, south-west Scotland. *Report of the British Geological Survey*, Vol. 19, No. 2, 13–18.

STONE, P. 1995. Geology of the Rhins of Galloway district. *Memoir of the British Geological Survey*, Sheets 1 and 3 (Scotland).

STONE, P, COOPER, A H, and EVANS, J A. 1999. The Skiddaw Group (English Lake district) reviewed: early Palaeozoic sedimentation and tectonism at the northern margin of Avalonia. 325–336 *in* 'In sight of the suture' the geology of the Isle of Man in its Iapetus Ocean context. WOODCOCK, N H, QUIRK, D G, FITCHES, W R, and BARNES, R P (editors). *Geological Society of London, Special Publication*, No. 160.

SUTHERLAND, D G. 1984. The Quaternary deposits and landforms of Scotland and the neighbouring shelves: a review. *Quaternary Science Reviews*, Vol. 3, 157–254.

TAYLOR, B J. 1961. The stratigraphy of exploratory boreholes in the west Cumberland coalfield. *Bulletin of the Geological Survey of Great Britain*, No. 17, 1–74.

TAYLOR, B J, BURGESS, I C, LAND, D H, MILLS, D A C, SMITH, D B, and WARREN, P T. 1971. *British regional geology: northern England (Fourth Edition).* (London: HMSO.)

TAYLOR, J H, and GAMBA, E A. 1933. The Oatland (IOM.) Igneous Complex. *Proceedings of the Geological Association*, Vol. 44, 355–377.

TAYLOR, S R. 1983. A stable isotope study of the Mercia Mudstones (Keuper Marl) and associated sulphate horizons in the English Midlands. *Sedimentology*, Vol. 30, 11–31.

THOMAS, G S P. 1976. The Quaternary stratigraphy of the Isle of Man. *Proceedings of the Geologists' Association*, Vol. 87, 307–323.

THOMAS, G S P. 1977. The Quaternary of the Isle of Man. 155–178 in *The Quaternary History of the Irish Sea.* KIDSON, C, and TOOLEY M J (editors). Geological Journal Special Issue, 7.

Thomas, G S P. 1984. The origin of the glacio-dynamic structure of the Bride Moraine, Isle of Man. *Boreas*, Vol. 3, 355–364.

THOMAS, G S P. 1985. The Quaternary of the Northern Irish Sea basin. 143–158 in *The Geomorphology of northwest England.* JOHNSON, R H (editor). (Manchester: Manchester University Press.)

THOMAS, G S P. 1999. Northern England. 91–98 *in* A revised correlation of Quaternary Deposits in the British Isles. BOWEN, D Q (editor). *Geological Society of London, Special Report*, No. 23.

THOMAS, G S P, CONNAUGHTON, M, and DACKOMBE, R V. 1985. Facies variation in a supraglacial outwash sandur from the Isle of Man. *Geological Journal*, Vol. 20, 193–213.

THOMPSON, J, and MEADOWS, N S. 1997. Clastic sabkhas and diachroneity at the top of the Sherwood Sandstone Group: East Irish Sea Basin. 237–251 *in* Petroleum Geology of the Irish Sea and Adjacent Areas. MEADOWS, N S, TRUEBLOOD, S P, HARDMAN, M, and COWAN, G (editors). *Geological Society of London, Special Publication*, No. 124.

TODD, S P, MURPHY, F C, and KENNAN, P S. 1991. On the trace of the Iapetus Suture in Ireland and Britain. *Journal of the Geological Society of London*, Vol. 148, 869–880.

TOOLEY, M J. 1985. Sea-level changes and coastal morphology in north-west England. 94–121 in *The Geomorphology of Northwest England.* JOHNSON, R H (editor). (Manchester: Manchester University Press.)

TUBB, S R, SOULSBY, A, and LAWRENCE, S R. 1986. Palaeozoic prospects on the northern flanks of the London–Brabant Massif. 55–72 *in* Habitat of Palaeozoic gas in NW Europe. BROOKS, J, GOFF, J C, and VAN HOORN, B (editors). *Geological Society of London, Special Publication*, No. 23.

VAN HOORN, B. 1987. Structural evolution, timing and tectonic style of the Sole Pit inversion. *Tectonophysics*, Vol. 137, 239–284.

VON ARX, R. 1994. East Snaefell Mine. *British Mining*, No. 50, 158–160.

VON ARX, R. 1996. A glimpse at Snaefell Mine. *British Mining*, No. 57, 34–46.

VON ARX, R. 1998. Kirk Michael Mine in the Isle of Man. *British Mining*, No. 61, 74–90.

VON GRAFENSTEIN, U, EICHER U, ERLENKEUSER H, RUCH P, SCHWANDER J, and AMMANN, B. 2000. Isotope signature of the Younger Dryas and two minor oscillations at Gerzensee (Switzerland): palaeoclimatic and palaeolimnologic interpretation based on bulk and biogenic carbonates. *Palaeogeography Palaeoclimatology Palaeoecology*, Vol. 159, 215–229.

VON GRAFENSTEIN, U, ERLENKEUSER, H, BRAUER, A, JOUZEL, J, and JOHNSEN, S J. 1999. A mid-European decadal isotope-climate record from 15 500 to 5 000 years BP. *Science*, Vol. 284 (5420), 1654–1657.

WARD, J. 1997. Early Dinantian evaporites of the Easton-1 well, Solway Basin, onshore, Cumbria, England. 277–296 *in* Petroleum geology of the Irish Sea and adjacent areas.

Meadows, N S, Trueblood, S, Hardman, M, and Cowan, G. (editors). *Geological Society of London, Special Publication,* No. 124.

Warren, J. 1999. *Evaporites: their evolution and economics.* (Oxford: Blackwell Science.)

Warriner, D, and Gillings, A. 1983. Exploration and survey of the Great Laxey Mine, Isle of Man. *Bulletin of the Peak District Mines Historical Society,* No. 8, 373–381.

Warrington, G, and Ivimey-Cook, H C. 1992. Triassic. 97–106 *in* Atlas of palaeogeography and lithofacies. Cope, J C W, Ingham, J K, and Rawson, P F (editors). *Memoir of the Geological Society of London,* No. 13.

Warrington, G, Audley-Charles, M G, Elliott, R E, Evans, W B, Ivimey-Cook, H C, Kent, P E, Robinson, P L, Shotton, F W, and Taylor, F M. 1980. A correlation of Triassic rocks in the British Isles. *Special Report of the Geological Society of London,* No. 13.

Warrington, G. 1997. The Penarth Group–Lias Group succession (Late Triassic–Early Jurassic) in the East Irish Sea Basin and neighbouring areas: a stratigraphical review. 33–46 *in* Petroleum geology of the Irish Sea and adjacent areas. Meadows, N S, Trueblood, S, Hardman, M, and Cowan, G (editors). *Geological Society of London, Special Publication,* No. 124.

Webb, B C, and Cooper, A H. 1988. Slump folds and gravity slide structures in a Lower Palaeozoic marginal basin sequence (the Skiddaw Group), NW England. *Journal of Structural Geology,* Vol. 10, 463–472.

White, N, and Lovell, B. 1997. Measuring the pulse of a plume with the sedimentary record. *Nature,* Vol. 387, 888–891.

White, R S. 1988. A hot-spot model for early Cenozoic volcanism in the North Atlantic. 3–13 *in* Early Cenozoic volcanism and the opening of the North Atlantic. Parson, L M, and Morton, A C (editors). *Geological Society of London, Special Publication,* No. 39.

Whittaker, A (editor). 1985. Atlas of onshore sedimentary basins in England and Wales: post-Carboniferous tectonics and stratigraphy. (Glasgow and London: Blackie.)

Wilkinson, I P, and Halliwell, G P (compilers). 1979. Offshore micro-palaeontological biostratigraphy of southern and western Britain. *Report of the Institute of Geological Sciences,* No. 79/9.

Wills, L. 1970. The Triassic succession in the central Midlands in its regional setting. *Quarterly Journal of the Geological Society of London,* Vol. 126, 225–285.

Wilson, A A. 1990. The Mercia Mudstone Group (Trias) of the East Irish Sea Basin. *Proceedings of the Yorkshire Geological Society,* Vol. 48, 1–22.

Wilson, A A. 1993. The Mercia Mudstone Group (Trias) of the Cheshire Basin. *Proceedings of the Yorkshire Geological Society,* Vol. 49, 171–188.

Wilson, A A, and Evans, W B. 1990. Geology of the country around Blackpool. *Memoir of the British Geological Survey,* Sheet 66 (England and Wales).

Wilson, E A. 1999. A bibliography of the geology of the Isle of Man. 345–361 *in* 'In sight of the suture' the Palaeozoic geology of the Isle of Man in its Iapetus Ocean context. Woodcock, N H, Quirk, D G, Fitches, W R, and Barnes, R P (editors). *Geological Society of London, Special Publication,* No. 160.

Wilson, H E, and Manning, P I. 1978. Geology of the Causeway Coast. 2 volumes. *Memoir of the Geological Survey of Northern Ireland* Sheet 7. (Belfast: HMSO.)

Wingfield, R T R. 1985. Isle of Man, Sheet 54°N–06°W, Seabed sediments and Quaternary geology 1:250 000 map British Geological Survey.

Wingfield, R T R. 1995. A model of sea-levels in the Irish and Celtic seas during the end Pleistocene to Holocene transition. 209–242 *in* Island Britain: a Quaternary perspective. Preece, R C (editor). *Geological Society of London, Special Publication,* No. 96.

Wingfield, R T R, Hession, M A I, and Whittington, R J. 1990. Anglesey, Sheet 53°N–06°W, Quaternary Geology 1:250 000 map British Geological Survey.

Wirtz, D. 1953. Zur stratigraphie des Pleistocäns im Westen der Britischen Inseln. *Neues Jahrbuck Geologie und Palaeontologie,* Vol. 96, 267–303.

Woodcock, N H, and Barnes, R P. 1999. An early Ordovician turbidite system on the Gondwana margin: the southeastern Manx Group, Isle of Man. 89–108 *in* 'In sight of the suture' the Palaeozoic geology of the Isle of Man in its Iapetus Ocean context. Woodcock, N H, Quirk, D G, Fitches, W R, and Barnes, R P (editors). *Geological Society of London, Special Publication,* No. 160.

Woodcock, N H, and Morris, J H. 1999. Debris flows on the Ordovician margin of Gondwana: Lady Port Formation, Manx Group, Isle of Man. 121–138 *in* 'In sight of the suture' the Palaeozoic geology of the Isle of Man in its Iapetus Ocean context. Woodcock, N H, Quirk, D G, Fitches, W R, and Barnes, R P (editors). *Geological Society of London, Special Publication,* No. 160.

Woodcock, N H, Quirk, D G, Fitches, W R, and Barnes, R P (editors). 1999a. 'In sight of the suture' the Palaeozoic geology of the Isle of Man in its Iapetus Ocean context. *Geological Society of London, Special Publication,* No. 160.

Woodcock, N H, Quirk, D G, Fitches, W R, and Barnes, R P. 1999b. 'In sight of the suture' the early Palaeozoic geological history of the Isle of Man. 1–10 *in* 'In sight of the suture' the Palaeozoic geology of the Isle of Man in its Iapetus Ocean context. Woodcock, N H, Quirk, D G, Fitches, W R, and Barnes, R P (editors). *Geological Society of London, Special Publication,* No. 160.

Woodcock, N H, Morris, J H, Quirk, D G, Barnes, R P, Burnett, D, Fitches, W R, Kennan, P S, and Power, G M. 1999c. Revised lithostratigraphy of the Manx Group, Isle of Man. 45–68 *in* 'In sight of the suture' the Palaeozoic geology of the Isle of Man in its Iapetus Ocean context. Woodcock, N H, Quirk, D G, Fitches, W R, and Barnes, R P (editors). *Geological Society of London, Special Publication,* No. 160.

Wright, J E, Hull, J H, McQuillin, R, and Arnold, S E. 1971. Irish Sea investigations 1969–70. *Report of the Institute of Geological Sciences,* No. 71/19.

Young, B. 1987. *Glossary of the minerals of the Lake District and adjoining areas.* (Newcastle upon Tyne: British Geological Survey.)

Index

See also Contents (p.iii to v) for main headings.

Note Subheadings used in this index are Basin, Biozone, Borehole, Fault, Formation, Group, Member, Mine and Well.